2-4-69

The U.S. Machine Tool Industry
from 1900 to 1950

The U.S.

MACHINE TOOL INDUSTRY

from 1900 to 1950

by Harless D. Wagoner

The M.I.T. Press

Massachusetts Institute of Technology

Cambridge, Massachusetts, and London, England

1485992

To

Helen Pearson Roell

Preface

The following history was originally written as a doctoral dissertation at the American University, Washington, D. C. and was completed in 1966. The idea of doing a history of the U.S. Machine Tool Industry was suggested by Dr. Charles M. Wiltse, who also served as a member of the dissertation committee under the chairmanship of Dr. Louis M. Hunter. I would like to thank not only Dr. Hunter and Dr. Wiltse, but also Dr. Edward L. Allen and Dr. Charles C. McLaughlin, who also served on the dissertation committee, for their advice and patience.

I am particularly indebted to Dr. David W. Bluestone for his most helpful suggestions and encouragement. I would also like to thank Senator Ralph E. Flanders for his useful comments. Thanks are also due to the staffs of the National Archives and Library of Congress, the Smithsonian Institution, the National Machine Tool Builders' Association, and the International Association of Machinists. Other individuals in the Department of Defense and other departments and agencies were very helpful although it was not possible to take full advantage of all available resources.

My wife, Josephine Tedeschi Wagoner provided such long and varied encouragement, support, and direct assistance that it is impossible to express adequately my indebtedness to her. Possibly, this is also a suitable place for me to acknowledge that without the help of my brothers I would probably not have been able to continue my education even through high school.

HARLESS D. WAGONER

Contents

Figures

Tables

PART I

THE MACHINE TOOL INDUSTRY

1

Introduction

The machine tool industry, while relatively small in terms of capital investment, output, or most other quantitative standards— as compared with such giant industries as iron and steel, automobiles, or chemicals—was of key importance in modern industrial development. Yet many phases of the history of the machine tool industry for the first half of the twentieth century have been dealt with only briefly and superficially in general economic histories and periodicals. Therefore, this history attempts to describe the major economic and managerial problems faced by the U.S. Machine Tool Industry in the period from 1900 to 1950 and to summarize the industry's development in appropriate perspective with contemporary development in closely related industries.

Definition of Machine Tool Industry Used

This history is concerned primarily with the business of producing and selling machine tools and with managerial problems and policies of tool builders rather than with the technical development of the tools themselves. "Machine tools" have been limited to power-operated metal-cutting tools thus conforming with the definition of machine tools used in the Census Bureau's Standard Industrial Classification (SIC 3541) ". . . tools that shape metal by grinding or progessively cutting away chips. . . ." This industry is most closely related to two other classifications: SIC 3542 "Metal Working Machinery, Not Elsewhere Classified" and SIC 3543 "Cutting Tools, Jigs, Fixtures, Etc." These three form the broader classification SIC 354 "Metalworking Machinery."

There were several reasons for confining the study to metal-cutting machine tools including the fact that the available statistics for this group of tools appeared more adequate than for other groups. Furthermore, the firms producing metal-cutting tools as their primary product seemed to have more in common with each other than with other machinery builders or metalworking firms generally. For most of the period to be covered, they were also represented by a strong trade association. This indicated that most of the leading metal-cutting machine tool builders thought of themselves as part of an independent industry with distinct problems and interests. Metal-forming machinery builders were not added to the National Machine Tool Builders Association (NMTBA) until almost the end of the period studied (1947).

Organization of History

The study is organized into three basic parts covering generally three chronological periods within the first half of the twentieth century, and a concluding summary which attempts to tie together the major problems and accomplishments of machine tool builders for the entire span of fifty years. A postscript was added which comments briefly on some major developments of the period between 1950 and 1963 but which is not intended to serve as a history of the industry during this period.

Chapter 2 summarizes some of the more important technical problems and developmental trends which had special significance for the machine tool industry and its economic development. Chapter 3 presents basic statistics on the size and location of the industry for the period from 1900 to 1950. Chapter 4 discusses the effects of unstable demand, prices, and profits; the industry's efforts to improve management, limit competition, solve manpower problems, adjust to wartime demand, and prepare for reconversion. Machine tool builders' problems are related to contemporary economic development and the growth of metal products manufacturing in particular.

Part II covers the period from 1919 through 1938. It attempts to describe and analyze the effects of an extended period of general prosperity followed by a major depression on the machine tool industry. The major topics covered include the delayed business reaction following World War I and efforts to measure, understand, and control business fluctuations.

Part III covers the problems of conversion and expansion for wartime production during World War II and reconversion to civilian production. So far as possible, the problems and programs discussed are viewed both from the standpoint of the federal government which had to develop adequate controls, priorities, etc., to meet wartime needs, and from that of the machine tool builders, although a large proportion of the source materials used, for this period, were from official files.

Earlier Histories of the Machine Tool Industry

When research was begun for this study, Professor Joseph Wickham Roe's *English and American Tool Builders* was almost the only volume available which attempted to deal with the development of the machine tool industry at any length. It, however, was concerned almost entirely with the technical side of the industry's development, and with selected tool builders. It also provided little information for the period after 1900.

Since 1958, Professor Robert S. Woodbury's monographs on gear-cutting machines, milling machines, and grinding machines have appeared as parts of what apparently is intended as a systematic historical treatment of machine tool development, but these do not cover the industry's economic problems. Professor Woodbury has also suggested that there is ample room for a dissertation on the application of machine tools to the automobile industry alone. Significant machine tool developments are also discussed in earlier works such as Ralph E. Flanders' *Gear Cutting Machinery*, and in a variety of articles in technical publications and trade journals.

Professor Wayne G. Broehl, Jr.,'s *Precision Valley*, which appeared in 1959, provides an interesting story of the development of three machine tool builders of Springfield, Vermont, but hardly provides a history of the machine tool industry as a whole. Professor William H. Brown included historical material on one major problem in his doctoral dissertation "Innovation in the Machine Tool Industry," a summary of which was published in the *Quarterly Journal of Economics* for August 1957. Dr. Robert Stanley Himes' doctoral dissertaton "A Study of The Machine Tool Industry With Emphasis on The Problem of Stability," examines at length the experience of the machine tool industry during the period from about 1921 to 1958 in light of the major business cycle theories and the experience of other industries. There are also a few histories of individual machine tool companies, but these provide little information on the economic problems and development of the machine tool industry in the twentieth century.

Sources

The primary sources used in the study included official records of several federal departments and agencies, official histories, the various volumes of the U.S. *Census of Manufactures, Historical Statistics of the United States,* various publications of the National Machine Tool Builders Association, and certain unpublished historical material available in the NMTBA Library.

Secondary materials used included a limited number of special monographs and company histories, general economic histories, professional journals, business periodicals, and the major machinery trade journals. These materials are listed in the bibliography and footnotes throughout the study.

It proved to be very difficult to compile adequate statistical material for the period prior to 1919 which would be reasonably comparable to data for the period 1919 to 1950. Even within the latter period there were also frequent changes in the definition and coverage of data compiled as well as in the method of tabulation and reporting. These changes made it difficult to compare data over a long enough period to show definite trends or compare geographical distribution for different years. One of the limitations of these materials which proved most frustrating was that while the NMTBA at various times questioned the accuracy of *Census of Manufactures* statistics relating to the machine tool industry, it compiled and released only summary information on shipments without geographical or individual company data which would make it possible to judge the validity of its objections to the *Census of Manufactures* data. Also the legal prohibition against release by the Bureau of the Census of data which might reflect individual company operations has resulted in troublesome and sometimes mystifying gaps in statistics for particular states and types of machines. There would, in fact, appear to be a need for a doctoral dissertation or critical monograph by a trained statistician on the development, limitations, and interpretation of the major statistical series relating to the machine tool industry.

The statistical problem became still more complex when efforts were made to obtain and analyze comparable statistical data for the principal machine tool using industries. It is believed, however, that the statistics which have been selected for comparison serve to illustrate basic relationships and indicate major economic trends. They provide some quantitative measure of the economic fluctuations taking place during the period studied and a basis for comparing changes in the machine tool industry. Therefore, while available statistical data were less complete, consistent, and accessible than would have been desired, they are considered adequate for this history.

2

The Changing
"State of the Art"

The following chapter summarizes the major technical factors affecting the evolution of machine tool design and construction during the first half of the twentieth century. It is intended to serve as an introduction and setting for the discussion of the machine tool industry's economic problems, policies, and attitudes presented in the remainder of the book. It is not intended to be a comprehensive history of machine tool development.

Prospect Ahead

By 1900, machine tools had developed to a high state of sophistication and performance when compared to the tools of 1850 or even 1875, but they were still being built individually or in small groups rather than manufactured. They were also beginning to feel the influence of recent technological developments which would make it necessary for many machine tools to be radically redesigned to provide greater rigidity, higher operating speeds, improved convenience and ease of operation, and the much higher output needed for low-cost mass production. Many of these developments originated in other industries but the machine tool industry was to have a major role in applying them to improve both machine tools and production methods. They included the development of high-speed tool steels and, later, cemented carbides, electric motors, geared and hydraulic transmissions and controls, and superior abrasives and grinding wheels.

Some technical developments and changes in production methods added to the adaptability of machine tools and made possible lower costs through longer production runs on major tool components. Thus the so-called unit method of tool construction—or in more modern terminology "modular construction"—involved the use of particular standardized components in a number of machines within a considerable size range and even, in some cases, in machines of different types. For example, the Cincinnati Milling Machine Company's high-powered milling machines introduced in 1907 were based on this system and were offered with a number of alternative features. These included cone and pulley, variable speed or constant speed motor drives, with the feed drive in inches per minute or per spindle revolution.[1]

High-Speed Steel and Machine Tool Design

The last decade of the nineteenth century brought into use a new class of tool steels which were to have revolutionary effects upon the metalworking industries and upon the design and construction of machine tools. The first of the so-called "high speed" steels were tungsten alloy steels and were successors to the older Mushet or air-hardening steel which had been invented in England in 1868. During the period between 1893 and 1898, Frederick W. Taylor experimented with cutting tools made from steels in which chromium was substituted for the manganese of the Mushet steel and which contained far less carbon than the older steel. In 1900, Taylor-White steel containing 8 per cent tungsten, 1.8 per cent chromium, 1.15 per cent carbon, 0.18 per cent manganese, and 0.25 per cent silicon was placed on the market. In the same year, the Bethlehem Steel Company brought out a tungsten-chromium-vanadium steel known as the 18-4-1. Other tool steels with special properties to meet particular classes of needs followed.[2]

High-speed steel made it possible to greatly increase cutting speeds and to take heavier cuts than had previously been possible. To make these changes practicable, however, it was necessary to increase the strength and rigidity of machines. High-speed steel

---

[1] Robert S. Woodbury, *History of the Milling Machine* (Technology Monographs, Historical Series No. 3. Cambridge, Mass.: The Technology Press, 1960), pp. 74–75.

[2] George S. Brady, *Materials Handbook* (New York: McGraw-Hill Book Company, Inc., 1947), pp. 331–334; J. W. Roe, *English and American Tool Builders* (New Haven: Yale University Press, 1916; Revised New York: McGraw-Hill Book Co., 1926), p. 277.

tools were harmed more quickly by "chatter" (vibration) and greater power was required to drive the tools. It is easy to over-estimate the immediate economic effects of these developments. Their initial impact was confined almost entirely to the roughing operations and they had little effect on finishing operations. The latter were frequently the most expensive since they involved much slower and more highly skilled work, and required frequent inspections to meet established tolerances.[3]

Nevertheless, the use of high-speed steels was gradually extended as it proved advantageous and economical in new applications. They were eventually found to be applicable to most machines and to all but a relatively small class of jobs where the volume was small and did not justify the additional tooling expense. However, while practical cutting speeds and feeds were increased rather rapidly during the first decade of the twentieth century, it must not be assumed that actual practice in most machine shops kept pace. The number of variable factors involved and the fact that each differed in its effect upon the cost of doing a particular job made it very difficult to determine the best combination for each operation. Speeds were increased and considerable reductions in cost accomplished but both lagged well behind what was theoretically possible.[4]

There were, moreover, definite limits on the reductions in cost which could be achieved from the use of high-speed steel. There were other phases of production operations which also needed attention and where significant economies could be made including improvements in control of work flow, better supervision and other phases of production management.[5] Senator Ralph E. Flanders recently wrote the author that about 1908 Mr. Taylor invited him to "join his group and write the definitive treatise on machine tool time study and practice. . . . I felt that he was mistaken in his impression that he had said the last word on these subjects. The rapid development of such cutting tools as tungsten carbide and others and the proliferation of electronic and automated machines proved that my judgment was correct."

[3] Fred J. Miller, *Metal Working Machinery* (Washington: U.S. Bureau of the Census, Census Bulletin 67, 1907), p. 14.

[4] H. I. Brackenbury, "Symposium on High-Speed Tools, No. 1291a, High-Speed Tools and Machines to Fit Them," ASME, *Transactions*, 1910, pp. 729–732.

[5] *Ibid*, pp. 774–776.

Influence of Electric Power and the Electric Motor

During the nineteenth century, machine tools were usually driven through systems of belts and pulleys transmitting power from steam engines or, still earlier, from water power or animals. Use of the electric motor to drive machine tools was first seriously proposed about the middle of the last decade of the nineteenth century, but most mechanics looked upon the early experiments largely as a fad. Electric power soon proved to have important advantages, however, including the fact that it permitted greater flexibility in the arrangement of tools and greatly simplified the problem of transmitting power. Electric motors also proved very advantageous where tools were operated intermittently since it was no longer necessary to keep an elaborate system of pulleys and shafting in continuous operation when a large part of the machines in a shop were shut down. By 1900, these advantages were becoming fairly well-known though all problems of adapting electric motors to machine tools had not been solved. One area of controversy related to the relative merits of individual motor drives for each machine versus group drives by which one motor provided power for a number of machines in a particular group through line shafts, pulleys, and belts. The first attempts to combine individual motors and machine tools in a single unit were made about 1901 but electric motors did not generally become integral parts of machine tools until the decade following World War I.[6]

The electric motor also made practicable the adoption of a system using portable, individually driven, tools for heavy work which could not be handled in the usual way even by very large machines. Instead of placing work in or on the machine itself, large pieces such as the ring or magnet frame of large electric generators were placed upon a floorplate, and tools were moved into position and fixed to the floorplate.

Electricity and the electric motor also made possible rapid improvement in the facilities provided by American machine shops for moving work or machines about the shop as needed. Electricity provided an ideal method of transmitting power to drive cranes which

[6] *American Machinist*, 25:1643–1645, November 13, 1902, "Progress in the Machine Tool Industry During the Decade 1890-1900," Thomas Caswell Rolt, *Short History of Machine Tools* (Cambridge, Mass.: The M.I.T. Press, 1965), p. 205.

were badly needed for transporting heavy work or equipment. The need to install electric facilities for this purpose led in turn to the extension of the use of electric power for other purposes.

During the first decade of the twentieth century, relatively little was known definitely as to either the amount of power lost by older systems of driving machines or the savings which could be realized by conversion to electric motor drives. Nevertheless, a good deal of emphasis was placed on potential savings in power by early advocates of electric motors. Some savings seemed certain in view of the fact that with the electric motor only those machines in actual operation used power.[7]

The introduction of electric power into the machine shop was accompanied by other important improvements in equipment and working conditions. Magnetic chucks were developed for machine tools. These made it possible to do many jobs conveniently and quickly which otherwise were difficult or even impossible to do at all. Electric power also gave birth to various devices for starting and stopping machines which were the predecessors of modern electric and electronic controls.

An important issue in the early development of electric power was the choice of direct or alternating current. Prior to the introduction of central electric utility plants, most manufacturing plants generated their own power by the use of steam engines or water power. Where plants converted to electricity but continued to produce their own power and the distances over which the power had to be transmitted were relatively short, direct current was normally used. The use of direct current in turn made possible the development of dependable variable speed motors. These combined with simple gear systems permitted very precise control of speeds. It is understandable, therefore, that during the early years of the twentieth century it seemed likely that the variable speed, direct current motor was the final answer to many machine tool problems. On the other hand, alternating current could be generated at higher voltages and transmitted economically over small wires for much longer distances than was practical with direct current. This meant a much smaller investment in copper for transmission lines and permitted the establishment of central power plants serving an en-

[7] A. L. DeLeeuw, "Economy of the Electric Drive in the Machine Shop," No. 1276a, ASME, *Transactions,* 1910, pp. 137–163.

tire community for domestic use, street lighting, and industrial power.

One of the major problems of adapting machine tools to electric motor drives or of developing suitable motor drives for metalworking machinery was that of achieving a reasonable degree of standardization. There was competition between the two types of electrical power, that is, direct and alternating current, and each appeared to have important advantages. However, the choice was not merely between these two types of power. The engineer also had to determine which of a number of voltages or combinations of voltages should be selected; whether a two or three phase system was preferable, and, if alternating current was to be used, whether twenty-five or sixty cycle current was needed. It soon became apparent that there was an urgent need for standardization which could only be achieved through cooperation between the tool builder and the motor manufacturers. The fact that central power companies were increasing in number and were offering power to manufacturing establishments at low rates also made standardization increasingly advantageous and necessary.[8]

Machine tool builders sought advice and assistance on use of electric motors from the electrical equipment manufacturers but were not always able to obtain much help. For example, in 1899 Brown and Sharpe asked the General Electric Company for information on the application of variable speed motors to milling machines and were assured that such advice would be supplied in a few days. Four months later the request was repeated but no material was supplied.[9]

Part of the difficulty of adapting electric motors, and particularly variable speed motors, to machine tool use was the size of the motors required, their cost, and inefficient power consumption at low speeds. The constant speed motor seemed to be at least part of the answer when combined with an adequate clutch and variable speed drive (power transmission) which could provide an adequate range of speeds without excessive loss of power.

The use of electric motors to drive machine tools became increasingly common during the period prior to World War I and the trend continued through the war period. Improvements were

8 *Ibid.*, pp. 166–167.
9 Woodbury, *Milling Machine*, p. 70–72.

made to provide wider speed ranges, reduce motor size for a given horsepower, and provide better balance of rotating parts at high speed. These were combined with improved geared transmissions, allowing higher speeds without excessive vibration and noise. Many improvements were also made in controls. Increased emphasis was placed on the advantage of using standard motors with standard armature shafts thereby reducing the number of spare armatures which had to be kept in stock and making possible the interchange of individual parts between motors.[10]

The following quotation sums up some of the important contributions of the electric motor to knowledge of machine tool design and metalworking practice:

> It is probably true that all of the existing knowledge in regard to the power and pressures exerted in machine-tool operation is due to the adoption of the electric motor as a driving means. And what is true of our knowledge of powers and pressures is also true of our information in regard to speeds. With an increase in our appreciation of the stresses of machine-tool members have come improvements in frame construction., particularly in designs to insure rigidity. With an increased knowledge of what speed means in production has come a deliberate attempt to gain greater convenience in machine tool handling. And with the adoption of chains and gears, which could not be run in the open because the device must be properly lubricated, has come an increase in the safety of machine-tool mechanism.[11]

Evolution of Electric Driving Mechanisms and Controls

The electric motor drive systems developed early in the twentieth century generally used a single electric motor to furnish power to move both work and tools. As machine tools became larger and more complex, it became necessary to provide complicated and expensive transmissions to connect the motor with the various tool and work handling mechanisms. It was found, however, that it was more convenient and economical to use separate motors with relatively simple transmissions to drive the various components. Electrical

[10] Charles Fair, "Selecting Motors for Machine Tools," *American Machinist*, 40:1107–1109, June 25, 1914.

[11] A. L .DeLeeuw, "Influence of Electric Motors on Machine Tools, *American Machinist*, 44:126, January 20, 1916.

controls were also designed which would stop the entire machine if one motor stalled, thereby avoiding serious damage to the machine or work.[12]

By the third decade of the twentieth century, alternating current motors were usually preferred by machine tool users but for some uses were still considered by tool builders to be less efficient and adaptable than direct current motors. F. E. Cardullo, Chief Engineer of the G. A. Gray Company of Cincinnati, reported to the American Society of Mechanical Engineers in 1929 that "The most satisfactory method of driving planers of medium and large size is by means of a reversing motor geared directly to the planer drive."[13]

During the twenties, most grinding machines and many other machine tools were still driven by means of countershafts. These were either driven from overhead shafting which transmitted power from a central source or by electric motors on the group-drive principle. The countershaft was in turn connected with the machine tool by belts. This system, while an improvement over earlier systems, was often cumbersome, rather unsightly, and not too efficient. Consequently, it was only a matter of time until a concerted effort was made to eliminate the countershaft, to improve the appearance of machine tool driving mechanisms, and to increase the efficiency of power transmission. One of the factors which made greater efficiency necessary was improvement in the metal-removing capacity of grinding wheels, and this required that more power be supplied.[14]

It was not economical, in the case of grinding machines at any rate, to cut down on the amount of power provided to the machine since it was essential for efficient grinding-wheel operation that the correct peripheral speed be maintained under the heaviest load. Failure to maintain the correct cutting speed also caused the surface of the wheel to break down with the result that it was no longer an accurate cutting tool.[15]

The introduction of individual electric motor drives for machine tools proceeded at a rapid rate during the twenties. One manufac-

[12] S. Einstein, "Machine-Tool Milestones, Past and Future," *Mechanical Engineering*, 52:959–962, November, 1930.

[13] F. E. Cardullo, "Motors for Planer Service," ASME, *Transactions*, 51: Part 2:169–184, 1929.

[14] R. E. W. Harrison, "Motor Drives for Precision Grinding Machines," ASME, *Transactions*, 51:Part 2:175, 1929.

[15] *Ibid.*, p. 178.

turer of lathes reported that between 1919 and 1929 production of individually motor-driven lathes increased from approximately 15 per cent to over 90 per cent. During this period, however, little progress appears to have been made in standardization of motor frame sizes, armature-shaft dimensions, foothole dimensions, etc. Each motor still had to be individually fitted to the machine in which it was to be used.[16]

The methods ordinarily used to select motors for machine tools were, in a number of respects, not very satisfactory. The machine tool builder often had little information as to the work the customer planned to do with the tool. To be safe, he generally recommended a motor of sufficient capacity to handle the maximum cut the machine tool was capable of, with the result that the tool frequently had far more power than was needed. In many cases, the customer specified the motor to be used. This was particularly so in the case of larger tools. A survey conducted by the NMTBA indicated that where the motor was of from ten to fifteen horsepower capacity, 57 per cent were specified by the user as compared with 30 per cent by the manufacturer and 13 per cent by dealers. In the case of motors of from one to ten horsepower, 47 per cent were specified by customers, 37 per cent by builders, and 15 per cent by dealers. The automobile industry, however, seemed a conspicuous exception to this general pattern. Thirteen out of fourteen of the largest machine tool firms reported that they customarily specified motors for all machine tools built for the automotive industry including special machines.[17]

The variable-speed electric motor with existing geared speed change mechanisms was not wholly satisfactory and particularly so after alternating current had largely replaced direct current. Machine tool designers began to develop various hydraulic power transmissions. These were not actually new—having been frequently employed in other industrial applications—but had to be adapted to machine tool use. This took place largely after World War I. Relatively simple and efficient units of comparatively small proportions were needed and the price had to be competitive with existing speed changing devices. Also it was necessary to adapt the

---

[16] Charles L. Cameron, "Methods of Motor Application and Controls on Lathes," ASME, *Transactions*, 51:Part 2:178, 1929.

[17] W. W. Nichols, "Economies Which May Be Effected in Power Transmission," ASME, *Transactions*, 52:Part 2:112, 1930.

transmissions to the needs of particular tools such as grinding machines which required relatively little power but a steady and smooth movement of the work slide. Broaching machines, on the other hand, needed a cushioning effect to protect the tool from shocks, great range and selectivity of working feeds, a choice of manual or automatic operation, and ease of control.

Whereas earlier machine tools required that the operator manually perform certain operations such as feeding a cutting tool into or across the work or moving the work past the tool, the invention and development of automatic or semiautomatic machine tools saw these functions transferred to the mechanism itself. Power was transmitted through a system of gears, spindles, and other mechanisms to advance or withdraw the cutting tool; for example, to cause the turret of an automatic lathe to "index" (move) from one station to another, or to produce other required movements. It was found that many of these movements could be performed efficiently by hydraulic mechanisms.

The principal advantages of hydraulic drive mechanisms for machine tools over purely mechanical systems were that the hydraulic systems offered a high degree of flexibility in speed ratios; providing a cushioning effect which reduced the shock to the machine when entering work or reversing, and were able to take extreme peak loads. It was possible to adapt hydraulic equipment to carry through a series of movements and to ensure that each motion would begin only after the preceding motion was completed. Some efforts were made during the twenties to standardize hydraulic drive and control equipment, but standardization was difficult because of the great variety of functions and speeds required by machine tool users.[18]

Scientific management and particularly time-and-motion studies, which were largely concerned with reducing direct labor costs, resulted in a rapid increase in the emphasis placed on convenience of operation. Simplicity in machine design and construction became less important than having controls within easy reach of the machine operator when in his normal working position. In the case of tools where it was not easy to fix a single position for the operator, dual or multiple sets of controls were provided to permit convenient

[18] J. P. Ferris and E. Wiedmann, "Progress in the Use of Hydraulic Equipment on Production Machinery," *Mechanical Engineering*, 54:477–482, July 1932; Woodbury, *Milling Machine*, pp. 95–96.

operation from various positions. Dials were provided to indicate the rate and direction of movement or rotation and the operator was, in some cases, also relieved of the job of manually changing the rate of rotation or traverse. In general, the trend of machine tool development was toward reducing the amount of physical effort and skill required to control tools while at the same time making it possible to rapidly produce work of high quality.[19]

Along with the emphasis on greater convenience of control, increased accuracy, and greater productivity, there was a demand for greater accessibility for maintainance and repair operations or complete overhauling. This need was met, in part, by the unit-design system of machine construction by which a machine tool was constructed of a number of more or less standardized and self-contained units. Under this system, a particular unit could be removed and replaced quickly and repairs were greatly simplified. In the interest of greater durability, the machine tool designer also drew upon other industries such as the automobile industry for sliding gears of alloy steel and integral keyshafts to improve drive and feed mechanisms. Antifriction bearings and centralized, automatic systems of lubrication were similarly adapted to machine tools.

Other advances in machine tool design to make them more nearly automatic in operation included various sensing or sizing devices which could accurately determine when a desired dimension was reached and cause the tool to withdraw. These were combined with devices which controlled a machine in performing a desired series of operations and, at the end of the period studied, led to numerically controlled machine tools, transfer machines, and automatic production lines.[20]

The latter developments took place largely after World War II and are beyond the scope of the present history. They should be viewed in relation, however, to the criticisms made by Professor Seymour Melman in his *Our Depleted Society* and by W. Paul Strassman for the nineteenth century in his *Risk and Technological*

---

[19] Einstein, "Machine Tool Milestones," pp. 960–961; Rolt, *Short History*, p. 237.

[20] Charles R. Hine, *Machine Tools for Engineers*, 2nd Ed. (New York: McGraw-Hill Book Compnay, Inc., 1959), pp. 401–422; Woodbury, *Milling Machine*, pp. 98–102; Rolt, *Machine Tools*, p. 237, "The most striking feature of machine tool engineering in the twentieth century has been the rapid and widespread adoption of powered control systems— . . . —on all but the simplest and smallest general-purpose tools."

Innovation that machine tool builders—along with many other businessmen—were not sufficiently aggressive and courageous in developing and applying new ideas and methods. Such "sins of omission" provide a partial explanation of some of the machine tool industry's chronic problems but are difficult to prove conclusively. It is also not possible to fix any specific responsibility in an industry as complex as the machine tool industry. Another aspect of this matter was covered by the late Dr. William H. Brown who developed the hypothesis "that both the introduction of new machine tools and the timing of their introduction can be understood as a planned attempt on the part of the machine tool firm to increase demand for its product."[21]

Specialization

That American machine tool manufacturers had gone a long way toward product specialization is indicated by the fact that by the beginning of the twentieth century no firm made—or even claimed to make—a complete line of machine tools. Considering the wide range of equipments included, of course, any such effort would have been rather foolhardy both technically and economically, and would have required that machines be built only on special order. However, it had been only a few years since many tool firms had in fact made such claims and operated on such a basis.

Specialization in machine tool manufacturing was accompanied by a considerable increase in the proportion of standardized interchangeable parts produced. Some parts such as screws, bolts, gears, and other components had been made on the interchangeable basis "for stock" for many years. These required relatively little in the way of expensive tools and gauges to produce. Many other parts, however, required rather elaborate and expensive equipment which could only be justified where a comparatively large number of machines of a particular type was to be produced by a single firm.

The development of the industry . . . led to an increasing application of the principle of interchangeable manufacture to the production of metal-working machinery, and this is one of the

21 William H. Brown, "Innovation in the Machine Tool Industry," *The Quarterly Journal of Economics*, LXXI, No. 3, August 1957, pp. 406–425, (article based on an unpublished doctoral dissertation, Yale University, 1952).

most prominent, important, and interesting features of the business as now carried on. Even some of the larger machines which, a few years ago were built one at a time and only upon orders, are now manufactured in considerable numbers by the aid of special tools and fixtures and with many if not all of their parts interchangeable.[22]

Many of the special machines built for the bicycle and later the automobile industry were adaptations and combinations of standardized units composed largely of individual parts or components which were manufactured in substantial numbers even though the completed assembly might have been designed to meet a highly specialized need. This does not imply, of course, that the machine tool industry had become a "mass-production" industry.

Standard Versus Special Purpose Tools

The machine tool user in deciding what machine tool he should purchase had two major alternatives. He might buy a "standard" machine produced by one or more machine tool builders as a regular item of manufacture. On the other hand, he might order a special machine designed to perform a particular operation or series of operations rapidly and with relatively little attention from the operator. Such special machines could often be considerably simpler in design than a standard machine. This fact tended to reduce the cost of producing special tools. However, machines which were unique or built on special orders were likely to be expensive—special design and engineering work were often required, some parts used could not be made in quantities, etc. Furthermore, the special machine could not be transferred readily from one product to another as demand shifted, and was likely to have little resale value. Nevertheless, prior to World War I, the use of special machine tools was increasing rather rapidly. This was particularly true in automobile manufacturing. Special machines were efficient and economical where a large number of identical parts of unusual shape or size were to be produced.[23]

A particular part could often be produced on more than one type

[22] Miller, *Metal-Working Machinery*, p. 18.
[23] John Riddell, "A User's View of Machine Tools," *American Machinist*, 33: Pt. 2:862–863, November 10, 1910; *American Machinist*, 38:371, February 27, 1913, "Single Purpose vs. Special Machine Tools."

of machine tool as well as on several models of the same general type. The choice of machine tool in any particular case was likely to depend upon a combination of several factors such as the number of pieces to be produced, the degree of accuracy and type of finish required, or merely on the fact that a particular machine was available. In a large manufacturing operation, the selection of machines was likely to be quite different from the case where a general machine shop was to produce only one or a small number of identical pieces and be able to handle a variety of work. In the former case, the cost of specialized tooling including if need be, the design and construction of new machine tools, expensive special jigs and fixtures, etc., could be prorated over a large volume of production to reduce the unit cost to a reasonable level. In the general shop, standard machines already available had to be utilized. In the latter case, primary reliance for the quality of the product had to be placed on the skill and ingenuity of the machinist rather than on production experts, tool designers, setup men, or elaborate accessories.

In some cases, it was more economical to select a machine which could complete a job in one operation. In others it was less costly to divide the work between two machines as, for example, between an automatic lathe performing a roughing operation and a centerless grinder completing a finishing operation. In other production operations, several standard machine tools could be linked by work-handling devices to form an efficient production line without incurring the cost or inflexibility of special machine tools.

The primary interest of the machine tool builder was in securing as wide as possible a market for his machines at acceptable prices. This meant that he often designed his tools to be adaptable to a relatively wide range of uses. Frequently, it resulted in standard machines being equipped with attachments and special features which were not required by particular users having a limited range of work. Since unnecessary equipment added to the cost of tools, some machine tool users suggested that machines should be designed in such a way that they could be sold without attachments and special features if these were not needed, or that tool builders should manufacture a line of simple machines for many types of commercial work.[24]

[24] Edson R. Norris, "Automatic Features on Machine Tools," *American Machinist*, 39:813–814, November 13, 1913.

The Automobile and Machine Tool Design

During the period covered by this study, the automobile industry was a particularly important factor in the evolution of machine tools and in the growth of the machine tool industry. Its most obvious role was that of customer for the machine tool industry's tools and "know-how" reflecting production techniques used in other industries. However, the automotive industry also contributed much to the development of better and stronger materials, to more economical production methods, to the progress of standardization and to the advance of machine tool design and construction. By the end of the first decade of the twentieth century, it was evident that the automobile industry was to replace the bicycle industry as the major machine tool user and leading influence on machine development.

The automobile today is, apparently, in about the position of the bicyle at the time when the diamond frame and the pneumatic tire had been accepted as final and leading features of the machine. . . . they have reached a standard stage so far as their leading features are concerned. Until recently improvements and changes which were not always improvements characterized the industry from year to year, . . . , this stage is now passed and automobile building is, from this point on, to become automobile manufacture, and we are led to ask if the influence of the bicycle in machine-tool development is to be repeated by the automobile.

. . . when the simplicity of the bicycle is contrasted with the complexity of the automobile it will be seen that the possibilities which now open up are far greater than those which existed in the early stages of bicycle development, and, for ourselves, we confidently look for rapid progress in the development of special machine tools for automobile work.[25]

One of the biggest problems which the automobile designer had to face was that of finding ways of building a machine which would withstand the vibration and shock to which the automobile was subjected by rough roads and comparatively high speeds. This need was met by the development of a series of alloy steels which were much stronger and tougher than earlier steels. Automobile

[25] *American Machinist*, 32:241–242, February 11, 1909, "The Coming Influence of the Automobile on Machine Tool Design."

buyers and builders also began to demand stronger, quieter running gears. This resulted in demands for improvements in the methods of gear production, and for better machines for grinding gears. The automobile industry was also responsible for the extension of the use of antifriction bearings of both the ball and roller types, and for rapidly extending the application of flooded or forced systems of lubrication. The latter had not been used for small machines but their advantages soon became obvious to machinery builders including machine tool builders. The automobile industry also helped to call attention to the importance and advantages of having controls located within convenient reach of the operator. Finally, the automobile industry and particularly the Society of Automobile Engineers took the lead in standardization of small parts.[26]

The reciprocal influence of the grinding machine and the automobile on each other can hardly be overemphasized. The technical aspects of this development are discussed by Professor Robert S. Woodbury in his *History of the Grinding Machine* and *History of the Gear-Cutting Machine* and need not be repeated here. The development of superior abrasives including silicon carbide (manufactured in the United States under the trade name "Carborundum") rediscovered in 1891, and artificial corundum (aluminum oxide) were followed by better grinding wheels and by the development of heavier and more rigid grinding machines capable of effectively using the new wheels in high-production grinding operations.[27]

The resistance of some machine tool industry executives and tool users, however, to new developments is also illustrated by the opposition which Charles H. Norton and others had to overcome in developing and introducing the much heavier grinding machines using larger and wider grinding wheels with higher speeds for rapid grinding. Experiments were begun on grinding of automobile crankshafts in 1903 and disclosed that the Norton grinder could do in fifteen minutes work which had previously required five hours.

[26] *American Machinist*, 38:119, January 16, 1913, "Influence of the Automobile on Machine Design;" *ibid.*, 38:161, January 23, 1913, "The Automobile and Machine Tools;" R. W. Woodbury, *History of the Grinding Machine* (Cambridge, Mass., M.I.T. Press, 1959), pp. 98–99, 105–108; V. S. Clark, *History of Manufactures* (New York: McGraw-Hill Book Company, 1929), Vol. III, pp. 162–163.

[27] Woodbury, *Grinding Machine*, pp. 90–95, 102–108.

By 1905, the Norton Company was doing this type of work for various automobile builders on a production basis. Automobile firms then began to buy production grinders for mass-production application first to crankshafts and, in 1910–1912 to hardened camshafts to eliminate another long and expensive series of machining operations.

The new grinding machines along with special milling and gear-cutting machines provided the automobile industry with better quality work at much higher production speeds and also reduced production costs. As a result of these and other developments, the automobile industry became the machine tool industry's best customer taking 25 to 30 per cent or more of the industry's output. By 1913, the Ford plant had thirty-three special purpose grinding machines in operation grinding vanadium steel drop forgings for transmission shafts. The Ford Company followed a policy of getting maximum production out of its tools and scrapping tools when it was convinced greater production could be obtained with new tools and production methods even though the original tools were relatively new and in good condition.[28]

The development of heavy vertical drilling machines was largely due to the automobile industry which used them for heavy drilling and for boring cylinders. Multiple-head milling machines of the planer type were also developed almost solely to meet the needs of automobile engine builders. The automobile and internal combustion engine provided the incentive for the development of new or improved machine tools. It was primarily up to the machine tool builders to design and build the machine tools.[29]

As the automobile industry grew in importance as a machine tool user, machine tool builders very naturally gave increasing attention to the industry's needs. Machine tools became heavier and more rugged, feed mechanisms were simplified, automatic lubrication was provided, alloy-steel heat-treated shafts and gears were adopted along with easily replaceable and adjustable slideways and bearings. Other features were adopted which improved the accuracy

[28] *Ibid.*, pp. 120–122; R. W. Woodbury, *Milling Machine*, p. 89; Woodbury, *History of the Gear-Cutting Machine* (Technology Monograph, Historical Series No. 1, Cambridge, Mass.: The Technology Press, 1958), pp. 121–123; Allen Nevins and F. E. Hill, *Ford, The Times, The Man, The Company* (New York: Charles Scribner Sons, 1954), Vol. I, p. 456.

[29] *American Machinist*, 44:81–82, January 13, 1916, "Influence of the Automobile on Machine-Tool Design"; Woodbury, *Milling Machine*, pp. 87–95.

of the product or the convenience and productivity of the machine tool. These efforts by the machine tool builder to improve his product were welcomed, as well as to a considerable degree stimulated, by the automobile industry.

There were other points on which the automobile manufacturers were not very well satisfied. For example, proper tooling—that is the provision of suitable jigs, fixtures, and cutting tools—seemed to be a secondary consideration to the machine tool builder and was often left entirely to the machine tool user. Machine tool builders countered with the complaint that users often failed to provide them with essential information regarding operating conditions, tolerances, and other requirements. It appears that where standardized jigs and fixtures could be used, the machine tool builder was more likely to supply these than where special appliances had to be designed for the individual user.[30]

Rate of Development of New Tools During World War I

The number of new machine tools introduced each year would seem to be an obvious indicator of the rate of machine tool development. On this assumption, the *American Machinist* at various times tabulated the number of new machines appearing in its columns. Since this journal attempted to cover all new machine tools as they appeared on the market, it was felt that this method should give reasonably adequate results. Its principal weakness was the fact that there was no effort to determine which machines embodied really significant innovations and which either represented only minor modifications of existing designs or were only copies of standard machines.

In 1914, a total of 503 new machine tools and machine shop appliances appeared as compared with 300 during 1913 and 375 in 1912. The total for 1914 included 53 drilling machines, 42 grinders, 39 punches, presses, and shears, 33 lathes, 21 millers, 18 boring machines, 12 sawing machines, and 10 automatics. For 1915, the total dropped to 425 and for 1916 to 329. Perhaps of more significance, however, is the fact that the number of lathes appearing increased from 35 in 1914 to 45 in 1915 and 77 in 1916 while the number of

---

[30] L. L. Roberts, "The Use and Application of Machine Tools," ASME, *Transactions*, 51:Part 2:33–34, 1929.

automatic machines declined from 10 in 1914 to 1 for 1915 and 1 for 1916. This result appears to have been almost entirely due to the fact that World War I produced a strong and rapidly growing demand for simple turning machines to produce shells while there was a temporary lull in interest in automatic machines.[31]

By 1915, the effects of the European war were strongly felt by the American machine tool industry. Past experience indicated that the number of new developments introduced tended to be greater in periods of slack business than in periods when business was unusually good. This experience did not appear to be borne out in 1915 since the number of items appearing did not decline as rapidly from the 1914 level as would have been expected even though American machine tool shops had never had more work. Actually, the machines which appeared in 1915 were the result of development efforts of preceding years and, in this area, the effects of the wartime demand had not been fully felt. The number appearing in 1915 was actually larger than in any previous years except 1914 and 1911. The fact that only one new automatic machine appeared each year in 1915 and 1916 is interesting in that we ordinarily associate automatic machines with high-speed mass production, and there was certainly an urgent demand for greatly increased production of munitions at that time. However, this need could also be met in most cases with simple lathes which could be produced and delivered much more rapidly than more complicated machines.

Production Standards and Methods in Wartime

Many firms which obtained munitions contracts early in World War I assumed that the standards of precision and uniformity required were relatively low in comparison to their regular line of work. It soon became apparent, however, that high standards were required to assure interchangeability and meet required performance standards. It also became clear that many American firms accepting munitions contracts really knew very little about manufacturing interchangeable parts and components despite the fact that this was an essential element of the so-called "American System" of pro-

[31] *American Machinist*, 42:837, May 13 1915, "New Machine Tools in 1914;" L. P. Alford, "Developments in Machine-Shop Equipment in 1915," *American Machinist*, 43:1169–1171, December 30, 1915; *American Machinist*, 46:41, January 4, 1917, "Developments in Machine-Shop Equipment in 1916."

duction. Their sole concern appeared to be with achieving and maintaining a high rate of production regardless of whether the product met specifications. They also complained strenuously if any European inspector rejected a lot because it did not meet specifications.[32]

Some of the difficulties were due to lack of training and experience on the part of newly recruited machinists and machine operators, carelessness, lack of an exact model of the item to be produced, or suitable standard and working gauges and inspection procedures to assure that all parts were within the specifications required.

The overriding emphasis on production rather than quality affected many tool building firms but was probably most strongly felt in new firms entering the tool business. In some cases, greater production was sought by simplifying tool designs to handle a particular type and narrow range of work. In others, however, production shortcuts, carelessness, and lack of experience resulted in production of machine tools which did not meet even minimum standards.

During World War I, there was a strong emphasis on speeding up production both of machine tools and war material and equipment. One method of achieving this end was to increase the speed of machine movements. In some cases, this appears to have been emphasized almost to the exclusion of consideration of other ways of achieving the result desired. For example, a great deal of effort was put on speeding up the movement of planer tables, but relatively little either on cutting down the time required to prepare work, place it on the planer bed, measure for cuts, change and grind tools, or on design of jigs and fixtures for the specific work at hand. In the case of the planer, most of these matters apparently were usually left to the ingenuity of the operator rather than being specified by a production specialist after careful analysis of the work to be done.[33]

Production engineering studies showed how in many cases 50 to 85 per cent of the time involved could be saved by the use of suitable jigs and fixtures. In many cases, also, the production engineer could effect substantial savings by eliminating such poor practices as that

[32] Earle Buckingham, "American Industrial Progress as Revealed by War Orders," *American Machinist*, 46:315–321, February 22, 1917.

[33] Charles Meier, "No. 1591 Metal Planers and Methods of Production," ASME, *Transactions*, 39:229–243, 1917.

of taking very short strokes with the planer which wasted power
and time in reversing and returning the table after each cut.

Machine Tool Productivity

Advances in machine tool design and construction resulted in increases in productivity of machines. For example, the following
figures illustrate the trend in productivity for splitting and straddle-
milling operations on connecting rods:

Date	Description	Production Per Hour
1910	4 pieces held in special fixture on table	40
1915	3 pieces held at each end of hand-index base	60
1920	6 pieces held in removable work-holding unit: load extra work unit while milling	90
1926	4 pieces held in automatic-index fixture	110
1928	4 pieces held in automatic-index fixture	125
1929	4 pieces held in automatic-index fixture	140
1930	8 pieces held in automatic-index fixture	248

The development of improved automatic or semiautomatic machine
tools also made it possible for one operator to tend several machines,
thus reducing unit labor costs.[34]

Research and Innovation

In the first two decades of the twentieth century, development of
new and improved machine tools and metalworking practices continued to be largely dependent on the independent individual efforts of a relatively small number of engineers, tool designers, and
skilled mechanics as it had during the nineteenth century. Efforts
by particular machine tool builders to develop, and to market, improved machines seemed to vary inversely to current demand for
existing machines. There continued to be, as there had been in the
nineteenth century, considerable resistance on the part of both
machine tool builders and many tool users to the introduction of
designs, methods of construction, or working methods which con-
flicted with or departed significantly from traditional practices.[35]

[34] Einstein, "Machine-Tool Milestones," pp. 959–962.
[35] For a discussion of the effects of technical and business inertia in the
nineteenth century, see W. Paul Strassman, *Risk and Technological Innovation*
(New York: Cornell University Press, 1959).

During the twenties, basic machine tool design changed much less rapidly than methods of production and special features of tools. A great many changes were made to increase tool capacity and to make tool operation more convenient. In general, most research activity and significant changes in tool design still took place during slack periods.[36] However, although the machine tool industry was generally prosperous during the second half of the twenties, and its principal concern was with filling orders for existing designs, there was some interest in research. This interest was directed almost entirely at finding solutions to immediate problems rather than to developing new basic knowledge. Much of what was learned to meet these particular problems was also not made available to other firms. This was true even though the machinery trade journals and the American Society of Mechanical Engineers (ASME) encouraged the development and exchange of technical information. For example, the ASME Committee on Cutting of Metals was active during 1928 in the following areas: (1) collection and correlation of data on cutting of metals from both domestic and foreign sources, (2) the practical relations between physical and chemical characteristics of cutting fluids and their performance, (3) establishment of a test code for tool steels, (4) experimental investigations on the machinability of metals.[37]

New developments or improvements in steel alloys and "stainless" steels as well as the growing popularity of plastics were largely the result of chemical and metallurgical research by firms in the chemicals and iron and steel industries. These indicated a need for more extensive and better organized research in the field of machine shop practice. However, because of the relatively small size of most machine shops, the problem of financing and coordinating research was more difficult than in industries which were dominated by a few large units capable of supporting substantial research programs or of taking the lead in developing cooperative research programs. The ASME attempted to suggest ways by which machine tool builders and machine shops generally could accelerate research.

Probably the only solution is a central institute or laboratory to be supported by contributions from the various trade associa-

[36] Brown, "Innovation."
[37] ASME, *Transactions*, 1928, MSP-51-1, "Progress in Machine-Shop Practice," Report of Executive Committee of Machine Shop Practice Division of ASME.

tions and individuals in the industry, but before such an institution can be established there must be an awakening to the true significance of fundamental and applied research. Much educational work lies ahead of any group undertaking to solve this particular problem, but the necessity is so great that it will justify large effort.[38]

While these efforts received some support from machine tool builders, and the impact of the depression caused many firms to give greater attention to development of improved machines, there is little evidence of any major change in the machine tool industry's approach to research or support of cooperative efforts. Major change in this area apparently had to wait at least until the end of World War II and, as noted in the previous reference to Professor Melman's *Our Depleted Society*, there is some basis for feeling that the post World War II efforts have not been adequate. It also appears that the development and introduction of new machine tools was influenced by machine tool builders' estimates of the most favorable time to market new machines and the costs involved in doing so.[39]

As machine tool demand declined during the period 1930–1933, tool builders gave greater attention to redesign of their products although improvements were not necessarily introduced immediately because some tool builders felt they should wait for the market to improve. Use of new materials for cutting tools was expanding and influencing tool design. These included tungsten and tantalum carbides which required that machine tools have greater rigidity, increased speed range, and wider feed range.[40]

Examples of design changes included a major re-engineering by Jones and Lamson of the Hartness flat-turret lathe. Jones and Lamson also introduced a new model thread grinder which soon comprised a major part of the company's sales. The Fellows Gear Shaper Company introduced an "hour-glass type" thread generator in 1930; a lapping machine in 1932, and several sizes of gear-shaping machines in the mid-thirties.[41]

[38] ASME, *Transactions*, 1929, MSP-52–1, "Progress in Machine-Shop Practice," Report of Executive Committee of Machine Shops Practice Division of ASME.

[39] Brown, "Innovation," p. 409–415.

[40] *Mechanical Engineering*, 53:898–900, No. 12, December 1931, "Machine Shop Practice."

[41] W. G. Broehl, Jr., *Precision Valley*, Englewood Cliffs, N.J.: Prentice-Hall, Inc., 1959), p. 142.

Standardization and Simplification

Some progress was made toward standardization during the thirties but it appears that the rate of progress was not fast enough to satisfy some government agencies. R. E. W. Harrison, Chief, Machinery Division, Bureau of Foreign and Domestic Commerce urged that the NMTBA and the machine tool industry push forward a program including the elimination of unnecessary sizes and types, standardization of simple elements within each particular group of tool builders, and cooperative effort on the basic problems of industrial standardization. He noted that the Lathe Group had notified the Ordnance Department that it had agreed on a simplified list of capacities and size designations although it had told the Navy Department that it could not classify its members by quality of product as the Navy had requested.

This is all to the good—it pleases the buying departments down here, and it is the first logical step in the program. However, as I see it, the activity should be an association activity, and should be extended to all the other groups. Cylindrical grinding machine manufacturers could now without prejudice to their commercial interests, I believe, announce their schedule of approved sizes and capacities, and possibly the milling machine group is in a position to do likewise, although I am not so well informed regarding the situation in this particular group.[42]

Possibilities for standardization and simplification of machine tool design and construction continued to be of interest to industrial mobilization planners concerned with the rapid expansion of production in the event of war. Simplification programs, of course, applied not only, or even primarily, to machine tools but also to the end product and production methods used. Thus efforts were made early in 1939 to reduce by 50 per cent the machine operations required to produce the M-1 Garand Rifle.[43]

[42] RG (Record Group) 151, Bureau of Foreign and Domestic Commerce, "General Machine Tools, 1933–1935," File 221.2. Letter from R. E. W. Harrison to Walter W. Tangeman, Vice President, Cincinnati Milling Machine Company, February 27, 1935.

[43] Ralph Elberton Smith, The Army and Economic Mobilization (Washington: Government Printing Office, 1959); p. 30; H. C. Thomson and Lida Mayo, Ordnance Department Procurement and Supply (Washington: Government Printing Office, 1960), pp. 161–162.

These efforts took place simultaneously with accelerated efforts to modernize equipment in major government installations such as the Springfield Armory some of whose machine tools antedated the Civil War and were more suitable for museums than for the production line. Retooling for production of new weapons such as the Garand Rifle was hampered by limited funds, as well as the technical problems inherent in standardization of weapon designs, and simplification of production methods necessary to mass production.

In November and December of 1941, similar memorandums were sent to army ordnance districts and arsenals and to navy bureaus, naval districts and navy yards urging greater efforts to get tool purchasers to accept tools of simplified design and with a minimum of accessories rather than more elaborate models. Examples were cited of what could be done:

> For example, the Betts type of simplified vertical boring mill is ideally suited to the production of ring-gears and ball bearing races for tank turrets. All of this work is of approximately the same diameter and of the same low height and these pieces can be machined on a boring and turning machine of this type. The Betts machine has a limited range of speeds because there is very little variation in the diameter of the work to be done, and the cross rail is of the fixed rigid type, bolted to short stubby housings instead of the adjustable-type cross rail on high housings to accommodate big work . . .[44]

As in World War I, one of the methods proposed to meet World War II production problems and tool shortages was for the technical bureaus and offices of the Services to do everything possible to relax specifications on tolerances and finishes consistent with necessary performance. It was believed that this policy, if aggressively pursued, would not only produce substantial reductions in the machine time required but would also make it possible to use many older tools which could not produce work meeting existing tolerances.[45]

[44] RG 80, Navy Department, Office of Procurement and Material, Machine Tool Section, 1942U to 1941W, File "M." Memorandum from Major General C. T. Harris, Jr., Assistant to the Chief of Ordnance to Ordnance Districts and Arsenals, December 5, 1941, "Machine Tools—Simplification of Requirements."

[45] RG 80, *Ibid.* Memorandum from Captain E. D. Almy, USN, to Undersecretary of the Navy James V. Forrestal, October 1, 1941, "Availability of Machine Tools."

Throughout World War II, there were many requirements both for new machine tools and accessories, and for improved production methods which would make it possible to use existing machine tools to produce new or modified weapons and other military equipment. Before all the wartime production problems were solved, it was apparent that further improvements in machine tools were needed to compete with older machines for postwar use in civilian production, but there was strong opposition to diverting attention or skilled manpower from the immediate problems of war production. Wartime developments in electronics and control engineering, moreover, were laying the ground for future major technical developments in machine tools as well as in many other industries.

Summary

Progress in machine tool design, construction, and operational controls during the first half of the twentieth century was remarkable and deserving of admiration. Nevertheless, it seems equally clear that progress was slower and the contribution of most tool builders less substantial than they would have been had the industry devoted a greater part of its efforts to research and development and had received more consistent interest and support from tool users and the federal government. Certainly, technical improvements in many machine tools were not great enough or frequent enough to convince many machine tool users that they should replace machine tools at anything approaching the rate which machine tool builders advocated, or which would have been necessary to keep ahead of, or even up with, recent industrial progress in some other industries and countries. On the other hand, more rapid technical progress in machine tool development might not have resulted in greater stability in machine tool demand or general prosperity for all or most firms in the machine tool industry. It is more likely that it would have meant more business and higher profits for some firms and an equally high mortality rate among other firms with smaller resources for research and exploitation of new developments.

By 1950, systematic and cooperative research and development under the control of large corporations, foundations, universities, and the federal government had largely replaced the efforts of individual inventors and engineers. To many, these collective efforts may well seem less interesting and individually satisfying than the contributions of the inventors and business pioneers of the earlier stages of the industrial revolution, just as complex theories of biological evolution are less dramatic than accounts of Divine Creation.

Machine tool designs and construction were modified to accommodate and exploit the characteristics of highspeed steel, cemented carbides, and abrasives in cutting tools, grinding wheels, and abrasive belts. The electric motor became an integral part of almost all machine tools and—with the aid of central power stations—freed machine tool users from the major limitations previously imposed on plant location and layout. Improved mechanical and hydraulic power transmissions and speed changing mechanisms were incorporated into machine tools to provide greater efficiency, increased flexibility, and quieter operation. Improved or radically new electrical and electronic controls were developed or adapted to machine tools which reduced the tool users' dependence on purely mechanical controls and, in many cases, radically reduced the amount of skill necessary to operate machines though they often complicated the problem of maintenance and repair. Also machine tools were made stronger and more rigid where higher operating speeds and greater cutting depths made this necessary. Lastly, a wide range of hybrid machines were developed by joining various basic units together with appropriate work handling devices in the so-called transfer machines or automatic production lines which became a symbol of modern mass-production industry.

The machine tool industry provided an amazing variety of specialized machine tools to meet the rapidly changing and often erratic requirements of machine tool users. It also made numerous functional improvements in standard machine tools and, at times, attempted to stimulate demand by nonfunctional changes in the appearance of machines or by adding or deleting particular accessories.

Also as machine tools became more complex, machine tool firms became less "integrated" and more dependent upon other firms and other industries for many components. By the end of the first half of the twentieth century, some machine tool plants were, in fact, little more than assembly plants. Many components and accessories were purchased from other firms in the machine tool industry while others were supplied by specialized plants supplying standardized components to various machinery industries.

3

1485992

Structure, Size, and Location

of the Machine Tool Industry

This chapter discusses the structure, size, and location of the machine tool industry as defined in Chapter 1. Some of the major factors influencing the location and growth of the industry are also indicated and provide a basis for some of the discussion in Parts II and III. The machine tool industry's relationships with major machine tool using industries are discussed in terms of their effect upon machine tool demand. Other industries which provide major raw materials and components used by machine tool builders are also identified and briefly discussed in terms of their importance to machine tool builders.

Roots in the Nineteenth Century

During the nineteenth century, production of machine tools progressed from the stage of an infant industry—in part native-born and in part imported—confined almost entirely to New England to that of a substantial and essential branch of American industry. Its center first moved southward into the Middle Atlantic states and Pennsylvania, and then west to Ohio and the Middle West. Its development and prosperity were closely related in each period of its growth to the expansion of other industries including textiles and textile machinery, small arms and ammunition, watches and clocks, the steamboat, railroads, farm machinery, and the bicycle. New products or improved designs of existing products required new machine tools in large numbers. Improvements in machine tool design and con-

35

struction, conversely, made new or better manufactured products possible and economical, and older tools obsolete.[1]

Form of Organization

By 1900 most machine tools were produced by corporations although it is probable that over half of the total establishments in the industry were not as yet corporately organized. Between 1900 and 1919, the relative importance of corporations in the industry continued to grow and in 1919, 79.4 per cent of the establishments reporting in the *Census of Manufactures* were corporately owned. They employed 94.3 per cent of the industry's employees and produced 94.5 per cent of the reported output of machine tools. Only in Indiana, Illinois, and Massachusetts did there appear to be a significant percentage of the industry under noncorporate ownership in terms of numbers of employees and output. In Illinois 28.4 per cent of the employees and 23.4 per cent of the value of products were in noncorporate establishments. In Indiana, 12.1 per cent of the wage earners and 16.9 per cent of the value of products were in noncorporate establishments. In Massachusetts over one-third of the establishments were noncorpoate but employed only 13 per cent of the employees.[2]

Size of the Machine Tool Industry

Production figures are one indication of the size of an industry. Unfortunately, available machine tool production and shipment statistics for the period prior to 1919 are not very adequate and probably not very reliable. Shipments of machine tools in 1900 probably amounted to about $19 or $20 million as compared to about $160 million in 1919. When these figures are adjusted to allow for the changing value of the dollar over this period the increase is about $65.7 million or 307 per cent for 1919 as compared to 1900. No corresponding figures for numbers of machine tools produced or shipped are available for 1900 but it seems likely that the increase between 1900 and 1919 was small and that the average

[1] Joseph Wickham Roe, *English and American Tool Builders* (New Haven: Yale University Press, 1916; Revised New York: McGraw-Hill Book Company, 1926), p. 277.

[2] U.S. Bureau of the Census, *Census of Manufactures,* 1919, Table 22.

cost per machine tool increased very substantially both because of the increasing size, weight, and complexity of machine tools and the declining value of the dollar.

It seems reasonable to assume that trends in production are more accurately reflected in data for years in which an industry operated at what may be considered normal levels. On this assumption, data for the machine tool industry for the years 1919, 1929, and 1939 were compared. During these years, the industry was operating at a relatively high level, but not at peak level. Information for production for 1919 and 1929 was adjusted to make it more comparable with that for 1939 by using only the figures for the metal-cutting types.

Production for 1919 and 1929 was about equal (1929 was about 3 per cent higher) in dollar value, and production for 1939 was about 17 per cent higher in terms of dollar value than in 1919. It was noted that NMTBA reports of machine tool shipments for the same years showed that 1929 was about 14 per cent higher than 1919 in value and 1939 about 24 per cent higher than 1919 (See Appendix Tables 5-7).

The most obvious explanation for the fact that the NMTBA figures for value of shipments were greater than those reported in the census is that the NMTBA figures represent the delivered price of the tools to the customer whereas the census totals reflect production valued on an f.o.b. basis. There are consequently two variable factors—one being the difference between the delivered price and the price at the factory without the distribution cost and the other the fact that the NMTBA figures represent shipments while the census figures reflect production and include additions to inventory.

The census figure for the value of machine tool production in 1929 was substantialy lower (about 14 per cent) than the NMTBA figure for value of shipments. One explanation for this lower value may be that the NMTBA shipments figure represents the actual price of tools shipped in 1929 whereas the census figure probably represents an end-of-year valuation of the production following the financial "crash." Since the average unit price for machines shipped increased in 1930 and 1931 over 1929, it is questionable how much effect the crash should have had on inventory valuation.

It is apparent that volume (number of units) of production and shipments declined very substantially between 1919 and 1939 and that conversely, their value rose substantially (about 24 per cent based on the NMTBA figures for shipments and 17 per cent for the value of production based on census data). Clearly, the unit price and cost rose. Part of this increase was due to changes in the design and construction of many tools which made them heavier, more complex, and more expensive to build. Whether this accounts for all the increase seems doubtful, however. Unit prices, based on the NMTBA figures, increased until 1931 when they reached a peak average of $4,200 per unit. They then began to decline; at first slowly, and then more rapidly, until a low point of $3,325 per unit was reached in 1936—about 21 per cent reduction. Unit prices then rose again until they were $4,265 in 1938, but declined rather substantially in 1939 to an average of $3,883 per unit. The high of 1938 was on a very low volume of shipments as compared to either 1937 or 1939 and must have included a disproportionate number of the larger, more complex high-precision and high-cost special machines. It is possible that there may also have been a significant number of price increases based on the improved demand in 1937. This seems unlikely in view of the fact that the industry was still operating below capacity. Furthermore, no information was found to support this possibility other than general statements indicating that many machine tool builders felt the main possibility for improving profits was to raise prices even though this might have some negative effect on the volume of sales. Other statements, however, emphasized the need to expand sales and reduce costs if possible, rather than raise prices.

The *Census of Manufactures* data for 1947 were used rather than those for 1949 since a complete canvass of manufacturing industry was made in 1947 while the figures for 1949 were based on a sample. The census report shows that in 1947, there were 315 establishments reporting in the machine tool industry (SIC 3541) as compared with 224 for 1939. The large difference in the number of establishments reporting in 1947 versus 1939 exaggerates the actual increase in the number of machine tool building establishments which was nearer 10 per cent than the 40 per cent indicated. Total shipments (primary and secondary products) were reported as $493.8 million in 1947 compared to $221.3 million in 1939. Shipments of machine tools alone by the machine tool industry were reported at $356.4 million in 1947. In the same year, other industries reported machine tool production of $58.3 million. In 1939, the machine tool industry was reported to have produced $171.0 million of machine tools and other industries about $10.5 million. It was noted that the census figures for 1947 were substantially higher than the NMTBA estimates (by about one sixth) whereas those for 1939 were lower by roughly the same proportion. According to NMTBA estimates about 51,500 machine tools were shipped in 1939 compared to 60,000 in 1947 and a low of 34,500 in 1949.

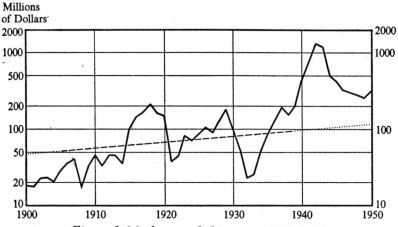

Figure 1. Machine tool shipments, 1900-1950

Source: NMBTA estimates.

In Figure 1, an attempt is made to depict graphically the trend in production over the period studied using NMTBA shipments figures. These figures are not adjusted for price changes because no suitable price index (or set of indices which could be linked) with which to adjust them was found. A ratio chart is used so that relative growth of the industry is shown. A least squares fit to the logarithms of the data for the years 1905 through 1935 was made to obtain the trend line shown. Note that the period selected for the calculation includes both a wartime peak (1917–18) and a severe depression trough (1932-33). Hopefully, then, the distortion introduced by one extreme is balanced by that introduced by the other. Nevertheless, since the basic data consist of unadjusted figures, the moderate slope shown is probably too steep. Therefore, when judged by production, it appears that the growth rate of the machine tool industry was at best very slow during the period studied.

Employment is in many ways an excellent index of the condition of the machine tool industry, although full analysis of this factor in production would require better statistics than are available. In 1939, the industry employed less than 40,000 workers; in 1940 the total rose to 57,000 and continued to increase through 1941 and most of 1942 until a peak of 120,000 workers was reached. Thus employment increased by approximately 200 per cent while the dollar value of machine tool shipments increased by over 500 per cent. The fact that shipments increased by so much higher a percentage than employment is probably due to a combination of factors including

1. increases in tool prices,
2. longer production runs,
3. standardization and simplification of some tools,
4. Long working hours

It is also probable that there was some actual increase in hourly output per man due to harder work because of the desire of both workers and management to aid the war effort.

Geographical Distribution of the Machine Tool Industry

By 1900, Cincinnati had become the leading machine tool center and had thirty establishments engaged in production of metalworking machinery with an aggregate production valued at $3,375,436. Philadelphia was second with eleven establishments reporting an aggregate output of $3,095,574. This included a wide range of tools as there was a lesser degree of specialization in Philadelphia than in most of the new production centers of the Midwest such as Cincinnati. Providence, Rhode Island ranked third among the machine tool production centers with fourteen establishments and production of $2,929,141. Production was generally diversified but included a large number of automatic and semiautomatic machines such as screw machines, turret lathes, and gear cutters as well as various types of milling machines. Hartford, Connecticut had eleven machine tool firms with a total output of $2,296,935, and Worcester, Massachusetts was fifth with twenty-four establishments reporting an output of $2,009,357.[3]

Available data on production of metal-cutting machine tools

[3] *American Machinist*, 25:1643, November 13, 1902, "Progress in the Machine Tool Industry During the Decade 1890–1900."

indicates that Ohio was far in the lead in this industry in 1900 with more than a third of the total output. Massachusetts was the second-ranking state, followed rather closely by Pennsylvania, Connecticut, and Rhode Island. Much farther back were New York, Illinois, New Jersey, Vermont, and Wisconsin, with Michigan a poor last. Census statistics for 1900 and even more so for 1905 (See Appendix Tables 1 and 2) show surprisingly large totals under the category "All Other States" on the assumption that giving additional state totals would disclose operations of individual firms.

Similar data for 1919 (See Appendix Table 13) show a total more than ten times as large in dollars. Due to price increases including particularly those during World War I, the increase in physical production was actually much less. Ohio retained its position as did Massachusetts, but the latter was closely followed by Rhode Island. These were followed by Connecticut, Pennsylvania, Illinois, and Michigan. Farther back came Vermont and Wisconsin with almost equal production; then New Jersey, New York, and Indiana.

Available data for 1900, 1905, and 1919 show a somewhat different geographical distribution of production of major types of machine tools and show even greater differences if specific types of tools are compared. In 1900 and 1905, Ohio was the leading producer of lathes, boring and drilling machines, planers, shapers and slotters, threading machines, shearing machines, and sawing machines. Rhode Island led by a small margin in milling machine and grinding machine output.

In 1919, Ohio continued to lead in lathe production and in the other major types in which it had led in 1900, but had also taken the lead in milling machines. Massachusetts had moved far into the lead in production of grinding machines with Pennsylvania a poor second while Rhode Island had been relegated to the "All Other States" category of the *Census of Manufactures*.

Relatively, machine tool output grew most rapidly in Michigan and Illinois. This growth was due primarily to the development of the automobile industry in the case of Michigan and to the expansion of farm equipment, construction machinery, and tractor production in the case of Illinois. Relative growth, however, appeared to be almost as great in Wisconsin, Rhode Island, and Vermont. The rate of growth in Pennsylvania was the smallest of any state for which separate data were reported, and its relative share of the business declined drastically.

Comparisons between the geographical distribution of the machine tool industry are complicated by the lack of full comparability of much of the available data. For example, *Census of Manufactures* data for 1939 reflect only the metal-cutting machine tool (SIC 3541) producers while the data for earlier years include certain types of metal-forming machines and portable tools. The proportion of the latter to the metal-cutting machine tools varies enough from state to state to significantly affect the ranking by state. It is estimated, for example, that data for 1937 for Illinois and Pennsylvania should be reduced by about 40 per cent if only the metal-cutting machine tool establishments are to be compared. In the same way, figures for New Jersey and Rhode Island should be reduced by about 30 per cent; Ohio by 25 per cent; Connecticut, Indiana, Michigan, New York, and Vermont each by about 20 per cent; Massachusetts by 10 per cent, and Wisconsin by 5 per cent.

There does not appear to be any really satisfactory method for adjusting the data for 1919, 1929, or other years prior to 1939 to provide estimates of production or shipments by state covering metal-cutting machine tool producers, though this was done for the national totals based on the subtotals given for each type of machine. The NMTBA did not compile and release shipments or production estimates by state during the period studied. It is understood it intends to do so in the future. Other published information on machine tool production for states and regions appears to be based on the *Census of Manufactures* data and usually ignores the problem of changing definitions.

Changes in geographical distribution of the machine tool industry for the first half of the twentieth century, as a whole, appear less radical than those of the second half of the nineteenth century. Nevertheless, if machine tool data for the major tool producting regions are considered in terms of each region's relative share of machine tool employment or production, it is seen that the same basic trends continued into the twentieth century. There were intraregional shifts, however, which were relatively larger than those between regions. When data for the major machine tool building states are compared for 1900 and 1954, the intervening years appear to have brought drastic changes including some for which no explanation was found. (See Figures 2 and 3).

The three principal machine tool regions were New England, the Middle Atlantic States, and the East North Central States. New

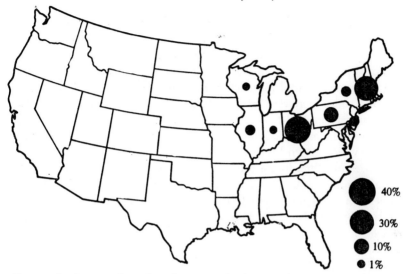

Figure 2. Geographic distribution of the machine tool industry, 1900.

Source of Data: Fred J. Miller, *Metal Working Machinery*, U.S. Census Bulletin 67. Based on Production of selected types of machine tools.

Figure 3. Geographic distribution of the machine tool industry, 1954.

Source of Data: U.S. Department of Commerce, Bureau of the Census, *Census of Manufactures*. Based on the number of wage earners in the machine tool industry.

England increased its relative share of the machine tool industry between 1900 and 1919 from 35.0 per cent to 39.9 per cent, but lost ground between 1919 and 1954 when its percentage had declined to 33.6 per cent. Within this region, Connecticut increased its share of the machine tool industry from 10.8 to 13.7 per cent while Vermont's share increased from 1.7 to 6.0 per cent. Massachusetts' share declined from 15.7 to 12.2 per cent between 1900 and 1919 and to 7.0 per cent in 1954. Rhode Island, however, followed a somewhat mystifying pattern by increasing its share from 6.8 to 13.6 per cent in 1919 and then losing ground until it had only 6.9 per cent of the business in 1954. The most probable explanation of the increase between 1900 and 1919 is that it was a temporary development resulting mainly from temporary demand generated by World War I.

Comparison of the distribution of wage earners in machine tool production for 1919 and 1939 in terms of percentages show that New England's share declined from 39.9 per cent to 33.2 per cent. (See Appendix Tables 3 and 4).

The relative importance of the Middle Atlantic Region declined from 18.6 to 13.0 per cent in 1919; to 10.6 per cent in 1939, and to 9.8 per cent by 1954. Within this region, New Jersey and Pennsylvania dropped between 1900 and 1919 and continued to drop until in 1954 their share was only 1.0 and 2.1 per cent respectively. New York's share declined from 5.6 in 1900 to 3.0 per cent in 1919 but then increased again to 6.7 percent in 1954.

The relative share of the East North Central States was about the same for 1919 as for 1900 but grew to 53.0 per cent in 1939, and to 53.4 per cent in 1954. As previously noted, the major increases were in Michigan (from 0.5 to 11.3 per cent); Wisconsin (2.0 to 7.0 per cent); and Illinois whose share increased from 3.3 to 8.9 per cent between 1900 and 1954. Ohio remained far in the lead but its percentage dropped rather drastically from 37.4 per cent to 24.2 per cent.

The *Census of Manufactures* data for 1919, 1929, and 1939 indicate that Ohio's machine tool industry produced almost the same value of products for each year with 1929 being a little higher than 1939 and 1919 slightly lower than 1939 (See Appendix Table 5). It should be noted that the *Census of Manufactures* data distributed by state represent all products of the machine tool industry rather than merely machine tools. The Bureau of the Census reports that the value of secondary products of one industry is usually largely offset by the production of other industries. However, this does not appear to have been the case in the machine tool industry whose secondary products in 1939 were valued at about $48 million while machine tools produced by other industries were valued at only about $10.5 million. The main distorting factor, however, is the fact that some establishments and states produce high percentages of secondary products while others produce few, if any. For example, the machine tool builders in Vermont appear to have produced few secondary products whereas the principal machine tool builder in Rhode Island produced a high percentage of secondary products. However, since the present study is concerned with the machine tool industry rather than merely machine tool production, total output as well as machine tool production should be considered.

Massachusetts was in second place in 1919 and 1939 with production amounting to slightly over one-third that of Ohio. Its 1939 production was slightly greater in dollar value than that of 1919 ($24.6 million in 1939 and $23.4 million in 1919). Connecticut was in second place in 1929 followed by Illinois with Massachusetts in fourth place. Massachusetts' production declined from 1919 to 1929 whereas Connecticut's production in 1929 was about 50 per cent higher than in 1919 but declined about 15 per cent for 1939 as compared to 1929. Rhode Island followed Massachusetts in production in 1919 but had a slightly higher percentage of wage earners engaged in machine tool production. The *Census of Manufactures* did not give Rhode Island's production for 1929 or 1939, on the ground that to do so would disclose an individual firm's operations. It is difficult to see why this should be any more true in 1929 and 1939 than in 1919 and 1947 when figures for Rhode Island were published. Actually, a single large firm accounted for a very high percentage of the machine tool industry's production in the state throughout the period. Michigan and Illinois moved ahead of Pennsylvania and gained somewhat on the leading machine tool producing states. This was a continuation of a trend noted in the first and second decades of the twentieth century.

Within the New England States, the same trends continued between 1919 and 1939 as were previously noted for the entire first half of the twentieth century—that is, Connecticut and Vermont increased their percentages from 10.3 to 12.4 and 3.8 to 4.7 respectively. Massachusetts' percentage declined from 12.2 to 7.2 and Rhode Island's from 13.6 to 8.9. Similar intraregional shifts were also noted in the Middle Atlantic States where New York increased its share from 3.0 to 5.4 per cent while New Jersey lost ground from 3.1 to 2.3 per cent. The shifts within the East North Central States differed somewhat from the longer range shifts previously noted in that Ohio increased its percentage from 26.1 in 1919 to 29.5 in 1939. Wisconsin increased from 4.4 to 7.0 per cent, Michigan from 6.0 to 7.7 per cent, and Illinois from 6.1 to 7.4 per cent.

These changes do not conform to any obvious pattern but suggest rather that the machine tool industry has been quite mobile and greatly influenced by major industrial changes such as the rapid development of the automobile and farm equipment industries and the stagnation of the railroad equipment industry. In other cases, such as Vermont, continued success during the period studied appears to have been due to the fact that a small group of companies continued to produce high-quality machine tools under competent management for sale to a diversified and widely distributed market.

Number and Size of Firms in the Machine Tool Industry

An effort was made to identify all establishments whose primary business during at least part of the period from 1900 to 1950 was the production of metal-cutting type machine tools (SIC 3541), and to obtain enough information for each firm to provide a measure of their relative importance in terms of employment in machine tool production and shipments of machine tools. Some employment data were found in National Recovery Administration (NRA) files for what were probably most of the major machine tool firms operating in April 1934. This was a low point, but not the lowest point, of the great depression. Data on both employment and shipments for a wartime peak period in 1942 were extracted from War Production Board reports. The employment figures are for December 1942, whereas shipment information is for April 1942 when production and shipments were still rising at a rapid rate. It is felt that the 1942 figures are reasonably representative of the peak capacity of the machine tool industry for the period under study, whereas those for 1934 reflect a period of severe depression when a large part of the industry's capacity was idle.

The data were tabulated by state and by size of establishment groupings based on employment in machine tools production. Establishments were classified as follows:

a. Over 500 employees in machine tool production were classified "Large."
b. 100 to 499 employees in machine tool production were classified "Medium."
c. 1 to 99 employees in machine tool production were classified "Other."

Firms for which no data on employment or shipments was secured or which made machine tools as a secondary product were included under "Other." The above data appear in Appendix Tables 8-11.

A total of 532 establishments was identified of which 57 were classified as "Large," 105 as "Medium," and the remaining 370 fell in the "Other" category. The last group seems very large but includes many firms which produced machine tools for a very short period, such as during one of the two major wars, and which were liquidated, merged, or converted to other products. This group probably represented no more than 10 per cent of machine tool production, employment, or shipments totals.

The large machine tool firms range from the Cincinnati Milling Machine Company which had 6,902 wage earners employed in machine tool production in December of 1942 and 1,400 in April of 1934 to comparatively small firms with a little over 500 wage earners producing machine tools in December 1942. The twenty-five largest firms (See Appendix Tables 8 and 9) had about 53 per cent of the industry's wage earners and shipments in 1942 and 61 per cent in 1934. These figures would seem to confirm the theory that large firms fared better than small or medium-sized firms in periods of depression. However, since the available data for 1934 are less complete than that for 1942, it is doubtful how much emphasis should be put on this comparison.

Seven of the largest twenty-five firms were located in Ohio; four each in Connecticut and Vermont; three in Massachusetts; two each in Pennsylvania and Wisconsin; and one each in Michigan, New York, and Rhode Island. Four Ohio firms were among the largest twelve firms having over 2,000 wage earners producing machine tools in December 1942. Rhode Island's one large firm, Brown and Sharpe Manufacturing Company, was second in terms of machine tool employment in 1942 with the Bullard Company of Connecticut in third place. The Warner and Swasey Company of Cleveland, Ohio was in fourth place followed by another Ohio firm, the National Acme Company, in fifth place. The fifty-seven large firms together had 71 per cent of the machine tool wage earners in December 1942 or, to put it another way, about one-sixth of the establishments had over seven-tenths of the employees.

The 105 medium-sized firms had about 27 per cent of the machine tool wage earners in December 1942 although they represented about a third of the machine tool producers in operation. The remaining 50 per cent of the machine tool builders probably employed no more than 3 to 5 per cent of the total wage earners in December 1942.

Ohio had fifteen firms which could be classified as "Large" (having over 500 wage earners producing machine tools). All of these firms remained in operation throughout the period through World War II with one being merged in 1948 and another in 1950. Ohio also had thirty establishments which fell in the "Medium" range, of which one was liquidated in 1921 and another in 1947. Three were merged at the end of World War II (1947-1948). Ohio had eighty-six other establishments which produced machine tools within the period studied of which twenty-seven were liquidated prior to World War II and ten were merged. The remaining establishments were probably a very minor factor in terms of Ohio's machine tool production and a considerable number of them were liquidated, merged, or fully converted to other products during or shortly after World War II.

Connecticut and Massachusetts were about equal from the standpoint of the number of establishments producing machine tools. Connecticult had four "Large" establishments and five "Medium" of which one was liquidated in 1950. The State had a total of forty-six other establishments which produced machine tools of which sixteen were liquidated, merged, or converted to other products. The remaining thirty establishments were a minor factor in Connecticut's machine tool production. Massachusetts had seven establishments in the "Large" class but the largest was about half the size of Connecticut's largest. Massachusetts also had ten "Medium" establishments, three of which were liquidated at the end of World War II (1946-49). It had thirty-seven other establishments which produced machine tools of which twenty were liquidated, merged, or converted to other products. Michigan, New York, and Illinois had almost the same number of establishments making machine tools within the period studied (forty-eight, forty-six, and forty-five respectively). In Michigan, the medium-sized establishments were much more important than in the other states where most of the employment and production was accounted for by a few large firms. Michigan had a larger number of firms (nineteen) liquidated, merged, or converted to other products, but these, with one exception, were minor machine tool producers. Pennsylvania had a total of twenty-eight machine tool producers and Wisconsin twenty-six, with other states far behind in terms of number of establishments. There were instances, as in the case of Rhode Island, where a single company represented a large percentage of the state's machine tool industry.

During the period between 1919 and 1939, the number of new machine tool builders was much smaller than for the period 1900 to 1919. The number of "Large" and "Medium" establishments entering the machine tool business between 1919 and 1939 was twenty-five compared to seventy-one for the preceding period. In this respect, Michigan led with four and Ohio with three new establishments. Massachusetts added two new machine tool builders.

During the first half of the twentieth century, few of the large- and medium-sized machine tool establishments were liquidated, although some did change ownership, a few were merged, and others underwent periods of severe strain and reorganization (See Appendix Table 14). Somewhat more frequently, the larger firms acquired the assets of, or particular machine tool lines from, smaller companies or became more integrated by establishing or buying foundries to provide castings needed for major machine tool components. There were few cases where machine tool builders acquired unrelated businesses or where diversified companies acquired major machine tool plants, although both types of business consolidation became more common in the period after World War II.

There was a high mortality rate among the small machine tool builders whose numbers far exceeded their relative importance as machine tool producers. Liquidations and mergers were highest during periods of depression or recession such as 1921-1922 and 1930-1934, but some occurred even in periods of general prosperity. This was probably due to a variety of factors some of which had nothing to do with the level of demand for machine tools. For example, some of the small firms entered the machine tool business with few assets either financial, managerial, or technical and quickly failed. Others were members of other industries and produced machine tools during short periods of peak wartime demand with no intention of continuing in the machine tool business.

Of the twenty-five largest firms, twenty were in business in 1900 and remained in business through the first half of the twentieth century. Two additional firms in this group began operation in 1903 and one each in 1909, 1916, and 1919. A total of thirty-eight of the large firms were in operation by 1900; fifteen more were formed by 1919 and one each in 1921 and 1931. Of these firms, only two were liquidated prior to 1950—one in 1949 and one in 1947. These were the Canedy-Otto Manufacturing Company of Chicago Heights, Illinois, which was sold at public auction in 1949 and purchased by the Cincinnati Lathe and Tool Company; and Wm. Sellers & Company which was absorbed by the Consolidated Machine Tool Corporation of Rochester, New York, in 1947 when Sellers' Philadelphia plant was closed.

The failure rate among medium-sized firms during the period from 1900 to 1950 was somewhat higher than for the large firms and averaged about 0.26 per cent per year. Actually, the liquidations were concentrated into seven years with a rate of 1.72 per cent in 1921 and rates varying between 1.56 and 3.33 per cent in the years 1945–1950 with the peak in 1949.

As previously indicated, the number of liquidations was much higher among the smaller firms averaging 1.83 per cent per year for the entire period covered. There were some liquidations in most of the years but the peak of 9.95 per cent was reached in 1921 followed closely by 1922 when the rate was 7.4 per cent. The other years in which the rate was high were 1924 (4.47 per cent), 1933 (4.12 per cent), 1914 (4.06 per cent), and 1932 (3.47 per cent). Somewhat surprisingly, the peak production and demand year of 1942 showed a rather high failure rate of 2.84 per cent. The rates for 1947-1949 were 2.82, 2.27, and 2.28 per cent respectively.

A comparison of the average percentages of liquidations among machine tool builders and for all types of business is included in the Appendix Table 15. This indicates that, in a number of years, the rate for the machine tool industry was lower than that for all businesses. These appeared to be mainly years of industrial expansion while the machine tool rate was much higher in other years when industrial activity was stable or declining. There were exceptions to this pattern, however, as in the period from 1939 to 1942.

The average life of the firms which were liquidated or went out of the machine tool business during the period from 1900–1950 was calculated from the available data for 154 firms. The average life for large firms was approximately forty years; for medium-sized firms, it was about 35.5 years; and for other firms, 13.4 years. During the same period, an additional sixty-three machine tool firms were involved in mergers including five large firms, nine medium-sized firms and forty-nine other firms.

Expansion of Machine Tool Using Industries

In order to better understand the changes which took place in the machine tool industry it is desirable to look at some of the changes taking place in other industries. The period from 1899 through 1919 was generally one in which manufacturing expanded much more rapidly than population. It has been estimated that manufacturing production for 1919 was more than double that for 1899. Most of the increase appears to have been due to mechanization and improvements in production methods since the only significant gain in the work force was in the period from 1904 to 1909.[4]

Production Index

Census Year	Index	Census Year	Index
1899	100	1914	169
1904	122	1919	214
1909	159		

Most of the increase in output was in metal products including automobiles, trucks, agricultural equipment, and industrial machinery for whose production a variety of improved machine tools was essential. The reason for this trend may also be illustrated by comparing statistics of capital investment in key manufacturing industries. (See Table 16).

These industries displayed a wide range in growth of capital

[4] H. U. Faulkner, *Decline of Laissez Faire, 1897–1917* (New York: Rinehart and Company, Inc., 1951), pp. 115–117, 147; U.S. Bureau of Census, *Historical Statistics of the United States, Colonial Times to 1957* (Washington: Government Printing Office, 1960), pp. 7, 409.

investment ranging from the locomotive and railroad equipment industry where the increase in value of investment was only 89 per cent to the motor vehicle industry whose capital increased by 255 per cent. Capital for manufacturing generally increased 164 per cent. It would thus appear that manufacturing production increased considerably more rapidly than did capital invested. No comparable data was found on the amount of investment represented by metal-cutting machine tools, though it may be assumed that nearly all the tools produced from 1900 to 1919 were still in use —not necessarily in the hands of the original purchaser—plus a considerable number of tools produced during the years prior to 1900. Some tools still in use dated back to the Civil War, but the total depreciated value of tools over thirty years old in 1919 was probably negligible.

The most spectacular growth during this period was in passenger automobiles which rose from $6.0 million in 1900 to $1,296.6 million in 1919 or by 21,500 per cent (See Appendix Table 20). Production of the first automobiles was made possible by the existence and prior experience of general machine shops, the sewing machine industry, the bicycle industry, steam engine builders, small arms producers, carriage and wagon makers, and machine tool builders. The automobile industry's rapid growth provided a new and growing market first for general purpose machine tools and soon for special high production tools designed to meet the industry's needs for rapid production of standardized parts. The automobile industry was primarily responsible for the rapid growth of machine tool production in Michigan and also provided new business to many firms in Ohio, Wisconsin, Indiana, and other states. It was also largely responsible for the rapid development of the construction machinery industry for road building. It seems obvious that the influence of special demand such as that of the automobile industry had the greatest and most direct influence on the location of builders of special tools for the particular industry. It had less influence on the location of firms building a varied line of general-purpose machine tools and perhaps also other products having a wide market.[5]

[5] E. W. Miller, *Geography of Manufacturing* (Englewood Cliffs, N. J.: Prentice-Hall, Inc., 1962), pp. 3–7; R. S. Woodbury, *History of the Grinding Machine* (Cambridge, Mass.: The M.I.T. Press, 1959), pp. 98–99; W. S. Woytinsky and E. S. Woytinsky, *World Population and Production* (New York: The Twentieth Century Fund, 1953), p. 1149.

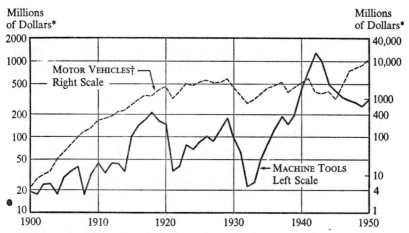

Figure 4. Machine tool shipments and motor vehicle production, 1900–1950.

Sources: NMTBA estimates.

U.S. Department of Commerce, Bureau of the Vensus, *Historical Statistics of the United States—Colonial Times to 1957.*

* Logarithmic vertical scale used.

† Includes passenger cars, trucks, and buses.

In Figure 4, production indices for machine tools and motor vehicles are plotted. Again, a ratio chart is used to show relative growth rates. Note that from 1914 on, with exception of the war periods, the shapes of the curves are quite similar.

While production and sales of automobiles rose rapidly year after year through 1916 when World War I caused a temporary reduction in passenger car production, these statistics do not indicate the fact that many automobile builders failed and went out of business or were absorbed by other firms and that only a few firms grew rapidly. In some cases, plants and machine tools were taken over by other firms. Some automobiles, moreover, were technical successes but commercial failures for various reasons despite the fact that the market for low- and medium-priced automobiles seemed almost unlimited. Some automobile firms emphasized high quality in engineering and construction and style in coachwork while others, of which Ford is an outstanding example, concentrated on mass production of a standardized low-cost vehicle which would provide comparatively reliable, though not luxurious, transportation.

The machine tool industry provided automobile builders with advice and assistance on production problems as well as a variety of machine tools. In addition, it was not only a source of skilled machinists but also of production experts such as Walter E. Flanders, who was hired by Ford in the Fall of 1906.[6] This contribution of manpower by the machine tool industry was not—with the exception of normal advice and service to customers—voluntary and was frequently lamented by machine tool builders. Nevertheless, it was of considerable importance to the automobile industry as well as being a drain on the resources of the machine tool industry.

Production of agricultural equipment in the United States increased from about $100.6 million in 1900 to $187.8 million in 1914 and to $396.6 million in 1919 (See Appendix Table 20). Like the development of the automobile, the expansion of agricultural equipment production and farm mechanization after 1900 was closely related to the development of the internal combustion engine first for stationary power and later for use in tractors and trucks. Between 1910 and 1919, the number of farm tractors in use rose from 1,000 to 158,000 and the number of trucks from zero to 111,000. World War I which generated labor shortages also stimulated farm mechanization and indirectly demand for machine tools to build agricultural equipment.[7]

World War I and the years immediately preceding it also saw the birth and development of another industry which would eventually be a major machine tool user. U.S. aircraft production grew from one in 1910 to 14,020 in 1918 before again falling drastically to 780 planes in 1919.[8] The full impact of the aircraft industry was not to be felt, however, until World War II.

The railroad equipment industry and railroad maintenance shops were major customers of the machine tool industry during the second half of the nineteenth century and some of the more important tool builders specialized in large machine tools used by this industry. A record production of 2,300 locomotives was reached in 1890 but was drastically affected by the panic of 1893, falling to

6 Alan Nevins and Frank Ernest Hill, *Ford, The Times, The Man, The Company* (New York: Charles Scribner Sons, 1954), Vol. 1, p. 334.

7 V. S. Clark, *History of Manufactures* (New York: McGraw-Hill Book Company, 1929), Vol. III, p. 315; Faulkner, *Decline of Laissez Faire*, pp. 331–332; *Historical Statistics of the U. S.*, Series P250–306, p. 420.

8 Woytinsky, *World Population*, p. 1171.

less than 700 before beginning to recover. By 1899, however, locomotive production again exceeded the 1890 level and in 1900 a total of 3,153 locomotives was produced. Production continued to rise, with a setback in 1904, until 1907 when a peak of 7,362 locomotives was produced. This peak was followed by another drastic reduction to 2,340 in 1908 and 2,877 in 1909. There were similar rather drastic fluctuations until a new peak of 6,475 units was reached in 1918 followed by a sharp reduction to 3,272 in 1919 (See Appendix Table 21).

Railroad equipment output (locomotives and cars) grew from $130.0 million in 1900 to a peak of $734.0 million in 1918; dropped to almost bottom in 1933 when only $13.6 million in railroad equipment was produced, and then improved somewhat until 1937 when it amounted to $119.1 million. The diesel locomotive appeared about 1925 and by 1950 was rapidly replacing the remaining steam locomotives on American railroads.[9]

Both railroad equipment and the machine tools used in their production and maintenance had a long useful life. After production of steam locomotives began to decline there was little demand for new machine tools for this segment of the industry or for railroad shops for their maintenance. Introduction and expansion of production and use of diesel locomotives provided some new business for machine tool builders, but this business went to other firms than those which had produced tools for the steam locomotive builders. Whereas steam locomotive production had been concentrated in the Baldwin Works and the American Locomotive Company, the General Motors Corporation became dominant in the production of diesel locomotives. As previously indicated, the decline of the steam locomotive was a major cause of the decline in Pennsylvania's importance as a producer of machine tools since it was a major producer of heavy machine tools for railroad equipment producers and railroad maintenance shops.

Between 1900 and 1913, the tonnage carried by United States railroads more than doubled, reaching 300 billion ton miles, but this tonnage actually required fewer locomotives and cars than in preceding years because of the fact that locomotives, cars, and rails were able to handle heavier loads. The freight tonnage rose to

[9] Clark, *Manufactures*, pp. 136–139; *Historical Statistics of the U.S.*, Series P250–306, p. 421.

408,778 million ton miles in 1918 but fell somewhat to 367,161 million in 1919.[10]

The railroad equipment industry in the twentieth century was much less important as a machine tool customer than it had been in the last half of the nineteenth century. Nevertheless, some machine tool builders still hoped or expected that this trend would be reversed and that the railroads and railroad equipment industries would embark on a major modernization program after World War I. This hope may have caused them to delay or limit their efforts to develop other machines and find other markets.

Conversion of the shipbuilding industry from wood to steel, including construction of important shipbuilding operations on the Great Lakes, provided a substantial demand at the end of the nineteenth century for some types of machine tools to produce propulsion machinery and other equipment. However, the shipbuilding industry performed very erratically during the first two decades of the twentieth century, varying between 190,000 and 300,000 tons in most years between 1900 and 1913, falling to 156,000 tons in 1914, and then rising again until 3,580,000 tons were launched in 1919 and almost 4,000,000 tons in 1920. Between World Wars I and II, shipbuilding again declined drastically in the face of foreign competition and reduction in naval construction.[11]

It has been noted that proximity to major tool users was a major factor directly affecting the establishment and location of many machine tool builders. The large machine tool using industries, however, were strongly influenced by the availability of labor and particularly skilled mechanics from other industries. These were important factors influencing the location of major metalworking plants along the Great Lakes and in the Pittsburgh area.

The principal raw material used by machine tool builders was gray iron castings usually supplied by independent foundries. There was a trend, during the first decades of the twentieth century, among the larger tool builders to acquire or establish their own foundries and thereby free themselves from dependence on the not always very reliable services of the custom foundries. Machine tool

[10] Clark, *Manufactures*, p. 141; *Historical Statistics of the U.S.*, Series P73–86, p. 431.
[11] Clark, *Manufactures*, pp. 145, 313; Woytinsky, *World Population*, pp. 1160–1161.

builders also required various sizes and types of bar steel which were purchased through local distributors rather than directly from the steel mills. Since the cost of these materials was a relatively small part of the total cost of the finished machine, it does not appear that material transportation costs were a significant factor influencing the location of machine tool plants. The machine tool builder purchased other machine components including, particularly, electric motors and controls, and often the transmissions used to transmit power from the motors to the cutting-tool, table, and other moving parts. They also often purchased various accessories from firms specializing in these items. It would be interesting to analyze the types and amounts of semifinished materials and components purchased from other firms; to relate these to the operations performed by the machine tool builder, and to the distribution of machine tool output to the using industries. Adequate data for this purpose were not found for the period covered by the history. Machine tool establishments were certainly not purely assembly plants in the same degree as many automobile plants, but they tended to become more rather than less dependent on other firms and industries for major components as well as basic materials and rough castings.

Since iron and steel were basic raw materials from which machine tools were built, and machine tools were, in turn, required to work a large part of steel produced at some stage in the process of converting the raw material into finished products, it would seem probable that there would be a correlation between demand for machine tools and production of iron and steel. Consequently, data on physical production for steel ingots and castings were compared with available data on machine tools. Unfortunately, in the case of machine tools, physical volume data (number of units) were not available for the period 1901–1918, and were not too satisfactory, in any case, due to the wide variation in machine tools and the changes which occurred in them over the period from 1900 to 1950. Shipment data in dollars are affected by changes in price levels and in the value of money. However, where fluctuations within short periods were compared, the above limitations were not considered too serious. In Figure 5, machine tool shipments and long tons of steel ingots are plotted using two different logarithmic

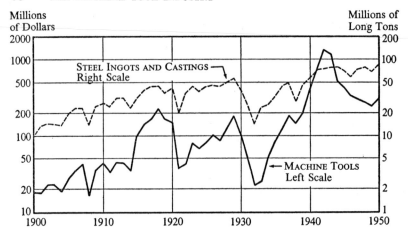

Figure 5. Machine tool shipments and production of steel ingots and castings.

Sources: NMTBA estimates.
U.S. Department of Commerce, Bureau of the Census, *Historical Statistics of the United States—Colonial Times to 1957.*

scales—one for dollars and one for long tons. The left scale therefore applies to machine tools, the right to steel ingots and castings.

Peak years for steel production and machine tool shipments were compared with interesting but not too helpful results. Thus steel production reached peaks in 1902 and 1906 ahead of corresponding peaks in machine tool shipments. In 1910 and 1913, peaks for both were reached in the same year while steel production reached a World War I peak one year ahead of the peak for machine tools in 1918. The situation was reversed in World War II when machine tool shipments peaked in 1942, two years ahead of the peak for steel output. Steel production rose substantially in 1920 over 1919 whereas machine tool shipments were declining. Both steel and machine tools peaked in 1923, 1926, 1929, and 1937. In both 1944 and 1948, steel output reached peaks while machine tools were declining.

If low points are considered in relation to the preceding peaks, the results are as follows. Steel production in 1904 was about 7 per cent below 1902. Machine tool shipments for 1904 were more than 22 per cent below the previous peak of 1903. Steel output in 1908 was about 40 per cent below the previous peak in 1907 while machine tool shipments fell almost 60 per cent in 1908 compared to 1907. Steel output in 1911 was about 9 per cent lower than in 1910 while machine tool shipments fell about 26 per cent between 1910 and 1911. Steel output for 1919 was about 27 per cent below the previous peak of 1916 and in 1921 was about 58 per cent below the 1916 level. Machine tool shipments fell about 84 per cent between their peak in 1918 and the low of 1921.

Steel output in 1924 was about 16 per cent below 1923 while machine tool shipments fell only about 12 per cent. In 1927, steel shipments were about 7 per cent below 1926 while machine tool shipments fell by about 17 per cent. Steel shipments fell about 76 per cent between 1929 and 1932 while machine tool shipments fell by about 88 per cent. In 1938 steel shipments were about 44 per cent below 1937, while machine tool shipments declined about 25 per cent (the second time machine tool shipments fell by a smaller percentage than steel output). Steel output fell about 26 per cent between 1944 and 1946, their low point since 1939. Machine tool shipments declined from their peak in 1942 until 1949 by about 88 per cent in number of units. From the above figures, it is apparent that machine tools declined more sharply than steel output in all except two instances, 1924 and 1938.

Between 1900 and 1910, the farm equipment industry was a more important consumer of steel than the automobile industry. However, the latter industry was expanding rapidly and quickly became a more important user of machine tools. The early peaks in farm equipment production coincided with those for steel and preceded those for machine tools by about a year. Production of farm equipment continued to increase through World War I until a peak was reached in 1919, a year later than for machine tools and about three years after the peak in steel output was reached. By World War I, tractor production was also becoming a significant factor and continued to expand until 1920. Production of automobiles was temporarily reduced during 1918 by over 25 per cent. American industry was still in the "tooling-up" process when World War I ended. This was probably the main reason why machine tool production also reached a peak in 1918 unlike the situation in World War II when machine tool production reached a peak in 1942 long before the war ended.

Age and Distribution of Machine Tools in the Principal Tool Using Industries

Machine tools held by the primary machine tool using industries are reflected in the various "Inventories" of metalworking equipment published by the *American Machinist* at intervals of five (or more recently four) years since 1925. This information is based on a sampling procedure rather than a complete survey of the metalworking industries and may not be accurate in all respects. However, it should be adequate to indicate generally how many machine tools were in the hands of different industry groupings (See Appendix Table 17).

The *American Machinist* "Inventory" for 1940 estimated that there were about 942,000 machine tools in use by U.S. industries. The largest number was held by the "Fabricated Metal Products" industry with about 359,000 units in place. About 76 per cent of this total were over ten years old as compared to the overall average of 72 per cent for all industries. The second largest accumulation was in the "Motor Vehicles and Parts" industry which had about 130,500 machine tools. About 63 per cent of this industry's tools were over ten years old or considerably less than the overall average though far above the percentage for 1930. The "Shipbuilding, Ordnance, Miscellaneous" industry grouping had about 73,800 machine tools or slightly more than the "Metalworking Machinery" group with 71,300. The "Metalworking Machinery" group had 71 per cent of its machine tools in the over ten years old category as compared with 76 per cent for the "Shipbuilding, Ordnance, Miscellaneous" industry.

The overall number of machine tools in use by U.S. industries rose rather rapidly between 1925 and 1930 by about 25 per cent (see Figure 6). It then began a slow decline until 1935 and a somewhat more rapid decline between 1935 and 1940 when the influence of World War II began to take effect. The number of units over ten years of age rose rapidly from 1925 to 1935 by almost 200 per cent, and then declined slowly until about 1945. No data on the number of units over twenty years old was compiled prior to 1940 when it appears that about 110,000 machine tools were over twenty years old. Since all the World War I machine tools would have been at least twenty years old by 1939, this would indicate that

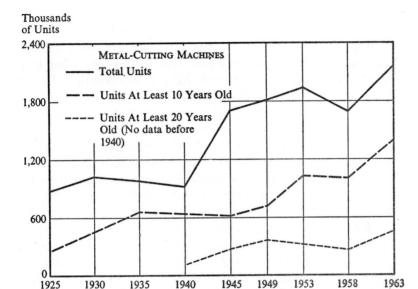

Figure 6. Age of machine tools.

Source: *American Machinist.*

roughly four out of five World War I tools had been scrapped. This proportion, however, is almost certainly too high since the *American Machinist's* inventories did not cover all the government-owned tools, many of which were of World War I vintage or earlier.

The *American Machinist* also tabulated the inventory data by type of machine, thus giving some indication of both the varying average age of different types of machines and of the types which were currently being preferred. In 1930, for example, about 50 per cent of all tools in use were over ten years old, but in the case of vertical boring machines about 76 per cent were more than ten years old whereas only about 24 per cent of internal grinders were over ten years old. The smallness of the latter figure apparently was due to the recent rapid increase in the use of this type of grinding machine both because of the improvement of the machines and the increased use of heat-treated steels. Planers showed the next highest percentage of machines over ten years old with about 69 per cent in this category. This is not surprising since relatively few new planers were being built. Planers were generally considered to have a long life and had been in use for many years. Engine lathes were third in the percentage of machines over ten years old with about 60 per cent as contrasted with the newer types of automatic lathes where only 29 per cent were over ten years old. The latter percentage was probably influenced by the fact that relatively few automatic lathes were produced during World War I. The only other type where the percentage over ten years old was significantly below 50 per cent was multiple spindle upright drilling machines.

The information for the earlier years indicates among other things that the percentage of machine tools over ten years old held by the "Motor Vehicles and Parts" industry remained steady between 1925 and 1930 at 27 per cent but then rose until in 1940, 63 per cent of the industry's machine tools were more than ten years old. This tends to confirm that the industry generally had modified its policy of replacing tools in the direction of retaining them for longer periods. It tends to support the claims of machine tool builders that their machines were being built to last longer. It can also be partially accounted for by the reduced level of motor vehicle production in the period from 1930 to 1940 as compared with the peak year of 1929, and by the fact that few major changes in automobile design or construction had occurred (See Table 17).

The information for the "Fabricated Metal Products" group shows that the number of tools over ten years old declined very substantially from 59 to 49 per cent between 1925 and 1930, then increased rapidly from 49 per cent to 76 per cent in 1940. These figures reflect a "boom and bust" situation in which the industry was first expanding and modernizing at a rapid rate followed by general stagnation during the depression years.

Information on the "Metalworking Machinery" industry was not reported for 1925 or 1930 but the percentage of machine tools over ten years old rose from 66 per cent in 1935 to 71 per cent in 1940.

The "General Industrial Machinery" industry apparently modernized between 1925 and 1930 sufficiently to reduce the percentage of machine tools over ten years old from 52 to 47, and then held most of its tools until, by 1940, 78 per cent were over ten years old. The "Agricultural Machinery" industry seems to have followed a somewhat steadier course regarding tool replacement in that between 1925 and 1930, the number of machine tools over ten years old declined from 65 to 58 per cent and then increased to 69 per cent in 1940.

The "Railroad Equipment" industry had 56 per cent of its machine tools over ten years old in 1925 and this percentage rose to 74 per cent in 1930—the highest percentage of any industry surveyed. Rather surprisingly, the percentage dropped to 71 per cent in 1935, probably more as a result of scrapping the oldest and most obsolete equipment and shops than as a result of new purchases of machine tools. It then rose again to 83 per cent in 1940.

Overall the number of machines over ten years old rose from 44 per cent in 1925 to 52 per cent in 1930, 67 per cent in 1935, and 72 per cent in 1940. These figures are consistent with the fact that machine tool demand was depressed during most of this period.

The percentages of machine tools over ten or twenty years old were, of course, affected both by industry policies regarding the scrapping or selling of obsolete tools and those governing the purchase of new machines. Some shops, when not pressed for space, kept machine tools in place long after they ceased to be of much value, and even though they were used only a small part of the time. Others followed much stricter policies of selling or scrapping obsolete equipment either to make room for other equipment or just because it was considered to be harmful to employee morale and efficiency to have obsolete equipment on the shop floor. This was true even when the space was not actually immediately needed for other equipment. It is also apparent that where acquisition of new equipment was concentrated in a short period, there was a corresponding rapid increase in the percentage of machine tools over ten or twenty years old after this lapse of time. This accounts for the increase in the percentage of machine tools over ten years old in 1930. Despite the fact that there was considerable modernization during the period 1925 to 1930, it was more than balanced by the higher output during World War I. Thus it is estimated that 540 to 550 thousand new machine tools were shipped during the five years 1915 through 1919 as compared with about 156 thousand in the period 1925 through 1929. The number shipped in 1930 was the lowest since 1921. Clearly, the percentage of tools over ten years old could have been maintained—assuming the 1925 to 1930 rate of acquisition of new machine tools—only if there had been a general and very aggressive program for scrapping older machines produced during or before World War I.

For the period from 1919 through 1939, the NMTBA's reports of the number of new machine tools shipped indicate that approximately 420 thousand machine tools were shipped in the ten year period from 1919 through 1928, about 263 thousand between 1929 and 1938, and about 52 thousand in 1939 or a total of about 735 thousand of which over half would be over ten years old in 1940. It is assumed that with the exception of tools exported, almost all the tools shipped from 1919 through 1939 were in use in 1940 plus a part of those delivered between 1915 and 1919 as well as some pre-World War I machine tools.

A total of about 1,762,000 machine tools was in use by the metalworking industries in 1949. This represented an increase of about 51,000 or 3 per cent from 1945, and 820,000 more than 1940, or nearly double the 1940 level. Of the total for 1949, 43 per cent were over ten years old and 21 per cent over twenty years old. The small percentage increase in the total volume between 1945 and 1949 together with the very large increase between 1940 and 1945 made it almost certain that there would be a correspondingly large increase in machines over ten years old in the period from 1949 to 1953.[12]

About 376,000 machine tools of the 1949 total were held by a rather miscellaneous industrial grouping "Fabricated Metal Products" (including SIC 2514, 2522, 2523, 2541, 34, 375, 379, 39) consisting of 6,963 plants with twenty-one or more employees each. Of the total number of machine tools, about 45 per cent were more than ten years old, and 23 per cent over twenty-years old or slightly above the overall averages. It is believed that of this very large number of machine tools, the number of relatively low-cost machines was probably substantially higher than in the "Motor Vehicles and Parts" industry.

The second largest aggregate holdings of about 241,000 machine tools was held by the "Shipbuilding, Ordnance, Miscellanous" group (SIC 19, 332, 336, 3391, 3393, 351, 373). This group was in considerably better shape than the average since only 36 per cent of its tools was more than ten years old and 18 per cent over twenty years old. Both this group and the preceding one are so broad, how-

[12] *American Machinist*, "The Mid-Century Inventory of Metalworking Production Equipment," Nov. 3, 1949; U.S. Senate Joint Committee on Defense Production, 82nd Congress, 2nd Session, Report 1107, *Defense Production Act, Progress Report No. 13, Machine Tools* (Washington: Government Printing Office, 1952), pp. 8–10.

ever, that the total figure doesn't give a very precise picture of how machine tools were distributed.

The third largest holding of machine tools in 1949 was the 162,-000 held by the "Electrical Equipment" industry (SIC 361, 364, 365, 366, 369). About 37 per cent were over ten years old and 18 per cent over twenty years old.

The fourth largest holding of machine tools in 1949 was the 147,-000 held by the "Metalworking Machinery" industry (SIC 354). Approximately 43 per cent of these tools were over ten years old (a small improvement from 1945) and 22 per cent were over twenty years old.

The "Motor Vehicles and Parts" industry (SIC 371) was fifth with about 139,000 machine tools of which 56 per cent were over ten years old and 28 per cent over twenty years old. Many of these tools were of the large, complex, specialized, and expensive types used for high volume production of engines and transmissions, and whose total cost was large in comparison to the number of units involved. However, in 1945, the industry had held 244,000 units or 87.7 per cent more machine tools than in 1940. The fact that all of this increase was in new machines caused the industry's percentage of tools over ten years old to drop to 37 per cent, their lowest point since 1930.

Most of the new tools were government-owned and were either sold after the war or placed in storage. It is not known how many were purchased by the automobile industry, but it appears that a large part of this industry's holdings of 139,000 in 1949 were tools of pre-1940 vintage, since the percentage of tools over ten years old had risen to 56 per cent. This was still less than the 63 per cent over ten years old held in 1940. In 1949, the automobile industry ("Motor Vehicles and Parts") had about 77,840 machine tools over ten years old, 38,920 machines over twenty years old, and 61,160 less than ten years old. It is also noted from the *Census of Manufactures* for 1947 that the industry invested about $185,000,000 in production machinery and equipment, but no information was found as to how much of this investment was for machine tools.

In the overall total of 1,762,000 machine tools in 1949 about 370,-000 were apparently over twenty years old. It would have required ten years to replace just these machines at the 1949 rate of production even if no tools were exported. Since a somewhat larger number were also between ten and twenty years old, it seems apparent there was a large potential replacement market. A major question mark, however, was how many of these machines were not really needed and were occupying plant space not required for the current level of manufacturing production which was far below the peak World War II levels (see Appendix Table 18). With the new machine tools added during World War II, there was probably little need for many plants to add new tools except where it could be clearly demonstrated that the postwar machines were so much better than the older machines that the latter were uneconomical to use.

Between 1945 and 1949, the largest relative increases in the number of machine tools held occurred in "Miscellaneous Machine Parts and Jobbing" industry (SIC 359) which increased by over 400 per cent from 17,235 to 100,847; the "Office and Store Machines" industry (SIC 357) which increased over 160 per cent from 17,307 to 45,645 machine tools; the "General Industrial Equipment" industry (SIC 356) which increased by over 70 per cent from 26,939 to 99,441 machine tools, and "Metalworking Equipment" industry (SIC 354) which increased over 60 per cent from 91,430 to 147,327. The largest reductions were in the "Aircraft and Parts" industry (SIC 372) which declined by over 80 per cent from 276,466 to 54,711, and the "Motor Vehicle and Parts" industry (SIC 371) which declined by about 40 per cent from 243,686 to 138,595 machine tools.

Identifying the major machine tool using areas and relating them to the producing areas is complicated by the fact that the available production information from the Census of Manufactures is by states whereas the user data in the American Machinist's "Mid-Century Inventory of Metalworking Production Equipment" for 1949 is tabulated by marketing areas which do not follow state lines. In the latter, eighteen urbanized industrial centers are identified, many of which include counties in two or more states. While these centers vary in both area and population, they are all comparatively small in area. There are also seven large geographical areas which include part or all of one or more states excluding the eighteen urbanized centers.

Of the urbanized centers, the largest number of machine tools was in the Boston area covering four counties in Massachusetts and one (Providence) in Rhode Island, which held 149,536 machine tools or about 35.5 tools for each 1,000 of population. The second largest concentration was in the New York area covering five counties in New York and seven in New Jersey, and which had 140,785 machine tools, but only 11.1 machines per 1,000 population. The Detroit area consisting of two counties in Michigan and one in Ohio was third among the urban centers with 122,443 machine tools or 40.4 per 1,000 of population. Detroit was second only to the Bridgeport area in terms of the ratio of machines to population though rather far behind since Bridgeport had 77.8 per 1,000 (See Appendix Table 26). Detroit was followed by Chicago, Bridgeport, and Cleveland with the other centers rather far behind in total numbers though some, such as Milwaukee, had a higher concentration ratio to population. (Milwaukee had 39.3 machine tools per 1,000 population). In the large geographic areas, the Midwestern Area consisting of Ohio, Michigan, Indiana, Illinois, and Wisconsin, except for the separate urban areas, was far ahead with 273,829 machine tools or 16.9 machines per 1,000 population. The southern area consisting of all the southeastern states except for the separate urbanized centers was second with 135,028 machine tools, but these represented only 4.6 per 1,000 population. This, of course, represented a large increase over the situation prior to World War II. The Middle Atlantic States, consisting of New York, New Jersey, and Pennsylvania, excluding the urban centers, were in third place with 130,111 machines or 16.2 per 1,000 of population. New England, Central and Mountain States, and Southeastern States were far behind in total number of machine tools, but New England had 17.4 machine tools per 1,000 of population, while the other two regions had only 2.7 and 2.2 per cent respectively.

If the totals for the Midwestern States are added to those for the urbanized centers in the same geographical area, the area formed corresponds to the "East North Central States" as used in the *Census of Manufactures.* This area had about 690,800 machine tools in 1949. This represented about 39 per cent of the national total of 1,762,000 which may be compared to 53.2 per cent of the nation's machine tools produced by the same area in 1947. This indicates that this area "exported," either to other areas of the United States or other countries, substantially more tools than it "imported."

New England had about 319,500 machine tools or 18.1 per cent of the national total. This may be compared with the 33.1 per cent of machine tool production in 1947 thus confirming the fact that New England was, in comparison to its own metalworking industry, an even larger exporter of machine tools than the East North Central States.

The Middle Atlantic States held about 449,105 machine tools or 25 per cent of the national total. This compares with production in 1947 of 12.1 per cent of the total production thus seeming to confirm that the Middle Atlantic States had become importers rather than exporters of machine tools. This was a substantial shift from the situation in 1900.

The Southern States, Central and Mountain States, Southwestern States and the Pacific Coast were all importers of machine tools, and the last three in particular still had very few machine tools in comparison either to their population or the huge geographical areas involved. There were, of course, within these areas industrial centers, such as Los Angeles and San Francisco which were becoming increasingly important in metalworking production.

Summary

The machine tool industry was not dominated by two or three large firms. Nevertheless, a relatively small group of companies of substantial size and resources did produce a high percentage of the industry's output and was able to survive the severe fluctuations in machine tool demand which followed the two major wars and the great depression of the thirties. The medium-sized companies also generally seemed to do reasonably well, but small firms found it much more difficult to maintain prices and continue in business during periods of recession.

In general, it appears that it was necessary to expand to a substantial size and to have sufficient resources, either from investors or retained earnings, to operate at an efficient level, maintain a reasonable level of development effort, and cover periodic losses when demand fell below the break-even point. Many small firms which entered the machine tool industry in periods of rapid expansion never reached this level and either were liquidated or decided after a few years that other production lines offered better prospects.

The number of new machine tool building firms established between 1919 and 1939 was much smaller than between 1900 and 1919 and was offset by the large number of liquidations, mergers, and conversions to other products during the recession of 1921–1922 and the depression of the thirties. Most of the firms liquidated or merged were among the smaller companies with limited resources. Some of the larger firms also experienced serious losses and, in some cases, underwent major reorganizations.

Most machine tool firms were corporately organized by 1919 and the individually owned firms or partnerships were largely among the smaller firms with a few exceptions. Corporations constituted 79.4 per cent of the machine tool firms reporting for the 1919 *Census of Manufactures* but employed 94.3 per cent of the industry's employees and produced 94.5 per cent of the output.

The principal geographic shifts in machine tool production during the first half of the twentieth century were in the increasing importance of Michigan, Wisconsin, and Illinois, and the declining importance of Pennsylvania and Massachusetts. The growth in the first three states was most closely related to the rapid expansion of the automobile industry, mechanization of agriculture, and road building. Most specifically, the growth in the machine tool industry was related to the replacement of the steam engine and animal power by the internal combustion engine. Conversely, the decline of Pennsylvania as a machine tool producer was most closely related to the stagnation of the railroad equipment industry and the decline of the steam locomotive. In the case of Massachusetts, its relative decline in production of machine tools appears to have been due to a more diverse combination of factors including the industry's failure to develop important new markets or to develop new equipment at a rapid enough rate.

New England, as a result of the performance of Connecticut and Vermont, maintained its relative position in the machine tool industry more successfully than did the Middle Atlantic States. In 1919, New England's share of machine tool production was higher than in 1900 mainly because Rhode Island's and Vermont's percentage of machine tool output approximately doubled. The growth in Rhode Island's share was not maintained, probably because it was largely due to demand generated by World War I. On the other hand, Vermont was able to maintain and improve its posi-

tion. However, the success of three of Vermont's leading tool builders in Springfield, Vermont and the Cone Machine Company of
Windsor, Vermont appears to have been despite rather than because of their location.

The major machine tool producing regions continued between
1919 and World War II to be the East North Central States, New
England, and the Middle Atlantic States. The East North Central
States increased their percentage of the industry mainly at the
expense of the Middle Atlantic States, but New England also lost
ground during this period. Ohio continued to be the leading machine tool producing state and regained some of the ground it lost
between 1900 and 1919. Massachusetts was in second place in 1919
in both production of machine tools and the number of wage
earners employed. By 1921, Connecticut moved ahead of Massachusetts in number of wage earners employed by the machine tool
industry and remained well ahead in 1939. Massachusetts was still
slightly ahead in machine tool production according to the *Census
of Manufactures* for 1939. Michigan and Illinois moved ahead of
Pennsylvania whose importance as a machine tool producer continued to decline. These shifts were closely related to the growth
of the automobile, agricultural machinery, and construction machinery industries, and the declining importance of the railroad
equipment industry.

There does not appear to have been a significant shift in the
regional distribution of machine tool production among the three
principal tool producing regions between 1939 and 1947. The Middle Atlantic States lost a little ground but this probably was due
mainly to some increase in machine tool production outside the
three main regions. Michigan showed the greatest gain of any of
the states while Ohio's share declined rather substantially. Connecticut was in second place in 1947 and 1939 while Michigan moved
into third place in 1947 well ahead of Rhode Island.

The relationship between the value of machine tools and secondary products produced by the machine tool industry remained
almost the same in 1947 as in 1939. On the other hand, the percentage of machine tools produced by the machine tool industry
as compared to machine tool production by other industries declined rather substantially from 94 per cent in 1939 to 86 per cent
in 1947, but this trend apparently reversed between 1947 and 1954

when the machine tool industry produced 93 per cent of all machine tools produced.

While the machine tool industry had worried about excess capacity during most of the period from 1919 to 1939, it was necessary in World War II to expand existing plants by about $160,645,000 in new facilities. This was about equal to three-fourths of the industry's net worth as of 1939.

During the period between 1939 and 1947, the percentage of machine tool wage earners employed by the four largest firms increased from 21.7 per cent to 23.7 per cent as compared with 13.8 per cent in 1935, thus indicating a continuing trend toward concentration of production. It was also noted, however, that the four largest firms reported "value added by manufacture" was somewhat lower than their percentage of wage earners thus suggesting that these firms were less efficient than the average in the industry. There did not appear to be any noticeable change in the degree of product specialization in the industry during this period, but production of any one type and size of machine tool continued to be limited to not more than four or five firms.

While the machine tool industry experienced a serious post-World War II recession, it was not as severe as that following World War I, though it was longer in duration. The large number of surplus used machine tools sold by the government at the end of World War II no doubt had a significant effect on demand for new machine tools though this factor was at least partially offset by accelerated wear on wartime tools, export requirements to replace machine tools destroyed or worn out during the war, etc.

Between 1925 and 1930, the total number of machine tools in use rose by about 25 percent while the number of machines over ten years old rose by about two-thirds reflecting the large number of machine tools added during World War I. Between 1930 and 1940 under the impact of the depression, the number of machine tools in use declined by about 10 per cent. The number of machine tools over ten years old continued to increase until 1935, but declined slightly by 1940. There was also a considerable range in the percentage of machine tools over ten years old in the different industrial areas. The Boston region had the highest percentage in 1953 followed by Indianapolis, with Philadelphia-Camden in third place. The newer industrial areas including the Los Angeles area and the Dallas-Houston area had the lowest number of machines and lowest percentage over ten years old.

The *American Machinist's* inventories of metalworking equipment for 1945 and 1949 showed spectacular increases in the number of machine tools held by some industries in one year followed by equally drastic reductions by the next inventory. Only one industry showed a reduction in 1945 over 1940 holdings followed by a large increase in 1949. The largest increases were in the "Aircraft and Parts" industry which increased from 8,780 in 1940 to 276,466 in 1945 followed by a decline to 54,711 in 1949; and the "Motor Vehicle and Parts" industry which increased from 130,518 in 1940 to 243,686 in 1945 and then declined to 138,595 in 1949. It was noted, however, that despite the large reduction in number of machine tools held by the "Motor Vehicle and Parts" industry, the industry invested over $185,000,000 in production machinery and equipment in 1947 contrasted to $15,366,000 for the "Aircraft and Parts" industry. While it is not known how much of these amounts was invested in machine tools, it seems certain that the quantity of new machine tools purchased by the "Motor Vehicles and Parts" industry was much larger than that for the "Aircraft and Parts" industry. Other major purchasers of machine tools in the period following World War II were the "Miscellaneous Machine Parts and Jobbing" industry, the "General Industrial Equipment" industry, and the "Metalworking Equipment" industry.

Comparison of the geographical distribution of machine tools with the distribution of machine tool production disclosed that the East North Central States were relatively more important as machine tool producers than for their machine tool holdings. They led the nation in both with 39 per cent of the machine tools in the metalworking industries and about 53.2 per cent of the machine tool production. New England was in a similar position with a much greater share of production of machine tools than holdings of such machines. The Middle Atlantic States and other areas held a higher percentage of machine tools than they produced. The Southern States had grown in importance for metalworking manufacturing, but still had relatively few machine tools compared with the three major metalworking areas. Los Angeles and San Francisco were important metalworking centers on the Pacific Coast, but did not produce significant amounts of machine tools.

4

Managerial Problems and Policies
1900-1919

This chapter describes some of the more important managerial problems faced by the machine tool industry during the first two decades of the twentieth century. The major policies and programs adopted or considered to solve these problems by individual or cooperative effort are briefly discussed. The views of leading machine tool builders are included as these were presented in their public statements. Many of the problems were not unique to the machine tool industry and it was not always possible to determine whether machine tool builders made original contributions to the understanding of the problems or to their solution. In fact, it is not certain whether any real progress was made toward solutions.

National Trade Association Established

By the turn of the twentieth century, many machine tool builders had begun to think of themselves and to act as businessmen or professional managers rather than—or as well as—skilled craftsmen following a trade. They were becoming more concerned with problems of selling tools, controlling price competition, cost accounting, or labor than with tool design and production. In the spring of 1902, a group of seventeen lathe builders met in Niagara Falls, New York in response to a call from William Lodge, President of the Lodge and Shipley Machine Tool Company of Cincinnati, to discuss mutual problems such as pricing and costs. Attendees at this meeting concluded that lathe builders' problems were not much different from those of producers of other types of machine tools.

Consequently, the following months were spent preparing for the establishment of an association which would be open to all machine tool builders.

Twenty-eight charter members attended the first annual convention of the National Machine Tool Builders' Association (NMTBA) when it met in Cleveland in October 1902. The machine tool builders who took the lead in forming the NMTBA hoped that cooperative efforts would stabilize business conditions and raise prices to a higher level. The uncertain and fluctuating character of machine tool demand, the increasing severity of competition, and the difficulty of maintaining prices at satisfactory levels were among the major problems facing the machine tool industry and presented a difficult challenge to the new association.[1]

The NMTBA was in part an expression of the business climate of the time reflected in the drive to organize business into trade associations and other mutual assistance groups spearheaded by the National Association of Manufacturers. It was an effort by owners and managers of comparatively small businesses to obtain by friendly cooperation some of the benefits the industrial giants were trying to achieve through mergers and the formation of corporate empires and alliances. It was a direct response to a number of problems which threatened to destroy many machine tool firms unless something was done quickly. It was, probably, also an effort on the part of some leading firms in the industry to maintain their positions.[2]

Price Increases and Stabilization

The immediate objective of raising prices to a higher level was the easiest for the new association to achieve. At the NMTBA organization meeting in May 1902, an agreement to raise prices by 5 per cent was reached almost immediately. In November 1903, the NMTBA adopted a resolution to the effect that

. . . there is nothing in the existing conditions to warrant a

---

[1] *Machinery*, 59: Part 2: 170–176, October 1952, "Looking Back on a Half Century of Service"; H. U. Faulkner, *Decline of Laissez Faire, 1897–1917* (New York: Rinehart and Company, Inc., 1951), pp. 331–332.

[2] Robert A. Brady, *Business as a System of Power* (New York: Columbia University Press, 1943), pp. 190–194.

reduction in prices and (the association) hereby resolves to maintain the present schedule of prices of machine tools . . .[3]

It reaffirmed the same resolution in April 1904, despite the fact that it noted that the machine tool business was even more "depressing" than prior to November 1902. The NMTBA urged that existing price levels be maintained despite reductions in demand which had formerly been quickly reflected in increased competition and price reductions. A strong position was taken in favor of maintaining prices and reducing production. This stand was widely publicized and was apparently endorsed by machinery dealers as well as machine tool builders. A resolution was also passed by the NMTBA convention in April 1904 to discourage the practice of placing machine tools with dealers on a consignment basis with the prospect that if they could not be sold the builder would have to take them back. The NMTBA leaders clearly intended to control price competition or perhaps to eliminate it entirely if this were possible. Some firms, however, were unwilling or unable to maintain prices, particularly in periods of depression, so it was against such firms that the NMTBA directed much of its persuasive effort and publicity.

One argument used by tool builders against proposals to reduce prices in periods of slack business was that small reductions would merely cause prospective customers to further defer buying tools in anticipation of further reductions in price while large reductions, which might be expected to result in additional orders, could not be made without reducing prices below costs. Since the latter were calculated by applying all current expenses and overhead as well as materials and labor to a reduced volume of production, costs per unit were higher than when production was greater. Price reductions were correspondingly more difficult to justify by this type of reasoning.[4]

[3] *American Machinist*, 27:605–607, May 5, 1904, Meeting of NMTBA, Cincinnati, April 26–27, 1904.

[4] *Ibid.*, 30:606–607, October 24, 1907, NMTBA Sixth Annual Convention, New York, October 15–16, 1907; *Ibid.*, 31:840–841, May 28, 1908, "Machine Tool Builder's Association," Atlantic City, May 19, 1908.

Cost Accounting Systems and Problems

During the second half of the nineteenth century, most machine tool builders were only incidentally concerned with costs. Wages paid for labor and prices paid for materials were for the most part based on prevailing rates and competitive factors. Company records reflected current income and expense but there was little accurate knowledge of production costs or overhead. Tool prices were usually based on competitive factors and frequently had little relation to the individual tool builder's costs or efficiency. When competition became severe, prices were likely to drop below the costs of even the most efficient firms with disastrous consequences to firms whose costs were higher or whose financial position was weak. There was also no greater standardization in accounting methods than in the products produced with the result that cost comparisons were likely to be misleading.

As a corollary to its interest in raising price levels, the NMTBA became actively interested in developing better, and more uniform, accounting methods. In May 1906, the association established a committee consisting of Messrs. F. A. Geier, E. P. Bullard, Jr., and C. H. Alvord to investigate accounting problems, and if possible, recommend a standard system of cost accounting "which will put all the builders in the field on the same basis and eliminate the possibility of anyone selling machinery unknowingly at a price below the cost of production."[5] Machine tool costs and cost accounting were also a major topic of discussion when the NMTBA met in May 1907. The report of the Uniform Cost Accounting Committee covered plans for collecting information from each member regarding his practice with respect to specific items of cost. This was followed in October 1907 by passage of a resolution authorizing the employment of an expert to visit NMTBA members to discuss with each their methods of handling costs.[6]

The association employed the Miller and Franklin Company, whose recommendations were distributed, in pamphlet form, at the

[5] *Machinery*, 12:Part 2:550 (Eng. Ed.), June 1906, Report of NMTBA Convention, May 1–2, 1906, Atlantic City, N.J.

[6] *American Machinist*, 29:745–746, May 23, 1907. Report of NMTBA Convention, Fortress Monroe, Virginia, May 14–15, 1907; *Ibid.*, 30:603–607, October 24, 1907, Report on NMTBA Convention, New York, October 15–16, 1907.

NMTBA Convention in May 1908. This cost accounting study disclosed that less than one-third of the association's members were using what the accountants considered good accounting systems. Some NMTBA members made no effort to figure costs, others included material and direct labor only, still others included estimates of overhead expenses, but omitted other significant items. In general, it indicated a widespread ignorance of the costs of doing business.

The NMTBA Cost Committee endorsed the findings of the Miller and Franklin Company study and recommended adoption of the methods it proposed. These did not include a completely "scientific" accounting system, nor provide for a uniform system of bookkeeping for general adoption. A schedule of items to be included in calculating costs was presented together with an illustrative system showing how the recommendations could be put into effect. The NMTBA Convention passed a resolution recommending adoption of the proposed methods by its membership.[7]

Progress in implementation of the recommended methods, however, proved to be slow and uncertain, despite continued efforts to secure their adoption. Two circular letters were sent out by the NMTBA, prior to its convention in the fall of 1908, in an effort to learn to what extent the proposed accounting system had been or was being installed. The replies showed that five members were using the system, seven indicated they might modify their existing systems to conform with those recommended, two planned to install the system at a later date when they were ready to make changes in their existing methods, four proposed to adopt the system with modifications, thirteen had no system but indicated they liked the one proposed, and twenty-four firms had systems of their own which they did not plan to change.[8]

In the period prior to World War I, the theory, principles, and procedures of cost accounting as applied to manufacturing operations were advancing rapidly. Two of the major elements of cost which were given much attention during this period were overhead and depreciation. One of the principal methods of allocating overhead developed was the so-called machine hour method. This method was based on the collection of all costs except materials

[7] *Ibid.*, 31:958–959, June 18, 1908, "A Uniform Cost System."
[8] *Ibid.*, 31:Part 2:638–639, October 29, 1908, "Machine Tool Builders Association," New York, October 20–21, 1908.

and direct labor by department and the allocation of these costs to the product on the basis of time required for the various machine processes. Numerous variations and refinements of the machine hour method were developed but all allocated production overhead costs on the basis of hours of machine operation.[9]

A. Hamilton Church presented a refined version of the machine rate system for allocating overhead expense to the NMTBA in May 1911. This method was based on the proposition that "every legitimate expense in a machine shop is incurred for the purpose of geting work up to, under, or away from the tool point." Each machine was charged with a number of annual rent charges which together represented the annual cost of the machine's capacity to produce. These were combined into a single hourly machine rent which was charged against all work done on that machine. The residue of expense left over due to idle machines was considered pure waste which must be charged directly to profit and loss.[10]

Depreciation was an important element of cost where expensive machine tools were used along with elaborate devices for holding and handling cutting tools and work. Machine tool builders were concerned with the problem of depreciation from two principal standpoints, namely; determining how depreciation should be handled with regard to their own productive equipment, and depreciation accounting by their customers. The latter seemed by far the more important consideration and particularly so in periods of slack business since it was closely related to machine tool users' replacement policies. The depreciated value of a machine tool was not, however, the sole consideration determining whether a machine tool was to be replaced.

Machine tool builders and dealers usually advocated that tool users adopt a "conservative" policy by which machine tools would be depreciated at a rate which would reduce the "book value" to scrap value within a period of ten years or less. They emphasized the effect of technical improvements in machine design, construc-

[9] S. Paul Garner, *Evolution of Cost Accounting of 1925* (Tuscaloosa, Alabama; University of Alabama Press, 1954), pp. 116, 118, 186, 345–346; A. Hamilton Church, "Proper Distribution of Established Charges," *The Engineering Magazine*, XXII, 1901; J. Lee Nicholson, *Factory Organization and Costs* (New York: Kohl Technical Publishing Company, 1909), pp. 54–57.

[10] A. Hamilton Church, "Distribution of the Expense Burden," *American Machinist*, 34:991–992, May 25, 1911.

tion, and operation which tended to make machines obsolete. Many tool users, on the other hand, saw little reason to replace a machine which appeared to be giving satisfactory service with a reasonable amount of maintenance even though it was fully depreciated, and improved models were available. This was particularly true where a machine was only in actual use during a fraction of the shop's working hours and the shop was operating at far below capacity as was often the case. Many machine tool builders took a similar position regarding replacement of their own equipment. No evidence was found that machine tool builders' views on depreciation and replacement of machine tools had any definite effect on machine tool users' investment practices.

Straight-line depreciation, by which the book value of a machine is reduced by the same predetermined amount each year regardless of machine use, tended to aggravate fluctuations in profits and losses in periods of prosperity and depression. It had little relation in many cases to actual market value, and slight relation either to machine deterioration from wear or technological advances. Consequently, accountants developed various methods intended to make depreciation charges more realistic. It seemed to them essential to fix different depreciation rates for different types of machine tools and for different operating conditions of the same machines. For purposes of asset valuation and analysis of profit and loss, the depreciation charges could, if desired, be adjusted from year to year to meet the needs or wishes of management. However, for tax purposes it was necessary to select and adhere to a method for calculating depreciation considered acceptable by the taxing authorities.

To determine the appropriate depreciation rate for machine tools required an estimate of the expected useful life of the type of machine and resale or scrap value at the end of this period. Life expectancy in machine tools, however, varied widely and resale value usually depended upon the used machine dealers' estimate of a machine's condition and age and of the likelihood of his finding a buyer needing a particular machine. There was ample room for wide differences of opinion regarding these items. For example, one writer in 1910 reported that for standard tools:

> . . . we find that the number of years of service averages about 15 with a loss in value of 50 per cent in lathes and planers, 60 per cent in drills. . . . A number of reliable concerns report that a

decrease of 10 per cent each year in value has always enabled them to finally dispose of tools without a book loss. This per cent varies and is as low as 5 per cent in some cases, A fair value for ordinary machine-shop conditions is 7½ per cent.[11]

Despite the NMTBA's efforts to promote greater uniformity in cost accounting practices the systems, even among those firms which had reasonably good accounting systems, were far from uniform in the period through World War I. The relatively slow progress made toward standardized cost accounting, as contrasted to accounting theory, was due primarily to the fact that many firms were either not convinced of the need for better and more uniform cost accounting or were unwilling to accept the effort, record keeping, and expense such systems entailed. Undoubtedly, some felt that their existing bookkeeping and accounting systems adequately met their needs or were peculiarly well suited to their own operations.[12]

Scientific Management and the Machine Tool Builder

Closely related to the machine tool builder's interest in improved cost accounting was a growing interest in "Scientific Management." This included both the specialized theories and devices advocated by Frederick Winslow Taylor and other systematic efforts to improve management practices and reduce knowledge or experience in management to a body of principles and techniques of more or less general validity and wide application. Many machine tool builders adopted at least some of the major principles and techniques of scientific management in such areas as time and motion study, the task system, division and specialization of labor, functionalization of management, production control, and cost accounting. The NMTBA constitution included as one of the association's primary objectives the "improvement of methods."

The development of scientific management during the first decade of the twentieth century paralleled, and to some degree accelerated, the mechanization of industry. One trend which is usually noted is that of the "transfer of skill" in many types of work from the

[11] W. W. Bird, "Depreciation of Machine Tools," *American Machinist*, 33: Part 2:767–769, October 27, 1910.

[12] Miller, Franklin, Basset, & Company, *Uniform Cost System Designed For the National Machine Tool Builders' Association*, 1920.

worker to the machine. Another is the multiplication of highly specialized jobs, many of which required only a very limited range of skills and experience to perform repetitive operations. Many workers, labor leaders, and socially conscious writers became very much concerned that eventually the need for highly skilled workers such as the general machinist would almost disappear. Other observers attempted to show that there would always be a need for highly skilled workers and for the exercise of judgment which could not be supplied by machines.[13]

Ralph E. Flanders, Jones and Lamson Machine Company, suggested that scientific management itself was a kind of "labor-saving machine" with both the advantages and limitations of such devices. He also contended that scientific management created rather than solved some of the economic and social problems arising from "maldistribution of wealth" and urged engineers to interest themselves in social problems.[14]

James Hartness, President of the Jones and Lamson Machine Company, took a less apprehensive view of the situation when he described time-study:

> It is a mechanical scheme of intelligent direction of work, and it depends for its success more on correct direction than on the workman's natural ability and inclination to devise his own methods.

Hartness noted that one of the principal features of scientific management was its emphasis on "the best use of the present means rather than the invention of new and wonderful machinery." He added that this principle should be a primary feature of all schemes of industrial management.[15]

One of the principal characteristics of most of the management systems advocated by Taylor and other management experts during this period was a high degree of centralized control. This centered usually in a planning department which was responsible not only for establishing production schedules, shop layouts, etc., but also

[13] Holden A. Evans, "What is to Become of the Machinist?" *American Machinist*, 33:Part 2:1095, December 15, 1910.

[14] *Machinery*, June 1912, pp. 764–765, "Scientific Management from a Social and Economic Standpoint."

[15] James Hartness, "The Human Factor in Manufacturing," *American Machinist*, 36:993–994, June 20, 1912.

for specifying precisely how each operation was to be carried out. The control thus imposed depended on elaborate records and required a constant flow of information from the shop to the planning department, and a corresponding flow of detailed instructions from the planning department to the shop.

Much of the detailed information initially required was gathered by two types of time studies. One involved the determination and recording of the time taken to complete particular jobs and thus accumulating data which could be used in estimating the time required for similar jobs in the future. The second method was based on the subdivision of a work process into a large number of elementary motions or elements, measuring the time required for each as accurately as possible, and systematically compiling these data for future reference. By adding together the time required for each of the elements required in a particular process, it was possible to estimate how long any job should take. It was necessary to analyze carefully the job to be done, determine precisely what operations were required, in what order they should be performed, and the best method of performing each. It was also necessary to have adequate supervision to assure that work was done according to the instructions and that the work was of acceptable quality.[16]

The National Association of Machinists (later International Association of Machinists) and other trade unions opposed the scientific management movement, as basically incompatible with trade unionism. Scientific management's emphasis upon centralized planning and control of work broken up into a large number of highly specialized jobs each of which required limited skill and experience threatened the craftsmanship upon which the trade unions were founded. Furthermore, the unions believed that it would result in perpetually changing job classifications and conditions to which the craft unions could not adjust. Despite their initial opposition, the International Association of Machinists did later admit as members those who had been trained in only a single branch of the machinist's trade.[17]

[16] Robert Thurston Kent, "The Utilization of Time-Study Data," *American Machinist*, 42:965–968, June 3, 1915.

[17] Harold M. Groves, "The Machinist in Industry" (unpublished Ph.D. Dissertation, University of Wisconsin, 1927), p. 376.

Wage Plans

Prior to World War I, machine tool builders made use of various plans of wage payment including straight hourly or daily rate systems, a variety of piece-work and premium payment schemes, and special schemes based on time-and-motion studies. The more elaborate schemes for "scientifically" setting wage rates involved establishment of detailed instructions for each job. They specified exactly how each operation was to be done and the tools, jigs, and fixtures, and cutting speeds to be used. These schemes, however, were not fully accepted by many machine tool builders. Generally, individual runs on particular machine tool parts were relatively short. Greater reliance was placed on the skill and experience of the individual machinist than was usual in mass production industries. Premium pay schemes which provided the worker an incentive to exercise his own initiative, inventiveness, and skill to increase production but were relatively simple to install and administer, seemed much better suited to tool builders' needs.[18]

In 1910, William Lodge, President of the Lodge and Shipley Machine Tool Company, emphasized the need to establish fair rates to start based on "historical" standards of performance, and said that their firm had been fortunate in that:

... we had a pretty accurate record of the cost of lathes of various sizes and of different sized lots, extending over a period of 12 years. This gave us a good basis to work from and with few exceptions, we took an average of the last three years of the record as a standard for time to be allowed. We knew that these times would be bettered in nearly every instance, but we were willing, yes, wanted the men to earn more to make it an object to strive for an increased output.[19]

Savings from reduced labor costs were divided equally between the workers and management. In order to ensure that foremen would have an interest in increasing production and help workers to meet or exceed their quotas, an allowance of $.02 per hour saved

[18] *American Machinist*, 31:Part 2:638–639, October 29, 1908, "Machine Tool Builders Association," New York, October 20–21, 1908.
[19] William Lodge, "Good Results From Premium Plan," *American Machinist*, 32:1017–1019, June 2, 1910.

was made from management's share of the savings. A charge of $.05 an hour lost was made against the foremen's premium earnings but apparently such charges were rather rare. An additional payment of one-half cent for each hour saved throughout the shop was made to the superintendent and his assistant from management's share of savings. A method was also established for paying bonuses to employees in the pattern shop. Lastly, an additional 2¼ cents per hour was set aside as a pension fund for workers reaching 65 with 25 years or more service with the firm.

In 1911, H. L. Gantt described a "task and bonus" system to the NMTBA convention. The sine qua non of this method was the availability of one or more highly skilled production specialists or "time-study" men capable of determining and specifying precisely the best way of doing each job and arriving at an accurate but fair estimate of how long each operation should take. The production expert was expected to be able to show a workman who failed to meet a quota how the job could be done in the time specified. Allowing too little time resulted in bad employee morale and possible loss of valuable workers while regularly allowing more time than necessary was reflected in higher costs or reduced profits and savings. The system also assumed that the work would be performed by the type of machinist or machine operator who was willing to do exactly as instructed rather than attempt to exercise his own judgment.[20]

Foremen were paid a bonus in addition to their regular pay if the quotas set were met or exceeded. The amount of the foreman's bonus was proportioned to the number of his men meeting their quotas with an additional amount if all workers earned bonuses. Gantt described the system as "a system of education with prizes for those who learn" and claimed that under it men learned more in a few months than in years under other systems.

The so-called "Maximum Pay Plan" introduced by the Bullard Machine Company was another effort to attract and hold workers without increasing labor costs. It was based on the principle that increased

. . . production not wage rate is the foundation of low cost . . . that skill in producing a specialized product can only be attained

[20] H. L. Gantt, "The Task and Bonus System," *American Machinist*, 35:920–921, November 16, 1911.

through long association with that product, and . . . that skill acquired through a long association produces work of superior quality.[21]

Employees were divided into six classes and minimum wages set for each class. Higher wages were to be determined by ability and a continued service bonus of 10 per cent was added as a deterrent to "job swapping." Standard times were determined for each operation. An employee's efficiency was computed by dividing the standard time by actual time. A 1 per cent bonus was then paid for each 1 per cent of efficiency above 75 per cent. No differential was paid for night work. Men were kept on the same shifts although rotating shifts were said to be preferable.[22]

One weakness of most of the premium or bonus systems, however, was that they concentrated on speeding up the worker and put little emphasis on finding new methods for achieving greater production without increasing the labor involved. Group bonus schemes were considered more effective where output depended on cooperation among all workers rather than unusual speed or skill on the part of the best workers. This was the case in virtually all assembly-line operations where the effective speed was likely to be that of the slowest worker or operation.[23]

The decline in business during the first half of 1914 stimulated the interest of machine tool builders in ways of reducing costs to maintain profits. NMTBA members were urged to seek to increase production in relation to investment and to reduce costs while, at the same time, maintaining or increasing wage rates. Special emphasis was placed on the value of bonus payments as incentives to greater output. Management was urged to increase its own effectiveness; give workers better drawings and provide more complete instructions as to the best method of doing each job.

Machine tool builders also became increasingly concerned about the waste involved in hiring and training new workers. Estimates of how much it cost to replace an employee varied widely but, in general, the costs increased in relation to the skill and experience

21 *American Machinist,* 44:922–923, May 25, 1916, "Bullard Maxi-Pay Plan;" *Machinery,* June 1916, pp. 918–919, "Bullard 'Maxi-Pay' Plan."
22 *Machinery,* October 1916, p. 118, "Working Hours of Bullard Machine Tool Co."
23 Fred H. Colvin and Frank A. Stanley, *Running a Machine Shop,* 2nd Ed. (New York: McGraw-Hill Book Company, Inc., 1948), p. 338.

required. Some managers, in this period, estimated their costs at less than $50 an employee, while a machine tool builder estimated his cost at about $150 each. This tool builder also estimated that, prior to World War I, to increase his permanent work force by fifty, he had found it necessary to hire almost 1,000 employees within a year.[24] Whatever the reasons, the turnover rate among new employees appears to have been very high. It was recognized, however, that the loss of men to other industries and the difficulty of getting good workers were not due entirely to offers of higher wages or better opportunities in other industries, but also to the general growth of industry at a faster rate than the supply of trained workers.[25]

Training Problems and Programs

The principal manpower requirements of machine tool builders were for skilled machinists, tool makers, and tool designers. In fact, many pioneer firms entered the machine tool business with almost no assets other than such skills and a few basic machine tools. One or more skilled machinists who had learned their trade in other shops could set up a business of their own with very little capital or equipment. In general, however, machinists received very little in the way of formal education. Many served lengthy apprenticeships but only a few shops actually had well-organized apprentice training programs with adequate instructors.

The great majority of students left school before they completed even a minimum education for the skilled mechanical trades. At the beginning of the last decade of the nineteenth century, about 80 per cent of students never reached high school. Less than 3 per cent graduated from high school. Most students left school at ten or twelve years of age to take jobs. Statistics such as these convinced many people that there was a need for more "practical training" at an earlier age in order to better fit students for jobs.

By the end of the nineteenth century, the machine tool industry

---

[24] Magnus W. Alexander, "Waste in Hiring and Discharging Men," *American Machinist*, 41:869–871, November 12, 1914.

[25] J. C. Spence, "On Inducing Ourselves and Our Men to Earn More Money; Some Points on Securing Efficiency Through Cooperation of Employer and Employee," *Machinery*, June 1914, pp. 85–86.

had developed to the point where a more reliable supply of skilled workers was needed. Increased foreign competition had also called attention to the need for better trained workers who were able to read engineering drawings and written instructions. Growing activity on the part of both labor organizations and the business groups organized to oppose union activities resulted in greater emphasis on training skilled or semiskilled workers. Lastly, the interest of professional educators and public administrators was shifting to put more emphasis on vocational training for workers and better professional training for engineers.[26]

Apprenticeship System

Relatively few machine tool or other manufacturing firms offered good opportunities for learning to be a skilled machinist or tool maker, although many claimed to have apprenticeship programs of some variety. Such training as was given was likely to be rather haphazard. It usually depended on the character and inclinations of the individual shop foreman, how much time and teaching ability he and the experienced machinists had, and the persistence of the apprentice in trying to learn as much as possible.

Some shop superintendents considered apprentices entering the shop at sixteen or younger almost worthless and preferred more mature young men of eighteen or nineteen. Apprentices were often described as "lazy, idle, stupid, careless, vicious or any one of a dozen other undesirable things," although there is no proof that this was more often the case than in the past. In part, the solution appeared to employers to lie in more careful selection of apprentices and greater efforts to retain the better prospects.

One source of difficulty both in securing and keeping apprentices was the fact that wages paid apprentices were very low and increased at a much slower rate—at least initially—than in the case of nonapprentices. The apprentice was supposed to receive valuable instruction for which he paid his employer a part of the value of his work. The value of his work was often considered to be that

---

[26] Milton P. Higgins, "Education of Machinists, Foremen, and Mechanical Engineers," ASME, *Transactions*, 21:646–767, December 1899; Monte A. Calvert, *The Mechanical Engineer in America, 1830–1910* (Baltimore, Maryland: The Johns Hopkins Press, 1967), pp. 56f.

of unskilled labor and the cost of instruction to be the difference between this value and the wages usually paid to other workers of equal skill and experience.[27]

The apprentice was also usually required to post a bond upon entering his apprenticeship. This was supposed to ensure his employer that he would not leave before completing his apprenticeship and would make a conscientious effort to complete it successfully. It also, however, made it difficult for some boys to enter an apprenticeship, and, along with the low wages paid during apprenticeship, eliminated some of the poorer boys who otherwise might be desirable apprentices.[28]

In May 1907 the NMTBA Committee on Apprenticeship proposed establishment of two systems of apprenticeship. The first was to be a general apprenticeship covering the entire machinist's trade as had been usual in the past. The second, was a special system in which the apprentice would be trained in a single specialized branch of the machinist's trade.[29] The Committee recommended that under both systems the apprentice be supplied with a set of tools at the beginning of his apprenticeship; that the tools remain the employer's property until the apprenticeship was completed and then be given to the apprentice. Successful apprentices were to be given diplomas bearing the seal of the NMTBA upon completion of their courses. The committee proposed that the general apprenticeship be for three years, and that wages be $.08, $.10 and $.13 per hour. The special apprenticeships were to cover two years with the wage rates being advanced by two-cent increments each six months from $.12 to $.18 an hour. The period for apprenticeship in operation of boring mills was to be 1½ years and the pay rates $.15, $.17, and $.20 per hour. In the case of drilling and milling, the apprenticeship was to be only a year.

In November 1908, E. P. Bullard, Jr., President, Bullard Machine Company insisted that the apprenticeship system was far from dead or dying and that no system of schools could take the place of shop training. He added that the cost of work produced by apprentices

---

[27] Forrest E. Cardullo, "Apprenticeship and Industrial Education," *American Machinist*, 29:244–246, February 22, 1906.

[28] *Ibid.*, pp. 245–246.

[29] *American Machinist*, 29:745–746, May 23, 1907; NMTBA Convention, Fortress Monroe, Virginia, May 14–15, 1907.

had been proven to be lower than the cost of that produced by journeymen, thus unintentionally confirming the charge made by labor unions and others that the apprentice system was sometimes used to secure cheap labor and weaken the position of journeymen machinists.[30]

Various explanations were advanced during the early years of the twentieth century as to why few boys, or too few of those considered the more desirable type, were interested in becoming machinist apprentices. Among these were (1) the lack of social status of machinists, (2) poor working conditions, (3) poor quality of apprentice training in many shops, (4) lack of opportunity for advancement of shop-trained men because of preference given to graduates of technical schools, and (5) the desire on the part of many boys starting work to make as much money as possible within a short time.

Part-Time or Half-Time Schools

Full-time vocational instruction by the public schools provided one alternative to apprenticeship training for those who were able to remain in school full-time, but this type of training also had its problems and deficiencies. The high cost of equipping and maintaining shops with modern tools and securing well-trained instructors were among the obstacles to provision of adequate training for machinists in the public schools. The "part-time" or "half-time" school was proposed as an alternative to overcome such difficulties. This was either a school with a "commercial shop" attached or a cooperative arrangement between schools and local industries whereby the student alternated periods of classroom work with actual shop work in the plant of a participating firm. When a school with its own shops attempted to duplicate conditions in a commercial establishment, including competitive sale of its products by which it could recoup its materials costs, there was criticism from commercial shops on the ground that such competition was unfair. On the other hand, if students were given only practice work, the training was criticized on the ground that it did not really prepare the student for his trade. The "half-time" school was considered by its advocates to meet these objections.

[30] *Ibid.*, 31:825–826, December 3, 1908, "Industrial Education at Atlanta."

There was considerable skepticism, however, regarding the claims made for the half-time school system, and it was doubted that many machine tool builders or other machinery manufacturers would agree to an apprentice system in which half of the apprentice's time was spent in school. Such a procedure did not appear to critics to be "commercial" and many firms were not willing to take apprentices of any kind. Trade unions also objected to such schemes since the unions attempted to regulate the number of apprentices that might be employed in proportion to the number of journeymen.

Cincinnati was one of the leading centers in the development of the part-time school. It combined training for the mechanical trades in the public elementary and secondary schools with part-time work in commercial shops. Similar training was provided for engineers by the University of Cincinnati and cooperating private firms. Some academic training was provided for apprentice machinists but the amount of time devoted to academic subjects was much smaller than in the case of engineering students.[31]

Early in 1908, Fred A. Geier, President of Cincinnati Milling Machine Company, reported that his firm had thirty-eight machinist apprentices. These boys were very weak in elementary arithmetic and were unable to read mechanical drawings. They had attended school for an average of seven years while the average for all boys in Cincinnati at this time was only five years. The firm decided to employ a "trained shopman" as a teacher and organize an apprentice school of its own. Each boy attended the school one evening a week for two hours.

Instruction in our apprentice school is direct and practical . . . we teach them to solve problems, and all the problems have a direct application to the work each boy is doing in the shop.

He exhibited specimens of work done by the apprentices before and after taking the training to demonstrate the rapid improvement which had been made. This arrangement, however, apparently did not last very long.[32]

In October 1909, Geier stated that while Cincinnati claimed to

[31] Calvert, *Mechanical Engineer*, p. 84.
[32] Fred A. Geier, "Engineering and Industrial Education," *American Machinist*, 31:710–712, May 7, 1908; *American Machinist*, 32:711–714, October 21, 1909, NMTBA Convention, New York, October 12–13, 1909.

have the oldest mechanics institute in the country, apprentices should not have to depend on night classes. Manual training courses had been established in the elementary grades and two technical high schools were about completed. Two firms had established their own shop schools. Also an agreement had been worked out between local firms and the Board of Education under which apprentices would attend the public schools four hours each week and would receive regular wages for this time. This arrangement was confined, at that time, to machine shops. The classes, moreover, were directed at problems encountered in the shop, and manufacturers' catalogs and blueprints were used for instruction. Geier reported that the classes had resulted in greater efficiency and had also proved to be a valuable inducement in recruiting apprentices.

The so-called "Fitchburg Plan" was another part-time training scheme considered by the NMTBA. Manufacturers cooperated with the high school to provide a four-year apprenticeship in which the first year was spent on school work; during the next three years alternate weeks were spent in school and in the shops. Apprentices worked in pairs so that one was in school while the other was in the shop. At the end of the school week, the boy who was to work in the shop the next week went to the shop on Saturday for an hour or half-hour prior to closing to get acquainted with the job his partner was working on and be ready to start work on the same job the following Monday. The training provided appears considerably more elaborate and required much more time in the classroom than was being allowed in the case of apprentice machinists in Cincinnati, but in both cases school work was closely oriented to shop needs.

Industrial or Vocational Schools Versus Apprenticeship

The major alternative to the apprenticeship system as a method of training machinists was the industrial or vocational schools. These were of two general types: (1) specialized vocational schools which taught a particular trade; and, (2) industrial schools providing a broader type of training ranging from purely manual skills to basic scientific knowledge and principles of manufacturing.[33]

[33] Milton P. Higgins, "Progress in Industrial Education," *American Machinist*, 30:715–716, November 7, 1907.

Defenders of the apprenticeship system often questioned whether mechanical skills could really be taught effectively in the schools. On the other hand, the leaders of the industrial school movement saw little reason to regret the decline of the apprenticeship system under which they felt skills were acquired very slowly by absorption rather than from actual teaching.

> The passing of the old apprenticeship system is not to be regretted, as it is hard to imagine a system so uneconomic and in some respects so unfair as this system. I, myself, served one of these "good old-fashioned apprenticeships" under extremely favorable circumstances, and have had the opportunity to observe many others; and can therefore speak from actual experience.[34]

It was claimed that industrial school training could be systematized to meet the needs of students on both the practical and academic sides. Even though some practical experience in a commercial shop was still needed to prepare a fully trained workman, this experience could be acquired in a much shorter time than under the apprenticeship system.[35]

While some leading machine tool builders took an active role in efforts to recruit and provide adequate vocational training to new workers and to encourage efforts of older workers to improve their skills, the impression left is that many other tool builders were more likely to complain about the passing of the "good old days" when there had been a much more ample supply of promising apprentices and skilled machinists and less competition for workers.

Problems Related to Machine Tool Demand

Machine tool demand can be classified in a variety of ways but possibly the more obvious broad classes are (1) demand resulting from industrial expansion, and (2) demand resulting from tool replacement. The first category can be further subdivided into (a) peacetime expansion, and (b) war related expansion. Peacetime expansion includes both demand created by the invention, develop-

---

[34] Dexter S. Kimball, "Industrial Schools and Apprenticeship," *American Machinist*, 33:Part 2:958–962, November 24, 1910.

[35] ASME, *Transactions*, No. 1367, 1912, 34:851–854, "Developments in Machine Shop Practice During the Last Decade."

ment, and marketing of new equipment and products, and increases in output of existing products. Similarly wartime demand results both from greatly expanded requirements for existing weapons and the introduction of new weapons. Replacement demand includes replacement made necessary by the normal wearing out of machine tools through use and that resulting from the introduction of new or improved machine tools or production methods making existing tools obsolete.

There are two primary types of machine orders, namely, dealers' orders and user or final purchaser orders. The importance of each type varies from one machine to another. In general, dealer "stock orders" are confined to standard or general purpose tools, whereas specialized machine tools are normally purchased directly by the tool user from the tool builder or by special order through a dealer.

The machine tool purchaser had two alternatives: he could buy merely the basic machine itself from the machine tool builder (in which case he had to produce the necessary jigs, fixtures, and cutting tools himself or buy them from some other firm); or he could request the machine tool builder to submit bids covering the complete tooling. In the latter case, the user needed only to provide an adequate statement of his requirements as to production, quality or finish, tolerances, previous operations performed, and locating points to be used. Since a decision to purchase machine tools for a particular need sometimes involved a choice not only between machines of the same type produced by different machine tool builders but also between different types of machines each requiring special tooling, it is easy to see that a great deal of work might be involved in preparing bids. The machine tool builder sometimes complained that the customer was unreasonable in his demands or that he failed to provide essential information. Some buyers countered with complaints that too few machine tool salesmen were really well-trained or reliable. Many salesmen, it was also charged, were so anxious to make sales that they made exaggerated claims for their machines. The machine tool builder, on the other hand, sometimes felt that the user did not give enough consideration to his own needs and production problems and tried to "pass the buck" to the machine tool salesman or builder. Some builders also felt that demands for special equipment and for extensive production engineering added greatly to the cost of machine tools but did not always add proportionately to the machine tool builder's profits since the latter could often make more from selling standard tools.[36]

Machine tool distributors claimed that their salesmen were better able to provide the free engineering advice expected by many machine tool buyers than the direct factory representative. The distributor was expected to be familiar with a variety of machines, whereas the factory representative was limited to his own line of tools. It was also claimed that, in some cases, the distributor would recommend another make in preference to those he was handling when the other machine was better suited to the buyer's needs. This was intended to give the buyer confidence in the distributor's advice and to improve the distributor's chances of getting future business.[37]

Machine tool builders sometimes challenged the advantages claimed for dealer sales organizations. For example, William J. Burger of the Warner & Swasey Company stated that:

. . . I find that the only information you get from the agent is the information you pick out of the circulars. If you really want to know something about the machine you must get the representative from the factory or write.[38]

The machine tool distributor also had his problems and complaints. The tool buyer seldom gave the machine tool salesman all the information he needed to estimate the production which could be obtained from a particular machine. Moreover, the information given the salesman often reflected ideal conditions rather than a realistic reflection of the work to be done. In such cases, the tool salesman either had to base his estimates on the ideal conditions with the probability that the buyer would be dissatisfied when the estimates could not be fulfilled in practice or give a very conservative estimate even though this might mean losing the order to a less cautious competitor.

The tool buyer wanted to know when he could expect delivery

[36] L. L. Roberts, "The Use and Application of Machine Tools," ASME, *Transactions,* 51:Part 2:33–34, 1929.
[37] George T. Trundle, Jr., "What Information Does the Machine Tool Buyer Need from the Machine Tool Salesman?" ASME, *Transactions,* 52:41–45, 1930.
[38] *Ibid.*

and frequently specified that he must have early delivery. The salesman, who ordinarily was selling on commission, wanted to make a sale and often agreed with the specified delivery time even when uncertain that it could be met. The machine tool salesman needed to be able to answer technical questions. The buyer wanted to know the range of feeds and speeds the machine provided; whether his standard equipment such as arbors and chucks would fit; the kind and size of bearings; whether the machine was to be motor driven, belt driven, or a combination drive. Distributors complained that machine tool builders did not give their agents enough information; that machine tool buyers wanted to see blueprints and detail drawings but that the tool builders ordinarily provided nothing but photographs.

Probably there was some merit in the complaints raised by machine tool builders, distributors and users, but to determine their validity and effect upon machine tool sales would require a major research project with access to company records, salesmen, and officials. No evidence was found that the machine tool industry's sales problems were essentially different from those of builders of other types of capital equipment. There is some evidence, however, that machine tool builders were not always alert to possibilities of stabilizing their business in new machine tools with greater effort to provide the jigs, fixtures, and cutting tools used with machine tools which normally had to be replaced more frequently than the machine tools.

Threat of Order Cancellation

In periods of rapid industrial expansion, the tool dealers' and builders' primary problem was to keep up with orders and meet promised delivery dates. Inventories declined drastically or disappeared entirely and order backlogs increased out of proportion to current shipments. There was a tendency in such periods for dealers to overestimate future sales. When the expansion rate began to decline, dealers found it increasingly difficult to find buyers, financing, or even storage space for the machines they had ordered. They then saw no alternative but to cancel, if possible, many of the orders placed with machine tool builders.

The tool builder was seldom able to anticipate such order cancellations sufficiently in advance to permit him to adjust his production schedule, inventories of materials and parts, orders for materials, and working force to meet the situation. In addition, since future productive capacity and future success depended to a large degree on retaining highly trained and experienced tool designers and machinists, tool firms wanted to avoid as much as possible the loss of such workers. Consequently, they were reluctant to stop or drastically reduce production until forced to do so by excessive inventories and lack of orders.

Machine tool builders were anxious, therefore, to find ways of ensuring that orders once taken would not be cancelled without their consent and, particularly so, during periods when demand was declining rapidly. In the fall of 1910, the NMTBA Committee on Cancellation of Orders and Dealers' Commissions in collaboration with a similar committee from the National Supply and Machinery Dealers' Association, recommended that quotations and order acceptances contain a clause stating

> Kindly note that all our quotations and acceptances are made subject to the understanding that the order is not subject to cancellation, provided shipment is made within the time specified.

This recommendation was adopted by the Convention but only after discussion which disclosed, among other things, that the action was "not intended to bind anyone, but to bring about a change in custom by placing before every customer the fact that such a change is to be inaugurated. . . ."[39]

The Dealers' Association also adopted the above resolution and by the spring of 1911 nearly all machine tool builders and dealers were using it. Builders were urged to use the clause in their contracts even though they did not sell directly to users. It was felt that this practice would tend to "add moral effect to the dealers' effort to hold the buyer to the legitimate obligation he assumes when he places an order for machine tools."[40]

[39] American Machinist, 33:Part 2:839–840, November 3, 1910, "Machine Tool Builders Convention."

[40] NMTBA, Official Report, Semi-annual Convention (19th Meeting), May 18–19, 1911, Atlantic City, New Jersey; American Machinist, 34:1039, June 1, 1911, "Non-Cancellation of Machine Tool Orders"; Forrest E. Cardullo, "Industrial Administration and Scientific Management," Machinery, 18:843–847 (Eng. Ed.), June 1911.

Little consideration appears to have been given to the fact that the tool buyer and user was also subject to unexpected declines in demand, cancellation of orders, etc., and could not always persuade or force his customers to take products which they no longer needed. This policy was probably based on the conservative theory that it was better to have fewer firm orders than to accept a larger volume of orders, a substantial part of which might be cancelled suddenly.

By the spring of 1915, tool builders were concerned that the war might end suddenly leaving them with a large number of machines in production. They feared orders would be cancelled and they would have no effective recourse. This had been the case in 1907 and the situation in 1915 appeared to some tool builders to be more dangerous. World War I, of course, did not end suddenly in 1915 or 1916. Reconversion problems and the adjustments necessary to return to a peacetime basis were not to come for over two years. Nevertheless, the NMTBA and many tool builders attempted to prepare for the impact of reconversion problems.[41]

"No Cancellation" clauses were incorporated in most machine tool contracts although it was not certain that this policy could be effective in the case of wartime demand. Some firms attempted to "put teeth" in the no cancellation provision by requiring substantial payments with orders and by specifying that the advance payment was for the last part of the order.[42]

Foreign Trade and Competition

During the nineteenth century when American industry, agriculture, and commerce were developing and expanding at a rapid rate, and the domestic demand for machine tools was growing also, only a few machine tool builders gave much attention to foreign trade. By the time the NMTBA was organized in 1902, however, increasing competition and periodic business recessions or depressions had convinced many tool builders that they should take a greater interest in foreign markets which might provide a stabilizing factor in machine tool demand. How this interest was to be translated into effective action to increase or even maintain America's existing share of world markets in the face of increasingly aggres-

---

[41] *Machinery,* 21:685, (Eng. Ed.), April 1915, "A Danger in War Orders."
[42] *American Machinist,* 42:573, April 1, 1915, "To Machine-Tool Builders."

sive competition from foreign—particularly German—machine tool builders was the problem.

One suggestion advanced was that U.S. machine tool builders cooperate to standardize major machine tool parts such as bearings and lathe spindles. The fact that repairs could thus be made more easily and that some components and accessories would be interchangeable would, it was hoped, cause foreign tool users to prefer American machines even though initially they might be equally or more expensive than tools built elsewhere. This was a logical extension of the so-called "American System" of standardized production to machine tool design and construction.[43]

The effects of tariff barriers on foreign business became a subject of frequent discussion. Many machine tool builders and dealers concluded that foreign tariffs put U.S. tool builders at a serious disadvantage and that the U.S. tariffs brought retaliation from other countries. Consequently, they began to advocate the reduction or even elimination of many of our tariffs. In the spring of 1905, Fred A. Geier of the Cincinnati Milling Machine Company reported on his observations during a European trip and urged that reciprocity treaties be negotiated providing for the mutual reduction of tariffs in an effort to encourage trade.

> The duty of our country in this crisis, . . . is to cease waging war against these nations with whom we desire to trade, and to enter upon some amicable treaties with them in which we shall give as good as we desire to take. . . . We want the world for our market, and we must enter that market by friendship and not by warfare.[44]

William Lodge, President, and P. E. Montanus, Secretary of the NMTBA endorsed the resolutions of the National Reciprocity Conference at Chicago in August 1905 advocating reciprocal trade concessions. They reported that the NMTBA would undoubtedly be asked to become a member of the Reciprocity Association.[45]

---

43 *Ibid.*, 26:1633–1634, November 19, 1903, New York Meeting of the NMTBA, November 10–11, 1903.

44 *Ibid.*, 28:608–609, May 4, 1905 "What Shall We Do About Our Foreign Machinery Trade;" *Machinery*, 11:471, May 1905 (Eng. Ed.), NMTBA Convention, Washington, D. C., April 11–12, 1905.

45 *American Machinist*, 28:570–571, October 1905, Fourth Annual Convention of the NMTBA, New York, October 16–17, 1905.

NMTBA representatives also attended a convention for the extension of foreign trade held in Washington during the winter of 1906–1907. This resulted in a list of recommendations to Congress intended to encourage foreign trade.[46]

The primary reasons for concern over foreign trade at this time were the fact that despite U.S. tariffs, imports of German tools to the U.S. were increasing between 1900 and 1905, while U.S. exports of tools to Germany were declining rather drastically. Yet German tariffs on machine tools were only from 5 to 10 per cent *ad valorem.*[47]

In the fall of 1908, the NMTBA appointed another committee to go to Washington to confer with government representatives regarding ways to stimulate foreign trade. At this time, machine tool builders were particularly concerned over the fact that European machine tool builders were successfully copying U.S. tool designs and production methods. These practices, together with tariffs, shipping costs, and wage differentials, appeared to be making it increasingly difficult or impossible for U.S. firms to compete successfully for European markets.[48]

By the end of the first decade of the twentieth century, differences in metalworking practices in Europe and the United States had become much less important than formerly. European users of turret lathes had adopted and were following closely American practice. The same types of machines were also generally preferred. European firms were showing greater interest in automatic lathes and screw machines. Much of Europe was undergoing a period of rather rapid industrial growth which brought increasing demands for metalworking machinery to rebuild or expand old plants and equip new plants.[49] American machine tool builders who traveled in Europe in this period observed with interest—and sometimes also with considerable apprehension—progress being made by foreign machine tool builders including particularly German firms. August H. Tuechter, President of the Cincinnati-Bickford Tool Company

[46] *Ibid.,* 30:745–746, May 23, 1907, NMTBA Convention, Fortress Monroe, Virginia, May 14–15, 1907.

[47] *Machinery,* "Will the Automobile Follow the Bicycle?" 13:79, October 1906.

[48] *Ibid.,* 15:235 (Eng. Ed.), November 1908, Annual Convention of NMTBA, New York, October 20–21, 1908.

[49] C. A. Tupper, "Machine Tool Trade in Europe," *American Machinist,* 35:257–259, August 10, 1911.

who spent three months in Europe in 1911 described how Germany had been able to build up her export trade. He laid particular emphasis on the knowledge and skill of German business representatives whose training included both practical experience at home in the shop and office, and an opportunity to learn the language and customs of the country in which they were to work. Tuechter also compared American and German machine tools and concluded that German standard machines compared very favorably with their American counterparts.[50]

Machine tool demand and production declined rather drastically during the early months of 1914 as part of a general depression in the metalworking trades. This trend was temporarily further aggravated following the outbreak of World War I in the summer of 1914 when shipments to Germany and Austria were cut off. By October 1914, however, some machine tool plants began to secure new business as a result of the war. By the spring of 1915, the machine tool industry generally had all the business it could handle and was rejecting some orders.[51] Total machine tool export shipments for fiscal year 1915 amounted to over 28 million dollars as compared with 14 million for the preceding year. Shipments to France were about $8.7 million as compared with $1.8 million, whereas shipments to Germany dropped from $2.2 million to about $.1 million in 1915.[52]

The outbreak of the first World War changed the foreign trade picture both with regard to German trade abroad and American trade with Europe. American tool builders, at first, began to give more attention to undeveloped South American markets. However, they concluded that expansion of these markets would require a relatively long time and was dependent upon the ability and willingness of American banks to provide favorable financing.[53] American banks had established branches in South America and were interested in encouraging the economic development of the con-

---

[50] August H. Tuechter, "European Machinery Building Trade," *American Machinist*, 35:1203–1204, December 28, 1911.

[51] W. A. Viall, "Conditions in the Machine Tool Industry," *American Machinist*, 43:870, 876, November 11, 1915.

[52] Ludwig W. Schmidt, "Machine Tool Exports During First Year of the War," *American Machinist*, 43:949–951, November 25, 1915.

[53] *Machinery*, 21:252 (Eng. Ed.), November 1914, NMTBA Convention, New York, October 22–23, 1914.

tinent. With such development, there would logically be expanded markets for the United States' capital equipment industries, including machine tools. On the other hand, most of Latin America was economically and culturally more closely oriented toward Europe than to the United States. Rapid expansion of the machinery trade in South America seemed clearly to be unlikely. In any case, long before it could get seriously started, the demand created by the war in Europe was occupying the machine tool builders' full attention so there was no immediate need to expand other markets.[54]

War Mobilization and Priority Problems

As World War I progressed, machine tool industry spokesmen became increasingly concerned over the relative priority assigned to machine tools. They objected to the view that munitions and other direct war production should have a higher priority than machine tools, that steel production should all go to ship construction, and that machine tool plants should be converted to direct war production. A campaign was, therefore, started to convince congressmen, members of the Council of National Defense and others of the importance of the machine tool industry to the war effort.[55]

Following establishment of the War Industries Board at the end of July 1917, a machine tool section was created early in October 1917. The War Industries Board, as originally created, had only advisory powers. It was not until it was reorganized in 1918 with Bernard M. Baruch as chairman reporting directly to the President that the board was given administrative control of industry.

One of the first acts of the Machine Tools Section of the War Industries Board was to request machine tool builders to supply shop schedules showing monthly output for a five month period from October 1917 to February 1918 and indicating machines which had been sold and those which had not. These data, when tabulated, showed the current situation and indicated shortages or overproduction. The inventory was used as a basis for advising the War

[54] R. E. Eldridge, "Establishment of American Banking Facilities in South America," *Machinery*, 21:255–257 (Eng. Ed.), November 1914.
[55] *American Machinist*, 46:872–873, May 17, 1917, "Machine Tools and the Matter of Priority."

Trade Board regarding modifications in their Conservation List to permit exportation of tools being produced in excess of U.S. needs. No attempt was made, however, to keep an up-to-date record of machine tool production.

Lists were obtained showing shipments of machine tools for countries other than England, France, Italy, and Japan, where these tools were stored, and selling and forwarding agents. This information was used to locate tools urgently needed by U.S. industry or our allies. A procedure was set up for commandeering machine tools intended for export with orders authorized by the Secretary of War. In some cases, these machines had to be modified to the English system from the metric system when they were to be used by American or British plants.

The Machine Tools Section also assisted the Chief of Ordnance to secure a number of experts in machine tool use who made time studies for production of the various forms of munitions and established a basis for determining machine tool requirements.[56]

An army proposal to establish a machine tool reserve of the larger and more difficult to procure machine tools was approved. Under this procedure, stock orders were issued to build up an inventory of such machines for disposition as required. A survey was also made of the larger sizes of machine tools which indicated a need to increase the available sources of supply. Contracts were let for the production of some of the tools in scarce supply by firms not previously building machine tools.

Some of the problems faced by the Machine Tool Section of the War Industries Board and the machine tools industry grew out of competition between various departments and agencies and their contractors. Thus it was necessary to try to reconcile not merely the total requirements but to establish approximately when particular machine tools would be needed; to determine whether more readily available models could be substituted for those in shortest supply, and to obtain the cooperation of the procuring agencies in the realistic scheduling of deliveries. Efforts were made to avoid or minimize hoarding such as had occurred at the air station at Hampton, Virginia where machine tools were delivered long before the

---

[56] *Ibid.*, 48:425–427, March 7, 1918, "The Work of the Machine Tool Section of the War Industries Board"; Benedict Crowell, *America's Munitions, 1917–1918* (Washington: Government Printing Office, 1919), pp. 64–65.

buildings were ready to house them. In this instance, the equipment was stored for months in the open under tarpaulins.[57]

Many contractors ordered machine tools with a careful eye for their potential value in peacetime production rather than merely to meet the immediate requirements of munitions production. This, for example, resulted in orders for scarce types of universal milling machines when plain millers would handle the war work satisfactorily. The limited powers and staff of the Machine Tool Section of the War Industries Board were not adequate to counteract such tendencies. Therefore, there was considerable agitation favoring the expansion of the Machine Tool Section's staff and authority to deal with the situation.[58]

The editors of the *American Machinist* urged that something similar to the British Machine Tool Board was needed. In Britain, a leading machine tool builder and his staff had been given wide powers.

> This board directs the whole machine-tool activities of the country in a way that has proven extremely beneficial to all concerned. It directs, or at least consents, to the purchase of every machine tool which may be needed for essential industries. It prevents new firms from going into building machines with which the market is already well-supplied and prevents the ordering of machines which may be scarce when a more common machine will answer for the work in hand.[59]

The editorial reported that the British Machine Tool Board required about 2,000 employees and was able to move tools from one shop to another. It suggested that the Machine Tool Section of the War Industries Board under George E. Merryweather could form a nucleus for such a board. The editorial added that there was no excuse for delay in deciding what machine tools would be needed even though all the details of war equipment design were not completed. Machine tool builders were said to be anxious to help in any way possible but needed a program. It recommended establish-

[57] *American Machinist*, 49:1093–1094, December 12, 1918, "Work of the Machine Tool Section of the War Industries Board."

[58] *Ibid.*, 48:425–427, May 7, 1918, "The Work of the Machine Tool Section of the War Industries Board."

[59] *Ibid.*, 48:848–849, May 16, 1918, "The Great Need of a Machine Tool Board."

ment of a committee of machine tool builders to work with the government. Major emphasis was placed on the full use of existing machine tool firms rather than bringing in new firms or expanding existing firms already loaded with work. The editors concluded . . .

> With an adequate board and a program for a machine-tool reserve, and this should include machines for all branches of the Army and Navy, we should do away with rush orders in one shop and no orders in the next; with overtime and layoffs, and the unsettled feeling which always goes with such uncertainty. This reserve need not include small machine tools at all, unless conditions change materially, as these can now be purchased from stock in most cases. There is certainly no need of ordering them in large quantities as was recently proposed, and from builders who have sprung up as a result of war conditions.

Wartime Expansion of the Work Force

During World War I, machine tool builders had to meet the problems of recruiting, training, and holding workers in the face of greatly increased demands for labor and a labor supply reduced by military recruitment. The methods used to meet these problems included (1) upgrading some workers, (2) extended application of the principles of specialization and division of labor, and (3) the addition of women to the work force. Employers also had to meet the "security" problem resulting from the fact that many of their workers were aliens, and that many of them did not want to become citizens but planned to return to their native lands.[60]

Women were hired by machine tool builders in significant numbers and by the end of the war numbered approximately 5,000 out of a total of 62,000 employees or roughly 12 per cent. Something over half of this total were in clerical or other minor salaried jobs and a little less than half were wage earners in the shops. The percentage of women production workers was, therefore, considerably less than the 12 per cent indicated above. Among the problems resulting from hiring women was that of providing suitable rest rooms and lockers. Greater emphasis was also put on cleanliness,

---

[60] Luther D. Burlingame, "War Work for Women," *Machinery*, 24:682–887 (Eng. Ed.), April 1918; *Ibid.*, "Industrial Americanization," *Machinery*, 28:30–32, September 1921.

orderliness, safety, and discipline than when the shops were an entirely masculine world. Results reported indicated that the women learned their jobs more quickly than men. This was attributed to the fact that foremen and other workers gave the women more attention during the "breaking-in" period. In addition, employers had a better choice in hiring women since more were available in relation to the demand.

Various preconceptions regarding use of women, including the belief that they could only be used in separate departments and that all "setting up" would have to be done by men, were disproven. Women were found to be particularly good on inspection work but they were used in a variety of other jobs. Proportionately fewer women than men left their jobs or were fired. Where they were discharged or resigned, the main reasons cited were tardiness, getting married, or health rather than the work or "job hopping."[61]

Efforts to solve the labor shortages also included hiring and using unskilled male and female workers as helpers for those jobs or portions of jobs which required a limited amount of skill. This allowed the skilled worker to handle more machines and more highly skilled work. This approach (used successfully by the British early in World War I) was a continuation and acceleration of trends toward specialization and "functionalization" of labor which had begun in the decade preceding World War I.[62]

The NMTBA supported efforts to counteract the efforts of wartime labor shortages and urged machine tool builders to stop competitive bidding for skilled men. It proposed that as an alternative, greater effort should be put on training and upgrading of both male and female unskilled workers to handle skilled work.[63]

During World War I, machine tool builders devoted a good deal of attention and discussion to ways in which they could make plant operations more efficient and management more "scientific." Often these efforts seemed largely to neglect or ignore the human element in the production process. The human factor, however, could not

[61] *Ibid.*, "War Work for Women," *Machinery*, 24:682–687 (Eng. Ed.), April 1918.

[62] Frederick A. Waldron, "Labor Dilution as a National Necessity," No. 1671, ASME, *Transactions*, 40:897–908, December 1918.

[63] *American Machinist*, 48:959–960, June 6, 1918, NMTBA Convention, May 16–17, 1918; *Machinery*, 24:942, June 1918, "The Machine Tool Industry and the War."

be ignored for long in a period of rapidly increasing demand and competition for labor. In small shops, owner, manager, and foremen were all in close touch with the workman and could stimulate his interest in his job and take a personal interest in his well-being. The larger tool building firms became conscious of a need for more formal personnel programs and policies to take the place of the close personal relationships possible in the smaller firms.

The owners and managers of most tool plants appeared anxious to avoid the development of either what they considered to be unwise social programs by a paternalistic government or a type of paternalistic company management which would attempt to provide a wide variety of services and benefits for the worker without special effort on his part. However, leading tool builders recognized that it was becoming necessary to establish better working conditions in the plant as well as to pay wages reasonably competitive with other major metalworking industries.

Some improvements in working conditions and provisions for promoting the comfort and safety of workers in the plant were recognized as being primarily or entirely the responsibility of management. Wherever possible, however, it was considered much better to encourage cooperation between management and workers and self-help on the part of the latter than for the employer to provide services without a direct contribution from the employee. Thus, cooperative efforts by workers with some help and encouragement from the employer were considered much preferable to compulsory programs of insurance imposed by a state or the federal government.[64]

Considerable progress in improving working conditions was undoubtedly made by and during World War I over conditions general in the latter part of the nineteenth century. Superintendents and foremen still attributed many accidents solely to worker carelessness, but much more attention was paid to making the machine shop a reasonably safe place to work. Also employers were becoming much more likely to accept a major responsibility for, and share the burden of, injuries from industrial accidents regardless of their cause.

[64] Luther D. Burlingame, "The Human Factor in Industry," *American Machinist*, 46:847–851, 931–934, May 17 and 31, 1917; Dr. Otto P. Geier, "The Human Potential in Industry," ASME, *Transactions*, 39:411–423, May 1917.

Machine tool builders gradually accepted the need to provide adequate first aid facilities in their shops. Similarly, they came to recognize the desirability of medical examinations for prospective employees and also, in some cases, for periodic medical examinations and limited medical care of employees. Dr. Otto P. Geier of the Cincinnati Milling Machine Company laid particular stress on the importance of an adequate in-plant medical program in a paper presented to the ASME in May 1917. The program advocated included complete physical examinations, (including dental), remedial treatment, emergency treatment, and preventive care.

What is needed is a doctor, a combination general repair and safety engineer, to look after the human machinery, to study stresses and strains on it, to give warning of a probable breakdown, to advise easing up on the load until the human mechanism has been readjusted, to do the hundred and one things that make for comfort of mind and body.[65]

It was generally felt, however, that such services should not be extended beyond the point where the shop was directly affected to the employee's family, unless, because of the isolated location of a plant, other facilities were not available.

A similar line of reasoning was followed in regard to food and recreational facilities. The company might be expected to provide physical facilities for an employee lunchroom but it was considered best to leave its operation to the employees. The company might also find it desirable to organize a suitable recreation program where adequate provisions for such were not already available in the community.

Opposition to Labor Unions

NMTBA members were urged to work directly with their men and to make a greater effort to "educate" their workers to the view that they had nothing to gain from "Unionism as it is now conducted."[66] Nevertheless, during World War I, the National Association of Machinists greatly increased its membership. It was able

65 *Ibid.*, p. 420.
66 J. C. Spence, "On Inducing Ourselves and Our Men to Earn More Money; Some Points on Securing Efficiency Through Cooperation of Employer and Employee," *Machinery*, 20:85–86 (Eng. Ed.), June 1914.

to make important gains in the machine tool plants and other machine shops including those in Cincinnati. Management of the latter firms working through the Cincinnati branch of the National Metal Trades Association had been very active and generally successful in fighting the unions and discouraging union membership. The union survived a premature strike—precipitated by employers. It was able to place many of the strikers in jobs in Detroit thereby reducing claims for strike benefits. A cutback in production in Detroit, however, forced many workers back to Cincinnati and helped to end the strike. A number of shops accepted the 48 hour week and made agreements with the union, although the Cincinnati Metal Trades Association claimed a complete victory over the union.[67]

The machine tool industry experienced greater labor problems as the efforts of the war in Europe increased. In the fall of 1915, NMTBA President W. A. Viall referred to the industry's labor troubles but said that the NMTBA was not concerned with labor questions. Rather it "tries to confine itself to the commercial side of our industry." He warned against efforts to distract the association from its main objectives. Viall also emphasized the machine tool industry's need for young men with both mechanical aptitude and executive ability.[68]

After World War I ended, the machine tool industry became seriously concerned over the loss of skilled workers to the automobile industry and the need to do something to prevent or reduce the drain on the tool industry's labor force. For example, Fred H. Colvin wrote in 1919:

> The machine-tool industry designed and built all the machinery which made possible large sewing machine and typewriter plants, the bicycle manufacturing establishments and the new automobile shops, which are now such an important part of our national industries. Yet in every case, the machine tool industry has suffered because all of the other industies have in turn offered inducements which made it extremely difficult to keep the men interested in the machine-tool shop.

[67] Groves, "Machinist," pp. 191–204.
[68] W. A. Viall, "Conditions in the Machine Tool Industry," *American Machinist*, 43:870, 876, November 11, 1915.

The automobile shops, for example, were able to offer half-trained apprentices several times the wages paid at that time, and as a consequence robbed the machine-tool shops of many young men on whom considerable time and money had been spent in training.[69]

He urged that all possible effort be exerted to secure and hold the skilled mechanic's interest and pride in his work, but the machine tool industry must also be able to offer competitive wages. Tool builders had placed too low a value on their products and were consequently unable to pay adequate wages. The value of machine tools to tool users should be determined by the amount of product produced with them. Wage rates and prices need not be raised radically but should be raised enough to attract the best type of workers.

Postwar Readjustments

During the summer and fall of 1918, the machine tool industry continued its efforts to maintain an adequate labor force and to catch up with requirements for tools in short supply. The NMTBA and the trade press emphasized the importance of the machine tool industry, its need for labor and scarce materials as compared to direct defense production, and the undesirability of converting major machine tool plants to production of munitions or other direct war production. The war ended, however, before U.S. industry had become fully tooled up for war production and before some of the major types of war equipment, such as aircraft powered by the highly publicized Liberty engine, reached the fighting forces in significant numbers.

As the war ended, machine tool builders' worries shifted to the problems of reconversion. These included the fear that tools already on hand would satisfy a large part of peacetime domestic needs and that foreign markets would not compensate for the probable slump in domestic business. Another question was whether and how rapidly the government would exercise cancellation privileges in war contracts and if contractors would then cancel contracts for

[69] Fred H. Colvin, "Putting the Machine Tool Industry Where It Belongs," *American Machinist*, 50:762–764, April 17, 1919.

machine tools. NMTBA President J. B. Doan told the NMTBA Convention in December 1918 that the government "should discourage cancellations of orders" and that "the placing of an order by a buyer and the acceptance of the same by the seller imposes an obligation on both to carry out the contract." He implied that this obligation existed regardless of any legal provisions for contract cancellation.[70]

Doan also expressed concern that machine tool builders might have trouble paying taxes on 1918 profits in the face of contract cancellations and reduced demand in 1919. He contended that most earnings in 1918 were represented by investments in buildings, equipment, tools, and by accounts receivable, and suggested that readjustments in taxes would be necessary and should be presented to Congressmen.

The NMTBA Convention passed a resolution on cancellation of orders urging "the principle already laid down by the Secretary of War that all cancellation and adjustments be carried out in a manner that will cause the least dislocation of industry, having in view the largest interests of the government, the employers and employees, allowing industry to return to its normal conditions as quickly as possible . . . " be carried out and that NMTBA members strongly support this policy.[71]

All machine tool builders were not so concerned about the postwar outlook and competition from tools built for war production. Some believed that European countries would buy most of the machine tools they would need to replace those destroyed or worn out from the United States and so would absorb a large part of the American output.[72]

American machine tool builders, and particularly the large number of small firms, faced many problems in attempting to build up an export business. The small firm could not maintain a selling organization in the various foreign countries which offered an actual or potential market. One possibility of overcoming some of

[70] J. B. Doan, "Problems Facing American Machine Tool Builders," *Machinery*, 25:300, December 1918.

[71] *American Machinist*, 49:1149–1150, December 19, 1918, "The Machine Tool Builder's Convention," New York, December 10–11, 1918.

[72] A. W. Henn, "The Machine Tool Trade After the War," *Machinery*, (Eng. Ed.), 24:1096, August 1918.

the difficulties was through cooperation. However, there was fear such cooperation might bring prosecution for violation of the Anti-Trust Laws. To avoid this, Congress enacted the so-called Webb-Pomerene Act to protect cooperative associations established for the purpose of engaging in foreign trade from prosecution under the Sherman Anti-Trust Act. It was claimed that the new act would put American industry on an equal footing with competing firms in Europe many of which already marketed their products through foreign trading corporations. Many years were to pass, however, before a "Webb-Pomerene Association" was formed for the machine tool industry.[73]

It appeared that while machine tool production had doubled during the war, the domestic market could not absorb more than 50 per cent of the tool output, and that it was necessary to try to obtain additional foreign business. During most of World War I, tool builders had plenty of orders, so they did not worry about trade barriers restricting their sales in foreign countries or about protection of domestic markets from foreign competition. At the end of the war, however, some tool builders again began to urge that the federal government should be more active in promoting favorable trade relationships to counter the effect of protective tariffs and aid U.S. firms to build up their export trade.[74]

Machine tool builders were particularly worried over the possibility that a loss of war business plus competition from surplus machines would result in a serious depression for the tool business. The NMTBA along with other business organizations used its influence with the federal government to assure that order cancellations, adjustments, and compensation would be administered in a way that would cause the least possible damage to industry. Whether as a result of these efforts by industry representatives or merely because the government agencies and Congress were sympathetic to business, this became official policy, and the direct and immediate effects of reconversion at the end of World War I proved less serious than many tool builders had feared or predicted.

[73] Ludwig W. Schmidt, "How Machine Tool Builders Can Cooperate in Foreign Trade," American Machinist, 48:839-841, May 16, 1918.
[74] J. W. Hook, "Future For Machine Tool Exports," Machinery, 25:454-456, January 1919; Schmidt, "Effect of Changes in Foreign Tariffs on the American Machine-Tool Industry," American Machinist, 48:1047-1049, June 20, 1918.

Summary

During the first decades of the twentieth century, machine tool builders became increasingly conscious of the need for cooperative action through the NMTBA and other business organizations but never reached full agreement as to what form such action should take or to what degree it was necessary to conform to common standards and practices.

The efforts of the NMTBA appear to have succeeded in raising machine tool prices and making machine tool builders more conscious of the need for adequate cost accounting systems. They did not, however, succeed in getting all machine tool builders (or even all NMTBA members) to accept and install a single uniform accounting system. They were also unable to prevent some price cutting in periods when demand for machine tools fell far below the industry's capacity.

Machine tool builders, or at least many of the larger firms, were active in developing and applying some of the techniques of "Scientific Management" although some techniques, such as time-and-motion studies, were usually considered to be better adapted to mass production industries. Even here, however, machine tool builders needed to take, and did take, an interest since the management procedures were applied by machine tool users and affected machine tool requirements.

Most machine tool builders appear to have preferred either straight hourly or daily pay systems or comparatively simple premium pay plans which could be installed and used without costly time-and-motion studies. These preferences were based on the fact that most machine tool plants produced finished machine tools and major parts in short runs which did not justify extensive study, special machine tools, or elaborate tooling. It was also felt that group bonus schemes gave encouragement to better cooperation among workmen and foremen in making production efficient, maintaining quality standards, and stimulating efforts to train new workers as rapidly as possible. Longevity payments were also sometimes added as a way of reducing costly and disruptive employee turnover.

The machine tool industry took greater interest in promoting foreign trade and in maintaining or increasing exports of machine tools than it had in the period before 1900. There is some evidence that these efforts had some effect in balancing fluctuations in domestic sales, but they did not, and probably could not, fully compensate for fluctuations in domestic demand and, at times, coincided with them.

Machine tool builders also attempted to solve some of the problems of securing, training, and retaining an adequate number of skilled machinists by improving and standardizing apprenticeship programs and by encouraging and assisting other employees to improve their training. The training offered both within the plant, and on a part-time cooperative basis with the public schools was closely related to the actual working problems met on the job in the participating plants. A system of special apprenticeships was established to simplify the problem of training new shop employees and to reduce the time required as an apprentice before the machinist could earn adequate wages. More specialized jobs were developed which could be filled by less skilled workers, and wage rates were adjusted to make them more competitive with other metalworking industries.

These efforts were stimulated by the growing demand for workers from the automobile industry and other expanding industries and were closely related to the broader problems of competitive wages, hours, and working conditions. They included a publicity campaign aimed at improving the social status of machinists as a way of encouraging more boys or young men to enter the machine tool industry.

None of these efforts appear to have been completely successful but they probably prevented the problems from reaching a critical stage.

During World War I, machine tool builders attempted to expand their work forces through upgrading workers, increasing specialization of jobs to permit more rapid training of new workers, and adding women in production, assembly, and inspection operations as well as in clerical work. Employment of women, except as office workers, appeared to be largely a temporary wartime measure which had little or no lasting effect upon hiring practices. No evidence was found of any effort to use nonwhite workers in skilled or semi-skilled production jobs.

Some progress was made in improving working conditions and in providing a minimum level of medical care and some other employee services. Efforts to impose mandatory unemployment and accident insurance schemes were generally opposed by machine tool builders as being uneconomic. Voluntary cooperative measures were advocated as an alternative. In these areas, it appears that machine tool builders followed the same general line as most other manufacturers though there were wide variations between the services provided by different firms.

Machine tool builders were also active in employer groups opposing the growth of unions in the metal trades. These efforts appear to have had considerable success though they did not prevent the growth of union membership. The NMTBA officially declared that it was not concerned with labor questions which were to be left to other employer organizations such as the National Metal Trades Association.

Machine tool builders, under NMTBA leadership, attempted to protect themselves from some of the effects of rapid changes in machine tool demand by the adoption of "No Cancellation" clauses in contracts. These clauses were apparently viewed mainly as educational devices to encourage restraint on the part of dealers and buyers rather than contractual provisions which could be strictly enforced regardless of their effect upon dealers or customers. Some efforts were made, however, to enforce No Cancellation clauses by requiring substantial advance payments and specifying that these covered the last part of orders.

During the U.S. mobilization effort in World War I, the NMTBA and machine tool builders tried to emphasize the importance of machine tools and the need for assigning a high priority to machine tool production. The industry also was well represented in the Machine Tool Section of the War Industries Board and successfully opposed efforts at standardization of machine tools which it considered unnecessary, unwise, and undesirable from the standpoint of future business. Efforts were made to satisfy war production requirements for machine tools by locating and commandeering tools intended for export to Germany or neutral nations, by diverting machine tools from nonessential civilian use to urgent war production, and by increasing production of needed tools. Machine tool shipment schedules were obtained from machine tool builders and tabulated but the information was not kept up to date.

The conflicting interests and efforts of the various government agencies were not fully resolved until after the end of the War in 1918. Efforts were made to reconcile requirements and establish realistic delivery schedules which would insure that machine tools would be provided where needed while avoiding lost time in both tool producing plants and those of end-product manufacturers. Measures such as creation of a Machine Tool Board with broad powers similar to the British Machine Tool Board, and a machine tool reserve were recommended but the war ended before much could be done to improve the control mechanism.

Machine tool builders were concerned about the effects of the large number of tools produced during the war on postwar domestic and foreign demand for machine tools. They were also worried about the effects of the cancellation of war contracts, and attempted to prove that the federal government should discourage cancellation of orders even where contracts provided for such cancellation and the government would have to pay for the machines. Adjustments in taxes and other measures were urged to ease the problems of reconversion. Efforts were also made to promote additional foreign business as a compensating factor to the expected decline in domestic business. The worst reaction from World War I, however, was delayed until late 1920 and 1921.

PART II

PROSPERITY AND DEPRESSION
1919-1939

5

The Nature and Effects of
Business Instability
1919-1939

The following chapter discusses the nature, timing, and magnitude of fluctuations in machine tool demand, production, and employment during the period from 1919 to 1939. It summarizes NMTBA efforts to develop adequate statistical reporting, and economic analysis to provide a warning of future recessions or depressions and also to give machine tool builders a clearer and more timely picture of their own position in the industry. It also describes some of the industry's efforts to stimulate demand and the role of the federal government in these efforts.

Postwar Economic Adjustment

The decline in machine tool business immediately following World War I proved less severe than many tool builders expected and many predictions regarding the nature and source of postwar business proved erroneous. Nevertheless, the postwar period did bring drastic changes in the machine tool industry as did the years of the great depression of the thirties. Between 1919 and 1921, the number of establishments engaged primarily in the production of machine tools declined from 403 to 348 or by approximately 13.6 per cent. During the same period, however, the average number of wage earners in the industry dropped from 53,111 to 21,307 or 59.9 per cent; the value of products declined from $212,400,000 to $67,-729,000 or 68.1 per cent. Value added by manufacture fell from

$153,366,000 to $43,751,000 or 71.5 per cent. In September, October, and November 1921, the number of machine tool industry workers dropped below 15,000. These figures include some producers of metal-forming machines. The total employment and shipments figures should probably be reduced by about 20 to 25 per cent to reflect this difference in definition of machine tools.[1]

Machine tool demand improved during 1922 and, because of the fact that prices were lower than prior to the depression of 1920-1921, the number of machines purchased was actually larger in comparison to the first three months of 1920 than was indicated by the statistics showing value of shipments. Demand for different types of machines varied rather widely, with the market for grinding machines and small automatic screw machines used by the radio industry being particularly active.[2]

By September, some machine tool firms including those building tools for the automobile industry were again working full time including night shifts. Other firms, however, reported little if any increase in business. By October, machine tool prices had increased by from 10 to 15 per cent over the level of the latter part of 1921. Materials prices were increasing and machinists were said to be in scarce supply. Stocks had been reduced to a point where new production for stock was needed although some firms were hesitant about again building up stocks. The potential danger of high cost inventories of finished or partially completed machines was less, however, than at the end of World War I due to the fact that both material and labor costs were lower.

While business and employment had no doubt improved, it is not clear why there should have been any real shortage of machinists for the machine tool industry. In January and February of 1923 employment of wage earners in the industry amounted to only a little over half the number employed at the end of 1919 and was below that in January 1921. The most likely explanation is that the increased level of manufacturing in general and the automobile industry in particular had drained away many of the more desirable workers. In each case, however, the 1922 level of operation

---

[1] U.S. Department of Commerce, Bureau of the Census, *Census of Manufactures: 1923.*

[2] *Machinery,* 28:834, June 1922; 28:1006, August, 1922, "The Machine Tool Industry."

was actually not very much above the 1920 level. (See Appendix Table 16). It is also possible that the number of machinists leaving the work force since 1919 was greater than, or at least equal to, the number of new machinists trained.[3]

The upward trend of machine tool demand which began in 1922 continued through 1923 and was accompanied by substantial increases in prices. There was some buyer resistance to these increases, however, and buyers warned tool builders that further price increases would result in curtailed buying. The latter warning was answered by A. W. Henn, President of the National Acme Company in *Machinery* with the claim that machine tools could not be priced solely with a view to encouraging buyers and that prices must cover "cost of production plus a reasonable margin of profit." He also insisted that machine tool prices were relatively low in comparison with some other types of machinery of similar quality and complexity. To support this view, he stated that machine tools cost only from $.20 to $.35 per pound while many other types of machinery sold for as much as $1.00 per pound.[4] It is interesting, however, that Mr. Henn chose to try to prove the reasonableness of machine tool prices by comparing per pound prices of machine tools with those of other types of machinery since, on other occasions, machine tool builders objected to price comparisons based on average per pound costs as unfair and misleading.

The NMTBA General Manager E. F. DuBrul compared machine tool building firms with shops in other industries during 1923. He estimated that in 1919, the average machine tool shop was about four times as large as the average in other industries in terms of capital invested, number of workers, value added by manufacture, or wages and salaries paid. The ratio in terms of material used, however, was much smaller. Average wages were paid by machine tool builders, but the proportion going to salaries was only about 21 per cent as compared to 27.3 per cent of the payroll for the average shop. He added that the machine tool builder had about $600 less in capital invested for each wage earner employed than in the average shop. On the other hand, the value added by manufacture

---

[3] *Ibid.*, 29:150, October 1922, "The Machine-Building Industries;" *Ibid.*, 29:228, November 1922, "The Machine Tool Industry."
[4] A. W. Henn, "The Upward Trend of Business," *Machinery*, 29:775, June 1923.

was about 66 per cent in the average firm in terms of material and fuel costs compared to 262 per cent for machine tool firms. The average manufacturer used $149 worth of material as compared to $38 for the tool builder, and $177 of capital for $150 in the case of the machine tool firm.

The above ratios, however, do not seem consistent since if both the total capital investment and number of employees were four times greater for machine tool plants than for other plants, it is difficult to see how investment per employee could be less. Also, how could other firms have greater capital investment if tool firms were four times larger on the average? The ratio of value added by manufacture indicated by DuBrul appears to be about the same as reflected in the *Census of Manufactures* for 1919 or about 2.6 times but is higher than that shown by the census figures for 1921 or 1923 which were only 1.8 and 2.3 times respectively. This ratio increased by 1929 when it was 2.9 but then declined and in 1939 was 2.4. The latter figure was probably reduced by the fact that the cost of materials, etc., included contract work which was not included in the figures for 1929 or earlier years.

DuBrul also reported that smaller firms—having an output of $100,000 per year or less—fared somewhat worse in the machine tool industry than in industry in general. The smaller shops represented about 44 per cent of the total firms in the industry but produced only about 3 per cent of the value added. Conversely, about 13 per cent of the machine tool builders produced 70 per cent of the value added, or an average of approximately $2,000,000 worth of tools compared to an investment of approximately $3,000,000 in capital. Here the intent appears to have been to warn other firms against entering the machine tool business.[5]

The fluctuating character of machine tool demand was emphasized as was the threat presented by large inventories of machine tools. DuBrul asserted that price reductions did not appreciably stimulate machine tool sales. He neglected to say that most of the machine tool industry's customers were also suffering from slack business conditions and were not in a position to make large investments in new machine tools even at bargain prices. DuBrul contrasted the inelastic demand for machine tools with demand

[5] Ernest F. DuBrul, "Economics of the Machine Tool Industry," *Machinery*, 29:564–566, March 1923.

for low-priced automobiles which he said was very sensitive to small price changes and represented a virtually unlimited market. He did not add, however, that this by no means assured that all motor vehicle manufacturers would prosper or find a ready market for their output.

DuBrul emphasized that long periods of depression made it necessary for machine tool builders to build up large reserves, in periods when business was good and profitable, if the firms were to survive the periods of idleness. He noted that several representative companies had earned about 9 per cent on investment during the ten years prior to World War I but that most of these earnings had to be retained as reserves against a further depression.

DuBrul concluded that as a result of lessons learned in the depression of 1921 and 1922, machine tool builders were very much concerned regarding the industry's economic problems. Because of this concern, they were more willing than formerly to contribute statistical information which could be used in studying the causes and effects of business cycles in an effort to find ways of moderating, if not eliminating, large fluctuations in business.

DuBrul reported in May 1924 that the machine tool industry as a whole had not received much if any return on its investment in 1923. This seems surprising in view of the fact that the value of shipments increased by 83 per cent in 1923 as compared to 1922 based on NMTBA estimates, that the number of units shipped increased by only 26 per cent, and that the unit price increased by 31 per cent. He contended that low profits in 1923 together with the losses suffered by the industry in 1921 and 1922 demonstrated a need to give further thought to problems still confronting the machine tool industry. He also recalled that in January 1921, the NMTBA had 222 members and said that 57 of these had either left the machine tool industry or were in the hands of receivers or creditors' committees.[6]

DuBrul said that the industry's biggest financial problem was that of excess capacity; that better salesmanship would help to increase sales, but that other measures were also needed. These included conversion of some firms to other products, consolidation, and cost reduction through concentration of production.

---

[6] *Machinery*, 30:767, June 1924, NMTBA Convention, Buffalo, May 22–23, 1924.

DuBrul warned that the problem of excess capacity could not be solved by "bargain sales below cost" or cutthroat competition, but that there was a need for greater research and competitive effort.

Business Cycle Predictions and Statistics

The delayed recession of 1920 and 1921 stimulated a marked increase in interest on the part of machine tool builders, dealers, and the NMTBA in development of statistical data and studies which might provide a more reliable key to future business trends. Machine tool firms were urged to pool statistical information through the NMTBA rather than attempt to rely entirely on their own information, experience, or judgment.[7]

In October 1921, DuBrul emphasized that without adequate statistics on production, shipments, stocks, and sales, each manufacturer must grope blindly in the dark.

> The first thing a man wants to know is whether he is getting his share of the business at any time. He can tell this if he knows the total number of machines in his line being sold in a month, and the total capacity of his group. . . . In no other way can he know, except by joining with his competitors in a composite report of conditions. When he has that report he can then compare his own conditions with those of the group as a whole.[8]

One explanation of the business cycle discussed by machine tool builders in the summer and fall of 1921 saw the roots of one recession or depression in the recovery phase of the preceding cycle. The theory was that as the period of prosperity approached, materials and labor costs increased more rapidly than selling prices, labor became less productive, and increases in order backlogs caused less efficient equipment to be brought into use. It also became more difficult to secure efficient executives. Orders were taken so far in advance of delivery at fixed prices that by the time delivery was made, the selling price did not cover costs; then, with a tightening of credit and higher interest rates, a downward turn in business soon followed. This downward trend occurred while machine tool builders had a large volume of unfilled orders and these presented

[7] *Machinery*, 27:193–194, November 1921, National Machine Tool Builders Convention, New York, October 18–20, 1921.
[8] *Ibid.*

a serious danger requiring exercise of business foresight. It was recommended that under such circumstances efforts be made to reduce contracts for high-priced materials even if this meant buying on a "hand-to-mouth" basis rather than building up high cost inventories. The machine tool builder was urged to anticipate this progression and to operate very conservatively, reduce inventories, and be prepared for a downward phase of the cycle.

No thought or weight was apparently given to the psychological theories of recessions which held that business fear or lack of confidence in the future was itself a major cause of recessions or that the steps taken by machine tool builders to cut back materials orders, inventories, and employment might have a significant and perhaps disproportionate effect in stimulating the downward movement in economic activity.[9]

DuBrul suggested that one of the causes of business fluctuations was the fact that most machine tool purchases were made during the wrong phase of the business cycle. He contended that during periods of depression machine tool activity was at a lower level than that for other types of machinery. When machine tool demand began to improve, the tool builder had to compete with his customers for materials and labor thus pushing up costs, while labor productivity declined. Demand for machine tools was satisfied before the economy reached its peak of prosperity, and order cancellations left the tool builder with excessive inventories even though he reduced production. DuBrul concluded:

> If, when material prices are low and labor is available, buyers of machine tools would place their orders for their own replacement requirements, the machine tool industry would thereby give employment to men who cannot be employed in consumer goods industries. Such employment would itself create demand for consumer goods on the part of such men and their families, and would thereby minimize the depression in consumer goods. The machine tool buyer would naturally get the benefit of lower prices.[10]

The above viewpoint, which appears to have been shared by many others in the machine tool industry, seems to portray the

[9] RG (Record Group) 151, Department of Commerce, Bureau of Foreign and Domestic Commerce, "Cooperation with Bureau—NMTBA, 1922–1926." File 711-N.

[10] Ernest F. DuBrul, "Buying Machinery at the Right Time," *American Machinist*, 56:385, March 9, 1922.

machine tool builder as the victim both of economic forces and of the shortsightedness of the machine tool users including particularly the producers of consumer goods. It is not clear, however, why DuBrul felt that tool users should not only be able to reliably predict future demand for their products, but also have adequate reserves or credit to permit them to invest in new tools in anticipation of increased demand. Apparently, it was felt that the tool user should be willing and able to risk new investments in capital equipment even when his existing plant was operating at a fraction of its capacity, investment funds were scarce, and future demand uncertain both as to timing and volume.

There were certainly some exceptions in which machine tool users had both the foresight and financial strength to take advantage of a slack period to clean out obsolete or little-used machines from their shops to make room for retooling. One example was when, in the panic of 1920–1921, Ford closed down for six weeks, cleared his plants of obsolete equipment, and then proceeded to improve working methods and layout and to install modern equipment. In 1920, also, the Lelands spent $4,249,000 for new machinery including $1,750,000 for special machine tools to produce postwar Lincolns. The high cost was due to a combination of high prices and the Lelands' insistence upon high quality both in the end product and in the production equipment.[11]

DuBrul emphasized that a trade association must gather scattered bits of information from its members and put these together in a systematic and coordinated whole. Some machine tool companies, however, preferred—either from a desire for secrecy or an unwillingness to pay the cost of obtaining necessary data and preparing reports—not to furnish the information requested by the NMTBA. In other cases, information was supplied but was not in a form in which it could be used. Finally, there was the problem of getting tool builders to use the statistics, even when compiled and analyzed by the NMTBA staff, and of establishing the validity of the NMTBA's economic analysis.[12]

[11] Allan Nevins and F. E. Hill, *Ford, Expansion and Challenge, 1915–1932.* Vol. 2 (New York: Charles Scribner Sons, 1957), pp. 167, 175.
[12] *American Machinist*, 56:672–674, May 4, 1922, "Machine Tool Builders Hold Spring Meeting," Atlantic City, April 25, 1922; *Machinery*, 28:707, May 1922. NMTBA Convention, Atlantic City, April 25–26, 1922.

Lessons to Be Learned from the Postwar Slump

By the spring of 1923 the machine tool industry was well on its way to recovery following the slump of 1920–1921, but NMTBA leaders were attempting to analyze and interpret the lessons to be learned from this and earlier recessions. NMTBA President, Edward J. Kearny posed two rhetorical questions: (1) "Have we learned anything from the long period of idleness?" and (2) "What steps can be taken in preparation for the next depression?" In answer to the first question, he listed six points: (a) demand for machine tools was subject to greater fluctuations than the most useless luxuries; (b) a curve showing past fluctuations in orders would have saved millions in 1920; (c) the beginning of a depression is the wrong time to build up stocks; (d) price reductions have no effect on machine tool sales; (e) idleness costs money but was unavoidable so far as could be determined with available knowledge; and (f) lack of substantial cash reserves at the start of a depression meant price cutting, loss of self-respect, discredit among competitors, humiliating pressure from banks, expensive refinancing, creditors' committees or receiverships. In answer to the second question, he suggested that tool builders study business trends carefully, and that at the first sign of a downward tendency, they should reduce the volume of work in process in order to prevent accumulation of a large inventory. Tool builders were also advised to try to accumulate cash surpluses to meet a future depression.[13]

Kearny called attention to a tendency to place increasing importance on competition as the primary price determinant, and suggested that usefulness to the buyer and cost of production should be the determining factors. He made a special plea on behalf of "individuality" in machine design and construction. He said there was room for progress in standardization, but warned that when machines of different makes closely resembled each other they also were close together in price. Kearny did not advocate the complete elimination of price competition or directly oppose standardization programs, but urged that both be used very carefully and with due attention to the dangerous consequences that might result

---

[13] *Machinery*, 29:776–777, June 1923. NMTBA Convention, White Sulphur Springs, West Virginia, May 9–10, 1923.

from energetic price competition or too much emphasis on standardization.

Six months later, Kearny estimated that machine tool production still amounted to only one-third of the industry's capacity. Many firms had been forced into receivership; surpluses had declined and net capital had been reduced. He expressed a belief that transportation and particularly the railroad was the key to progress and prosperity.

> The only thing that stands in the way of growth of transportation facilities is lack of capital. The capital will be forthcoming if there is prospect of security for the investment and a continued return that is satisfactory compared with what can be obtained in other industries. But the people are misinformed and led to believe false economic doctrines. When any considerable class is adversely affected, such for example, as the wheat growers or coal consumers, what is the first suggestion for relief? "Take it out of the railroads."

He urged that the Transportation Act of 1920 be continued in effect without "experimental amendments." This act, otherwise known as the Esch-Cummins Act, returned the railroads to private control after World War I, and was intended to encourage consolidation of weak roads with stronger lines into a few major systems. Kearny apparently expected or hoped that this would make the railroads more prosperous and encourage modernization which would include replacement of many machine tools. The railroads, however, proved much less anxious to consolidate than had been supposed and the act had much less effect than hoped. Possibly, the most remarkable feature of Kearny's address, however, was the fact that no reference was made to the automobile industry as providing either a present or future tool market, and the highly optimistic estimate of the railroad industry's role as a tool customer. Perhaps this tends to prove that it was easier to build machine tools than it was to predict accurately future economic developments.[14]

In October 1923, DuBrul referred to a special study of sales ratios which had been made by the NMTBA staff and said that such cooperative studies were necessary before the industry could combat

---

[14] Emory R. Johnson, *Government Regulation of Transportation* (New York: D. Appleton-Century Company, 1938), pp. 36–38, 319–322, 326–327.

the evils of unfair and unwise competition. He added that it was not sufficient to "bewail ignorance" but was necessary to try to educate the ignorant "as to costs and good business principles, through legitimate association work."[15]

DuBrul called attention to the efforts being made by the Department of Commerce to encourage industries to organize adequate statistical services and assured NMTBA members that such statistics could be compiled relatively cheaply once their collection was systematized.

The days of secrecy in business are largely over. With statistics and information a manufacturer can plan his own financing, sales, and production schedules more accurately. With specific information in hand, it is possible to slow down production of sizes or types that sell slowly and speed up on the faster sellers. Production schedules can be revised when a wave of cancellations is reported. No one will be misled in expanding his plant beyond reason because of a temporary spurt of orders.

Nevertheless, a good many members failed to supply statistical data to the association or to adhere to all of the policies it advocated. When business was good, there was little interest among tool builders in, or apparent need for, measures to prevent or control price competition. Many tool builders saw little advantage in supplying the NMTBA statistical and accounting information requested by DuBrul and the association's staff. In times of severe recession or depression, their attitude became more cooperative.

In May 1924, Ralph E. Flanders called attention to the fact that although the preceding year had been one of rather general industrial prosperity, machine tool output was only 36 per cent of the rate for the first quarter of 1920, that the average rate for the first four months of 1924 had been even lower, and that the prospect for the future looked still more doubtful. He attributed this situation to the fact that machine tool demand was deferrable in hard times, that there was a lag of several months from the time increased demand for end products began to be felt until it was reflected in greater demand for machine tools, that machine tool demand was the first to decline, that periods of high demand were shorter than

---

[15] *Machinery*, 30:183-184, November 1923, NMTBA Convention, Lenox, Massachusetts, October 2-4, 1923.

in other industries, and that changes in activity were more violent. Machine tool demand in the past, he said, had been based on expansion of domestic industry, and replacement or maintenance of existing equipment had been a relatively minor factor.[16]

Flanders analyzed some of the more basic economic factors and suggested that the United States was entering a period of slower expansion due to the disappearance of public land for agriculture and virtual stoppage of immigration. Moreover, he said, there was little foreign demand "in the countries that used to be good customers"—principally Western Europe and Great Britain—and the newer industrial countries such as Japan, India, and China had not developed rapidly enough to make up for the loss of the older trade. He also suggested the possibility that the "age of invention" was coming to an end; compared thirty-six-hour air mail service from New York to San Francisco with the replacement of the covered wagon by the railroad; and doubted that the former development would have as much effect as the latter. The machine tool industry was a "barometer of business expansion" rather than of business activity in general. It was also, he emphasized, "sensitive to major social movements quite beyond our control."

The machine tool industry had expanded rapidly to meet the needs of industrial expansion and wartime requirements but the rate of industrial expansion had declined. He hoped that it would not again be necessary to face wartime needs. He suggested the need for a new end-product industry to take the place of the bicycle and automobile—as the machine tool industry's best customer—but indicated that his hopes in this connection for the truck, tractor, and aircraft businesses had not been realized. He expressed a belief that the steady growth of industry and population would be a help in maintaining machine tool demand; that restriction of labor supply resulting from reduced immigration and other factors might increase demands for machinery; and that replacement of older machinery offered a possible market.

Flanders predicted a period of gradual improvement in business following one in which business would not be either particularly bad or good. Capacity operations might be again reached in three or four years or might require ten or fifteen years to achieve. He predicted that cyclic fluctuations would continue but would be less

[16] Ralph E. Flanders, "Prospects of the Machine Tool Industry," *Machinery*, 30:765–766, June 1924.

violent—"The lesson of the business cycle is being learned, and every individual manufacturer who adjusts his business to it assists in soothing its perturbations." Future events were to prove the above predictions overoptimistic. Nevertheless, Flanders presented a thoughtful and plausible analysis of the major economic factors affecting machine tool demand. His failure to foresee the major depression ahead may be attributed to the inherent difficulties in long range economic forecasting when there is little control over the economy. It was probably also to be expected that a trade association president would take a positive view and conclude a formal public address on a reasonably optimistic note.

Factors Influencing Tool Replacement

During the years prior to World War I and throughout most of the war itself, there was strong demand for machines to expand production. In the peak years, demand exceeded the capacity of the machine tool industry and the industry expanded to try to meet this demand. There was little incentive to try to introduce radically new designs since most plants had more work than they could handle filling orders for existing models. At the end of the war, however, this situation was rather drastically changed and demand fell off while available supply for peacetime use rapidly increased. Tool builders began to place much more emphasis on replacement business. Some machines had been overworked and undermaintained during the war and needed to be replaced, but this type of demand was balanced by the fact that many tools built for war production were no longer needed for this purpose. An alternative stimulus to sales was to introduce improvements in machine tool design and construction which would make much existing equipment obsolete.[17]

As previously noted, machine tool users, including machine tool builders, tended to retain and operate machines so long as they were in good condition and turned out satisfactory work. The machine tool builder or dealer had to prove that a new machine of the same type, or an improved model, would pay for itself within a short period of time through increased production, reduced labor, and lower overhead costs before a sale was likely.

[17] Myron S. Curtis, "The Economics of Machine-Tool Replacement," *Mechanical Engineering*, 49:966, September 1927.

All manufacturers, or at least all production managers, probably preferred to have the most efficient and adaptable equipment available and to keep all of it fully utilized, but it was rarely possible to achieve this ideal where machine tools were concerned. The principal obstacles were economic or managerial rather than technical and applied to virtually all industries although not in precisely the same way or to the same degree.

In the case of "defense" industries, the capital equipment utilization factor was likely to be low in peacetime when obsolescence rather than wear was the major factor determining when tools should be replaced, and very high during wartime. The reverse applied to some types of consumer goods industries. The major problems, so far as machine tools were concerned, were to determine when tools should be replaced for technical reasons and how rapidly new tools could be paid for through reduced costs or increased production. Such decisions, however, were usually contingent on estimates of potential future demand rather than merely an examination of current production costs, maintenance and repair records, and order books. In the case of peacetime industries, the problem of predicting future demand was a difficult one, but in the case of basically war related industries the problem was further complicated by a variety of political, strategic, and economic factors.

Replacement practice, of course, varied. Some firms followed a policy of getting maximum production from their machines (for example, by operating tools at higher speeds than recommended) even at the expense of higher maintenance costs and the need to replace their tools with improved models at relatively short intervals. The latter viewpoint was endorsed by the larger automobile firms and by some other industries. J. A. Smith, General Superintendent of the General Electric Company, stated:

> I believe it is thoroughly bad for shop morale to keep a lot of superannuated machine tools standing around. They occupy valuable space that ought to be devoted to a productive machine. They tie up motors that ought to be working. If your equipment is obsolete, sell it. If you can't sell it, scrap it. It is too expensive to have around the shop.[18]

18 *Ibid.*

However, the author was told by a mechanical engineer formerly employed by the General Electric Company that the company followed a policy under which it would replace machine tools only if the new tools would pay for themselves in one year. This raises the question of what was meant by tools being "obsolete" and suggests there may have been a rather drastic difference in viewpoint between the shop superintendents and those who controlled the company's business policies. It also is possible that there was a change in the company's replacement policy.

Certainly various factors entered into the determination as to whether a particular piece of equipment was considered obsolete. Among the more important of these were (1) improvements in the design of machine tools, (2) increased output requirements, (3) changes in product design, (4) elimination of uneconomical manufacturing operations, (5) changes in user's production methods, (6) effect on investment in materials in-process, (7) effect on space requirements, and (8) effect on power consumption. Each tool user probably put greater emphasis on some of these points than others and even considered a single factor to the exclusion of others. Undoubtedly, it was also sometimes difficult to obtain reliable data or give the proper weight to all considerations.[19]

The major components of machine tools varied greatly in rapidity of wear and needed to be repaired or replaced at different periods. Since frequency of repair and maintenance costs were a significant factor in determining when tools should be replaced, it was necessary to have adequate records of such maintenance costs. The fact that many tool users did not have such records was one of the reasons why older equipment was not replaced.

Many machine tool users demanded that new tools be a great deal better than the tools they replaced before they would agree to purchase new equipment. Automobile manufacturers, for example, frequently specified that new tools must pay for themselves within one year and explained this position by referring to the fact that changes were made in the product each year which might make the machine tools obsolete. This viewpoint seemed fairly reasonable when applied to special machines but much less so in the case

---

[19] L. C. Morrow, "Shop-Equipment Policies in Representative Plants," *Mechanical Engineering*, 49:970–974, September 1927.

of standard machines which were not replaced at anything approaching this rapid rate. Also the annual model changes often involved only minor changes in styling of bodies which had little effect on machine tool requirements. Other industries used longer periods ranging up to six or seven years used by locomotive repair shops.

There was a wide variation in the buying methods of machine tool users. Even though orders were in nearly all cases issued by a purchasing department, the actual selection of machine tools to be purchased was not usually made by the purchasing agent. In one plant, shop superintendents and master mechanics recommended purchases before the annual equipment budget was prepared; the supervisor of equipment reviewed the recommendations; the financial man authorized procuring of data; the purchasing agent secured proposals; and the machine tool committee made selections. The multiple approvals required for tool purchases and the "bureaucratic" procedures involved tended to discourage or delay procurement of new tools.

Machine tool users depended on various sources for information regarding new machine tool developments but the following appear to be the sources most used: (a) new equipment sections of the technical press, (b) advertisements in the technical press, (c) machine tool salesmen, (d) machinery expositions, and (e) plant visits.

Frederick V. Geier, Vice President of the Cincinnati Milling Machine Company, told the Machinery Builders Society in May 1930 that a questionnaire sent to 800 of the larger manufacturing companies in the United States revealed that none of the firms would buy new equipment unless it would repay its cost in less than five years and 43 per cent insisted that it pay for itself within two years. Geier also cited a prominent machine tool builder, who stated that his company rarely sold a machine unless the buyer netted a return of 25 per cent or more. Policies of this kind presented a serious problem to the machine tool and other machinery industries. Geier also indicated changes which had taken place in the thinking of machine tool designers regarding normal tool life:

> Formerly these engineers considered that the life of a machine tool design was from 10 to 15 years. Today they are convinced that design life is not over 5 to 10 years, and I suppose visitors at the Machine Tool Exposition last fall who enthused over one

of the new models exhibited would have been amazed to learn that a model to supersede that very one had been on the drawing board for many months.[20]

The NMTBA estimated at about the same time that a depreciation rate of from 10 to 15 per cent was necessary to recover the original cost of a machine before it became obsolete. Actual practice varied rather widely, however, one survey showing a range of from 7 to 33½ per cent and an average rate of about 12½ per cent. Since this average was within the range recommended by the NMTBA, the problem presumably lay with those firms using much lower rates.

An example showing the effect of obsolescence was a special machine built in 1924 which doubled previous output. Within 3½ years, a standard machine equalled this productivity and within five years a standard machine virtually doubled the output of the special machine and cost about half as much. Geier called attention to an "Index of Machine Tool Productivity" which showed a marked upward trend during the preceding ten years. Productivity for 1928 was about six times that for 1900.

. . . The five year period centering about 1906 shows a peak in productivity increase and reflects the changes brought about by the adaptation of machine tools to the use of high speed steel. It will be noted that since the war period there has been a steady upward trend in the productivity of new models, the index having crossed 60% increase in output. We can then fairly conclude that not only are new models coming on the market more frequently, but they are increasingly productive as compared to superseded models. This indicates plainly that obsolescence is growing both in frequency and in degree.

A major model changeover, such as Ford's shift from the Model T to the Model A in 1927, which involved all parts of the automobile including a new engine and transmission, was a major exception to the general picture of relatively slow and gradual replacement of individual machines. Such a model change required that many comparatively new machines be replaced along with those which were worn out. Other machines had to be rebuilt, thousands of new jigs, fixtures, dies, and tools built or purchased, and production lines rebuilt. Ford was reported to have purchased about 4,500 new

[20] Frederick V. Geier, "Amortization of Machine Tools," Paper delivered to Machinery Builders Society of New York, May 1930.

machine tools and to have invested $18,000,000 in new machinery and overhauling existing equipment.[21]

When Ford converted from the Model A to the "V-8," the changes made in tooling were less sweeping. The fact that this changeover took place during the depression probably caused Ford to retain in operation machines which would have been replaced during the twenties when the Model A was introduced.[22]

During the depression of the thirties, many of the largest machine tool users discarded the replacement policies followed during the twenties when many tools were replaced as soon as a new model became available. Under the tighter policies, machines were replaced only when they clearly could not do the work required. In view of the low level at which most industries were operating, low wages, and the surplus of labor available there was little apparent reason to replace tools. The machinery industries represented by the Machinery and Allied Products Institute (MAPI), National Machine Tool Builders Association (NMTBA) and other trade organizations attempted, however, to convince tool users that they should improve their depreciation accounting, develop an orderly program for capital equipment replacement, and take advantage of lower prices to modernize their plants.[23]

The Crash

The financial crash of 1929 was not immediately followed by a decline in machine tool shipments. In fact, a low point had been reached in 1927 when shipments of machine tools amounted to only 28,000 units selling for $87,000,000. Shipments increased in 1928 to 36,000 units valued at $128,000,000 and in 1929 to 50,000 units valued at $185,000,000, the industry's best year since 1918. In 1930, however, production again dropped very drastically to 23,500 units valued at $96,000,000, although unit costs per machine rose as they had for eight successive years. In 1931, there was a further radical drop in production to 12,000 units valued at $51,000,000 despite a further moderate increase in unit costs. In 1932, shipments reached

[21] Nevins, *Ford*, Vol. 2, p. 450.
[22] *Ibid.*, p. 595.
[23] W. G. Broehl, Jr., *Precision Valley* (Englewood Cliffs, N. J.: Prentice-Hall, Inc., 1959), pp. 146–147.

their lowest level since 1908 when only 5,500 units, valued at $22,-000,000, were shipped. The unit cost declined slightly for the first time in a decade.[24]

The number of wage earners in the machine tool industry reached a peak in October 1929 of 49,542, their highest level since early 1920 and the highest point they would reach until the end of 1939. Ironically, October 1929 was also the time of "Black Thursday" and the critical point of the great financial crash which was to be followed after varying time lapses by drastic declines in virtually all branches of industry and trade. Rather than leading the economic decline, as might have been expected in view of the machine tool builders' belief that their industry was the first to feel the effects of economic downturns and the last to start to recover, in 1929 and early 1930, machine tool production operations and employment were slow to decline. As previously noted, however, the first manifestation of a slowdown in demand for machine tools was normally felt in the volume of new orders received (particularly in new orders from tool users as distinguished from distributors). In this instance, however, there is little indication that machine tool builders or the NMTBA had, or recognized, any advance warning of the crash or did anything to prepare for it beyond the efforts of many firms to build up substantial reserves in periods of prosperity.

Causes of Depression

There was little difference of opinion among tool builders regarding the fact that the machine tool industry was subject to extreme and too frequent fluctuations in business, but determination of the causes and possible cure for the major depression of the thirties was a much more controversial area. Ralph E. Flanders in 1932 listed ten unbalancing factors in the existing industrialized economy. These were

1. Profits and output are unstable where there are large fixed charges for capital equipment and overhead and variable

---

[24] RG 151, "General Files, Machine Tools, 1933–35" file 221.2. Memorandum from LeVerne Beals, Chief Statistician for Manufacturers to the Assistant Director, Bureau of Foreign and Domestic Commerce, August 8, 1934, "Preliminary Report for the Machine Tool Industry."

labor costs are relatively low. Production tends to exceed effective demand.

2. Machine production results in unstable relations between price and volume of output due to the effects of high fixed charges.
3. Increasing production efficiency and greater application of machinery tends to throw a larger percentage of workers into relatively unstable occupations.
4. Increases in production tend to concentrate to a larger degree on comforts or luxuries rather than more essential goods and demand for the former is relatively unstable.
5. Large accumulation of profits tends to slow down business activity and to exaggerate fluctuations.
6. Economies from increased managerial efficiency tend to further upset the balance between production and purchasing power.
7. Possible slackening of rate of new investment required due to reduction in population growth and immigration.
8. Business and workers dependent on production of equipment and other capital goods are an unstable element in demand for consumer goods.
9. Dependence on foreign investment and trade.
10. Transfer of population from self-sustaining agriculture to urban industry.[25]

The so-called "economic maturity" theory advanced by Professor Alvin Hansen and others involved rather similar assumptions including:

1. That the frontier had been passed.
2. Foreign capital was looking elsewhere for opportunities for investment.
3. Inventions had been capital-saving rather than capital-using.
4. Capital requirements were being met from depreciation reserves and new savings were not needed.
5. Population growth was declining.[26]

[25] Ralph E. Flanders, "The Economics of Machine Production," *Mechanical Engineering*, 54:Part 2:605–612, No. 9, September 1932; Senator Flanders recently wrote the author, regarding this article that "In reviewing the causes of inflation I am astonished to find that I made no strong reference to the insane credit inflation of the late 1920's based on security prices which were completely unrealizable. That was the real cause of the inflation and is now largely under the tight hand of the Federal Reserve on margins."
[26] Broehl, *Precision Valley*, p. 144.

There were a variety of "underconsumption" and overproduction theories as to the cause of this and earlier depressions. There were also the so-called psychological theories which saw the loss of confidence on the part of businessmen, investors, etc., as the primary cause of the great depression. Many of these theories seemed to be plausible and attracted considerable numbers of adherents but they were not fully satisfactory explanations of the causes or cure of the depression.

To move closer to the immediate problem of what happened to the machine tool industry and determine whether the industry was the helpless victim of blind economic forces, the shortsightedness of machine tool users, etc., the question arises as to whether the machine tool industry had not raised its prices too much. They were increased from 1922 to 1931 by about 176 per cent, and attempts were made to offset reductions in volume of sales by price increases. Machine tool builders also were not very aggressive in reducing their costs and improving their products. As previously indicated, machine tool builders attributed the increases in prices to a combination of factors including improvements in the machine tools, increased labor and materials costs, and the necessity for setting prices high enough that the tool builders could develop adequate reserves in comparatively prosperous periods to carry them through periods of recession or depression. Spokesmen for the machine tool industry and many economists not connected with the industry insisted that machine tool demand was, like that for most other capital equipment, highly inelastic and that price changes had little effect upon the number of machines ordered. This view was apparently accepted by Dr. Robert Stanley Himes in his study of the machine tool industry.[27]

Dr. Himes summarized the formal and empirical theories of business investment as they related to the machine tool industry and indicated where demand for machine tools appeared to behave differently than for other producers' durable goods.

There are two respects in which machine tools may differ enough from other capital goods to warrant special attention.

[27] Robert Stanley Himes, "A Study of the Machine Tool Industry With Emphasis on the Problem of Stability." Unpublished dissertation, The American University, Washington, D. C., 1962, pp. 83f, 140–144.

These are: the highly differentiated, non-homogeneous nature of machine tools, and their great durability. . . .

Non-homogeneity means that while aggregate machine tool demand follows (or, more correctly, leads) the trend of general business conditions, there are many individual exceptions within the industry. . . . Evidence of varying demands for different types of machine tools during the same period of time is furnished by sales and profit data of the respective tool builders.

Durability of machine tools contributes to an "aggravation" of cyclical demand tendencies for all capital goods to the extent that it may exceed the average durability of such goods. The long life built into the machines, and its prolongation through the addition of improvements or by rebuilding, means that the purchase of new machine tools can be almost indefinitely postponed when business is poor. When the upturn comes, and increased production plus cost savings is a competitive must, the economic life of the equipment may be seriously curtailed as obsolescence sets in. As a result, a "bunching" of orders for new machine tools often occurs and thus the "typical" pattern of cyclical demand for machine tools emerges with its severe fluctuations in amplitude.

Efforts to Stimulate Domestic Business

During the summer of 1934, R. E. W. Harrison, Chief of the Machinery and Agricultural Implements Division of the Bureau of Foreign and Domestic Commerce, and a member of Army Ordnance's Board of Review, worked closely with NMTBA General Manager Herman H. Lind, to secure Public Works Administration funds for purchase of machine tools desired by the army air corps. This was a start on a program to modernize government installations, and Harrison urged the NMTBA to promote its extension.[28]

Harrison also urged that the trend followed by American firms of establishing branch plants in foreign countries as a way of overcoming tariffs and other restrictions on trade might have serious consequences for the United States in terms of further unemploy-

---

[28] RG 151, "Cooperation with Bureau–NMTBA–1927–1936," File 711-N. Letter from R. E. W. Harrison to H. H. Lind, July 25, 1934, "Machine Tool Advisory Committee for Ordnance Works"; "General Files, Machine Tools, 1933–1935," File 221.2. Letter from Harrison to Lind, August 25, 1934.

ment and that the U.S. Government take measures through subsidies, special tax benefits, etc., to reverse this trend and encourage American firms to concentrate their plants in the United States.

The *American Machinist's* "1935 Inventory of Metalworking Equipment" pointed out that 67 per cent of the installed machine tools were over ten years of age. A total of about 1,074,548 metal-cutting-type machine tools were estimated to be in place, of which 715,616 were over ten years old. Estimates were also made of the average number of machine tools required over the following five years (1935–1939) to maintain the existing average rate required to return the percentage of machines over ten years old to its 1930 level. It was estimated that the latter goal would require approximately the 1929 level of output. The *American Machinist* warned that failure to modernize the nation's metalworking machinery would mean an extended period of industrial inefficiency with high costs, a wide spread between material prices and those to consumers, and reduced purchasing power to further depress the existing standard of living. It added that to achieve this level of replacement required "courage and confidence" but that the necessity for such action was obvious. There appears to be no way of determining the effect of this type of publicity in trade journals, NMTBA releases, and other publications, but in the absence of clear evidence of increased demand for end products or special government action to stimulate investment in new equipment, it is unlikely that publicity had much direct effect on machine tool demand. Its main effects were probably felt in increased support for greater defense appropriations and preparation in the period immediately preceding and following the outbreak of World War II.

There were repeated attempts between World Wars I and II to obtain authorizations and appropriations to cover so-called "Educational Orders" which would have created additional demand for machine tools had they been successful. It was not until June 1938 that Congress authorized $2 million per year for this purpose for five years starting with fiscal year 1939. However, various delays including the fact that air corps planners could not freeze their plans or agree on what should be done with their share of the available funds, or if educational orders should be used at all for aircraft companies, prevented the educational orders from having significant impact before the production orders for World War II mobilization began to arrive.[29]

A program to modernize the Springfield Armory did get underway early in 1938 and Congress appropriated $1.8 million for retooling. Machine tool builders were invited to design and bid for new equipment to supplement older equipment still considered adequate. Efforts were also made to modernize the Frankford Arsenal and other arsenals during the thirties, but lack of funds prevented these efforts from having much effect. In 1939, it was estimated that 80 per cent of the machine tools in U.S. arsenals were eighteen or more years old. By comparison, of all tools in place in 1940, it was estimated that 72 per cent were over ten years old, and in 1953, about 19 per cent were over twenty years old.

Profits and Prices

During World War I wage rates, materials and other costs rose rather drastically, but it seems certain that machine tool price increases kept pace and—with the opportunity provided by wartime peak demand and the absence of price controls—had even run ahead of cost increases. As previously noted, machine tool builders were worried about what would happen to machine tool orders long before the war ended and tried, through measures such as the "No-Cancellation Clauses," to protect themselves against the impact of the end of the War. Nevertheless, most tool builders appeared to consider a postwar slump almost inevitable and to feel that prices would have to be reduced. They wished to keep price reductions to a minimum and to make them only as costs could be reduced.

The machine tool builders hoped to benefit from the fact that during the last years of the war they had been able to increase prices more rapidly than costs both by maintaining demand, so far as possible, and by also reducing costs ahead of price reductions. Thus labor, materials suppliers, tool users and end-product buyers would absorb most of the impact of reconversion and machine

---

[29] Iving Brinton Holley, Jr., *Buying Aircraft: Material Procurement for the Army Air Forces.* U.S. Department of the Army, (Washington: Government Printing Office, 1964), pp. 159–163; Ralph Elberton Smith, *The Army and Economic Mobilization,* Department of the Army (Washington: Government Printing Office, 1959), pp. 63–64.

tool builders would be protected as long as a reasonable amount of business could be secured. This line of reasoning—or "wishful thinking"—assumed that generally machine tool profit margins prior to World War I had been too low and that the war had provided an opportunity to readjust cost-price relationships to provide a more satisfactory margin of profit, greater reserves, etc. Undoubtedly, this was a very desirable objective from the machine tool builders' viewpoint, but it seems unlikely that all or even most machine tool builders were really convinced that such a favorable readjustment could be maintained in the face of falling demand and increased competition.

Wartime price increases had been greater, in many cases, than were made necessary because of design changes or increased costs, and some reductions in machine tool prices were needed. Since price increases on different machines and by different firms had varied widely, a flat percentage reduction was not practicable or equitable. Moreover, as noted, machine tool builders felt that price reductions should start with raw materials, food and living expenses rather than with a "finished product."[30]

In November 1920, NMTBA President Newton again opposed reducing prices on the ground that prices had to be related to production costs; that decreased output meant greater overhead per unit or dollar of production and had more than offset reductions in raw material prices. Research and development to improve machine tool design and construction also increased costs but any reduction in this area would be shortsighted. While the improvement in business which Newton had predicted the preceding spring had not materialized, the NMTBA President still insisted that price reductions were not a solution. Thus it seemed that while the tool builders argued that reductions in raw material and other costs should precede reductions in tool prices, they were not necessarily willing to reduce their prices when materials costs were reduced.[31]

Francis H. Sisson, Vice President, Guaranty Trust Company, however, warned the NMTBA that normal business conditions could

[30] Alexander Luchars, "Machine Tool Prices: Few Manufacturers Favor Price Reductions Under Present Conditions," *Machinery*, 25:705–708, April 1919.
[31] *Machinery*, 26:327, December 1920. NMTBA Convention, New York, November 11–12, 1920.

not be expected until price adjustments had brought prices to a level where normal business could be carried on "without the effects of inflation." Foreign exchange could not return to normal until production abroad reached a point where sufficient goods could be imported into the United States to pay for our exports.

That major price reductions did take place as business declined despite efforts of some industry leaders to hold the price line is indicated by the fact that by the spring of 1922 lathes which had sold for $3,900, $2,690, and $590 had fallen to $2,450, $1,695, and $370 respectively.[32]

The extremely fragmentary character of the information available on the machine tool industry's profits and costs makes it difficult to judge whether the price increases of 1922 and 1923 were necessary or wise. Based on the limited information in the *Census of Manufactures*, it appears that the machine tool industry's gross profits in 1919 after rent and taxes were deducted were about 21 per cent of the industry's invested capital. Since the census information for 1921 does not include either a valuation for "Capital" or payments for rent and taxes, the percentage of profit earned—if any—can only be estimated and appears to have been no more than 3 per cent (assuming that capital invested had declined through depreciation and liquidation to about $200 million from the 1919 level of $231 million). On a similar basis, the gross profit for 1923 would be about 16 per cent. The average unit price according to NMTBA estimates increased from $1,519 in 1922 to $2,203 in 1923 or by over 45 per cent. Even allowing for some improvement in the machine tools and some variation in the number of the more expensive machines sold, this increase seems rather large and could easily account for a substantial increase in profits. Whatever the average profit rate was, it undoubtedly represented a wide range of performance from the smaller or less efficient establishments which operated at a loss and were liquidated or converted to other products to the most successful firms which by 1923 were operating at a good profit even though the industry's total volume was still far below the levels of 1919 and 1920.

By 1932, it was clear enough that most firms in the machine tool industry, like those in many other industries, were faced with a

[32] *Ibid.*, 28:543, March 1922, "Prices of Machine Tools."

desperate struggle for survival, and that the country was in a major depression rather than merely in a limited period of economic adjustment. By 1933, 47 machine tool firms which had been in operation in 1931 were idle, had gone out of business entirely, or had produced less than $5,000 worth of tools during the year.

The effect of the depression on machine tool builders' profits is illustrated by the experience of three tool building firms in Springfield, Vermont. Jones and Lamson Machine Company showed a substantial loss in net profit in all of the five years 1930–1934, and a decline in end-of-year surplus from $1,135,701 for 1930 to $59,823 at the end of 1934 despite the fact that it paid a dividend only in 1930. This firm went into the depression with a substantial surplus which permitted it to operate at a reduced level and to develop improved designs in anticipation of better business conditions. Its losses in 1932 and 1933 amounted to about 45 per cent of sales and were $337,164 and $218,521 respectively. By 1935, business had improved so much that the company was again operating at a profit.[33]

The Fellows Gear Shaper Company fared considerably better; it suffered a net loss only in 1932 of $108,121 or 14.4 per cent of sales. It had an end-of-year surplus in 1930 of $1,122,949, paid dividends each year except 1933, and had a surplus at the end of 1934 of $765,783.

The Bryant Chucking Grinder Company operated at a net loss during 1931, 1932, and 1933 and in 1932 the loss of $36,202 represented 71.2 per cent of the company's sales. Its end-of-year surplus dropped from $198,688 at the end of 1930, to $115,062 in 1932, and was $147,417 at the end of 1934. The company paid small dividends in 1930, 1931, and 1934.

The losses suffered were due not merely to the loss in volume of business and the continuing costs of maintaining facilities and a nucleus work force, but also to the pressure on prices. This was apparently particularly strong in the case of Russian business which constituted a major part of the business available during this period.

As business began to improve significantly in 1935, 1936, and 1938, machine tool industry profits and net worth also improved.

---

[33] Broehl, *Precision Valley*, p. 134; See also Appendix Table 19 for profits in other years.

Profits before taxes in 1935 amounted to 10.2 per cent of the industry's net worth of $156,600,000. In 1936 profits rose to 24.6 per cent and net worth to $170,200,000. In 1937, profits before taxes amounted to 40.7 per cent of net worth estimated at $195,300,000. The "slump" of 1938 brought profits down to 16.4 per cent while net worth remained almost unchanged at $195,700,000. Profits and net worth both increased substantially in 1939 to 37.8 per cent and $215,300,000 respectively.[34]

That there were wide variations in profits of leading machine tool builders during the thirties is indicated by the information available on publicly held corporations filing reports under the Securities and Exchange Act. For example, the Bullard Company, Bridgeport, Connecticut showed net profits after taxes in 1936 of 32 per cent. This rate increased to 37 per cent in 1937 followed by a loss of 0.8 per cent in 1938 and net profits of 10 per cent in 1939 and 57 per cent in 1940. The Sundstrand Machine Tool Company, Rockford, Illinois showed net profits after taxes in 1936 of 31 per cent and 20 per cent in 1937 with losses of 11 per cent in 1938; profits of 26 per cent in 1939, and 64 per cent profit in 1940. More consistent performance was shown by the Monarch Machine Tool Company, Sidney, Ohio whose net profits after taxes in 1936 were 31 per cent, 43 per cent in 1937, a low of 24 per cent in 1938, 35 per cent in 1939, and 65 per cent in 1940.

Machinery Builders Organization Formed

The NMTBA worked closely with the Department of Commerce and other government agencies in various efforts to stimulate business, eliminate losses, and increase profits, although these efforts now seem clearly inadequate to meet the problems faced by the machine tool industry, the country, and a large part of the world. Some machine tool builders also tried to protect themselves from the effects of competition for available markets by collective action.

During the early thirties, W. H. Rastall and other officials of the Bureau of Foreign and Domestic Commerce attempted to advise machine tool builders on possible ways in which machine tool

[34] RG 188, Office of Price Administration, Industrial Division, Director's File, "History of Price Control in the Machine Tool Industry."

sales could be increased. These included more active advertising and selling efforts, and promoting a more adequate replacement policy on the part of machine tool users. Another suggestion was that machine tool builders take the lead in forming an association which would represent all machine builders and efficiently coordinate all machinery manufacturers' common interests. This was not practical with the approximately forty associations then representing machinery builders. It was pointed out also that, despite the large number of associations in existence, only about 10 per cent of machinery builders were organized.[35]

Rastall said that the NMTBA had done a great deal of work in the field of cost accounting and that conditions were sufficiently similar in other parts of the machinery industry for other groups to be able to benefit from the NMTBA experience. He called attention to the fact that German machine builders were much more fully organized than American firms and said this gave them an advantage in handling foreign trade.

Rastall suggested that tool builders consider themselves part of a machinery industry rather than merely part of the machine tool industry. The same suggestion was made to other machinery builders, such as textile machinery builders who tended to think of themselves as part of the textile industry rather than of the machinery industry. He estimated that there were a total of 10,000 firms building some type of machinery, and that they would be able to exert much greater influence if represented by a single organization.

This proclaimed need for an organization to represent all machinery manufacturers, rather than merely small specialized segments of this industry grouping, was partially met in the fall of 1933 by creation of the Machinery and Allied Products Institute (MAPI). Creation of MAPI, however, did not make a single unified industry of all machinery builders but rather provided a device for coordinating and pooling the efforts of the various machinery industries and their trade associations in some areas of common concern.

[35] RG 151, "Machinery-General-1932," File 221. Letter from W. H. Rastall to H. S. Robinson, Sales Manager, Cincinnati Shaper Company, January 13, 1932.

Self-Government Under the NRA

In August 1933, following enactment of the National Recovery Act in June 1933, the NMTBA established a committee of five members to draft a Code of Fair Competition for the Machine Tool and Forging Machinery Industry. Ralph E. Flanders, President of Jones and Lamson Machinery Company, was designated as Chairman, and the other members included J. G. Benedict, President, Landis Machine Company; Henry Buker, Vice President, Brown and Sharpe Manufacturing Company; E. A. Muller, President, King Machine Tool Company; and Herman H. Lind, General Manager, NMTBA. The resulting code was approved by President Roosevelt on November 8, 1933 with an exception specifying that the NRA Administrator had the right to approve or modify any action taken by the Supervisory Agency under Article VI of the code.

The Committee on Code presentation became the Supervisory Agency for 60 days after which it was replaced by an elected Supervisory Agency consisting of Buker, James E. Gleason, President, Gleason Works; H. M. Lucas, President, Lucas Machine Tool Company; R. M. Gaylord, President, Ingersoll Milling Machine Company; August H. Tuechter, President, Cincinnati Bickford Tool Company; William E. Whipp, President, Monarch Machine Tool Company; and NMTBA General Manager, H. H. Lind.[36]

Under the NRA, a total of 236 companies were identified as members of the machine tool and forging machinery industry as of April 1934. The total included 128 members of the NMTBA and 108 firms who were not members of the association. A total of 111 members of the NMTBA reported 1933 sales of $21,975,780 and seventy-seven nonmembers reported sales of $1,606,380. One hundred and eight members of the NMTBA reported that as of April 1, 1934, they had a total of 20,726 employees while seventy-one nonmembers reported total employment of 4,151.[37]

The Machine Tool and Forging Machinery Industry Code and other codes developed under NRA were an attempt to translate acceptable business practices and attitudes as represented by

[36] RG 9, National Recovery Administration, Code Authority Files, Machine Tool and Forging Machinery Industry, "History of the Code of Fair Competition for the Machine Tool and Forging Machinery Industry." Ms., pp. 1–5.
[37] RG 9, *Ibid.,* "Industry List," April 30, 1934, p. 12.

industry codes of ethics and other statements of approved business practices into enforceable legislation binding on all firms. Under it, the federal government gave official approval to cooperative action by industry, and industry self-government was to be made effective in suppressing competitive practices considered unfair by most members of an industry. As in most of the other industry codes neither the consumer nor labor was represented on the Code Authority which nevertheless proclaimed itself qualified to protect the interest of both and to refrain from acting in a spirit of narrow self-interest. It was probably too much to expect that labor would accept this arrangement without protest where its interests were seriously and directly affected as in the case of the supervision of minimum wage standards, apprenticeship rules, and work sharing programs.

Machine tool distributors were organized under a separate NRA Code for the "Machine Tool and Equipment Distributing Trade" rather than being included under the Machine Tool and Forging Machinery Industry Code. This arrangement was apparently preferred by both tool builders and distributors. It corresponded with the fact that builders and distributors had separate trade associations and that the Machine Tool and Forging Machinery Industry Code Supervisory Agency was virtually an arm or alter ego of the National Machine Tool Builders Association. It should be noted that, at this time, machine tool builders claimed to sell about 70 per cent of their output directly to tool users rather than through distributors.[38]

Included under the Distributors' Code were 369 machine tool dealers, manufacturers agents, and importers of machine tools with an estimated employment of 2,580. This industry estimated its volume of business in 1933 at $33,700,000 and its invested capital at $32,000,000. These sales figures appear high in view of the fact that the NMTBA estimated total shipments of machine tools in 1933 as only $25,000,000 (cutting type only). The distributors handled some tools, equipment, and accessories not produced by United States tool builders, used tools, and some machinery other than metal-cutting-type machine tools.

[38] RG 9, *Ibid.*, Machine Tool and Equipment Distributing Trade, File 139–13. "History of Code of Fair Competition for Machine Tool and Equipment Distributing Trade," 36 pp. Ms., June 15, 1935.

There apparently was little trouble with violations of the trade practice provisions of the Distributors' Code because most of the trade practices specified had been followed by the members of the industry for many years. Regarding the results of the code, the official history stated:

> The Code did not greatly benefit this Trade because there was very little need for the Code but the members secured the Code in order to cooperate with the President in his efforts toward recovery.[39]

The code provided a forty hour week in lieu of the approximately fifty hour week which had been usual and resulted in some increase in employment. No accurate statistics were collected for the industry but the increase in employment appears to have been about 10 per cent over the 1933 level.[40]

There were few complaints of violations of the code's provisions relating to wages, hours, and trade practices but the Supervisory Agency did not have funds to investigate whether all members were in fact complying with the code. The fact that many members did not pay their assessments or provide requested reports suggests either that there may have been noncompliance or lack of interest.[41]

Employment and Pay of Workers

Most of the rapid gains in membership made by the National Association of Machinists during World War I were lost during the business slump of 1921-1922 and in the face of aggressive anti-union activity lead by the National Metal Trades Association. The existence and potential threat of "unionism," however, appears to have caused the National Metal Trades Association, other employer groups, and individual employers to put greater emphasis on improving wages and working conditions than they would have otherwise.[42]

[39] Ibid., p. 8.
[40] Ibid., p. 12.
[41] Ibid., pp. 16–17.
[42] Harold M. Groves, "The Machinist in Industry" (unpublished Ph.D. dissertation, University of Wisconsin 1927), pp. 204, 379.

In 1922, Ernest F. DuBrul, General Manager of the NMTBA, attempted to answer the advocates of compulsory unemployment compensation legislation as represented by two bills then pending in Massachusetts and Wisconsin. Similar legislation was expected in other states and DuBrul supplied arguments which could be used against such bills. He contended that compulsory unemployment compensation would be "absolutely disastrous" for the machine tool industry because of the inelastic demand for tools. He emphasized that unemployment was greatest in times of depression which were also "financially the most dangerous for the employer." Thus the employer would be forced to "pay out unemployment doles" when he could least afford to do so.[43]

DuBrul asserted that the owner of a machine shop had no alternative when business slumped but to lay off his men, and ridiculed the idea that prices could possibly be set high enough in good times to pay for unemployment doles. If the employer attempted to do so, prices would be so inflated as to ruin the market. He also asked how the employer could possibly hope to find a basis on which to estimate the costs of such doles. DuBrul ridiculed a suggestion he attributed to proponents of unemployment compensation that employers be compelled to continue to produce for stock. The employer was certain to be burdened with some excess inventories of materials or partially finished components, and even if he had enough cash to carry him through a slump, he was almost certain to take a loss on such inventories when prices declined. He would be much better off in such cases if he laid off his workers promptly than if he attempted to continue producing. DuBrul further contended that most improvements in design occurred in periods of depression when the machine maker had plenty of time to devote to improvements and that the firm which continued producing for stock during slack times would be likely to find that its inventory had been made obsolete by better designs introduced by its competitors.

Obsolescence loss due to overstocking is an ever present and very large danger to machine builders in every depression. This danger makes it all the more imperative for them to shut down until cost conditions are stabilized at lower levels.

43 Ernest F. DuBrul, "Compulsory Unemployment Insurance and Its Effect on the Machinery Industry," *American Machinist*, 57:205–207, August 10, 1922.

DuBrul stated that employees lacked sufficient "economic education" to understand the necessity for wage reductions in bad times to bring down costs in line with prices. Wage cuts would probably result in strikes and charges that the employers were trying to provoke strikes in order to avoid having to pay unemployment compensation. He added that British experience with doles had shown that many workers preferred to remain idle as long as they received a small dole rather than try to find another job at lower wages. He predicted that if the Massachusetts and Wisconsin bills were enacted employers in these states would be at a serious disadvantage and that many no doubt would be put out of business.

DuBrul suggested that rather than place the burden directly on individual manufacturers, it would be preferable to provide "some scientific insurance basis" for calculating risks and cover industry generally. He then concluded, however, that to put insurance on an actuarial basis that would make each industry carry its fair share of the burden would be almost impossible.

> Insurance as a science can never insure things that lie so much in the domain of politics, so influenced by feelings and emotions, as unemployment. To ask the individual to do what cannot be done by scientific insurance is asking the impossible.

DuBrul apparently saw nothing inconsistent in asserting the right of machine tool builders to a sufficient margin of profit in good times to carry them through bad times, or that machine tool customers should continue to add to or replace machine tools during business slumps despite the fact that they might have no immediate, or certain future, need for such tools. During periods when business generally was good or particular industries were expanding rapidly, a machinist discharged by a tool building firm could expect to find a job in another industry or possibly in a different firm in the machine tool industry. In times of more or less general depression, however, he had little alternative and was not likely to have sufficient savings to cover extended unemployment.

Although the NMTBA generally opposed price reductions as a way of stimulating demand and discounted the influence of machine tool prices on demand, Mr. DuBrul appears above to assume that price reductions would take place and that wages should be adjusted downward to compensate for the price reductions. The employee was apparently expected to absorb a large share of the effect of reduced demand without assistance from government controlled insurance schemes or any assurance that wages during periods of prosperity would be adequate for workers to accumulate substantial savings to be used during layoffs.

The machine tool industry initially attempted to retain as much as possible of its skilled labor during the depression, but by 1932 machine tool industry shop employment had declined about 80 per cent from the 1929 level. From the standpoint of the workers involved, and particularly older and less skilled workers, the main problem was that in most cases there was little opportunity to find equivalent jobs elsewhere or even to find work of any kind.

There was a theory in Vermont, and perhaps other areas, that machine shop workers when unemployed could return to part or full-time farming. This theory seemed plausible where workers had been recruited from farms and where the unemployment was seasonal or a depression was limited in scope. However, in the major depression of the thirties, farm prices and demand were drastically reduced, and there was little opportunity for unemployed machinists or other manufacturing workers in agriculture except perhaps to raise some food for their own families.[44]

Employment of wage earners in the machine tool industry dropped from an average of 47,391 in 1929 (their highest level since 1919) to an average of 21,262 in 1931, and to a low point of 9,466 in March of 1933. Employment improved gradually during the remainder of 1933 and 1934 until it reached 18,255 in December 1934 and averaged 28,106 during 1935 with a peak employment of 32,962 in December 1935. The upward trend continued during 1936 and 1937 when employment averaged 37,477, a peak of 39,809 having been reached in October 1937. Employment dropped sharply in 1938 and amounted to only 30,331 in January 1939 before starting to recover as a result of war business, reaching 47,082 in December 1939. (As previously noted the statistics for years before 1939 include metal-forming tool producers as well as metal-cutting machine tool builders.)[45]

Statistics on wages and hours are not available for the machine tool industry for the period prior to 1932, but it seems certain that

[44] Broehl, *Precision Valley*, p. 136.
[45] U.S. *Census of Manufactures* for 1931, 1933, 1935, 1937 and 1939, "Machine Tools."

both weekly wages and hours worked by production employees declined rapidly from the peak levels of 1929. The main reduction in wages was due to reduced hours of work per week rather than the reduction in average hourly rates. The average weekly earnings for production workers in the machine tool industry in 1932 were $18.23 per week and the average work week was 29.5 hours. Average hourly wages declined slightly from $.618 in 1932 to $.579 in 1933 but this was offset by an increase in hours worked to 31.8 hours in 1933 and in weekly earnings to $18.41. During 1934, average weekly earnings increased fairly substantially to $22.53 as a result of both higher hourly rates and longer hours which averaged $.624 and 36.1 respectively. Again in 1935 both hourly rates and hours of work increased to $.638 and 40.9 respectively and weekly earnings averaged $26.09.

During 1936, average weekly earnings rose to $28.73 as a result of a small increase in hourly rates to $.647 and a larger increase in working hours to 44.4 hours. Average weekly earnings rose again in 1937 to $32.48 and hourly earnings to $.725 while hours rose only very slightly to 44.8 hours. Hourly earnings rose in 1938 but hours worked declined drastically, as the result of a large drop in orders, to 36.0 hours per week. Average weekly earnings in 1938 fell to $26.75.[46]

During World War I and most of the postwar period prior to the "1929 crash," the principal concern of machine tool builders was to devise methods of wage payment and management which would make it possible to obtain and hold good workers without excessive increases in production cost. As the depression gained momentum, however, the problem was largely that of finding enough business to keep even a drastically reduced work force reasonably busy during a reduced workweek and to avoid a complete shutdown of operations. By the time the National Recovery Act was passed, the wage problem was largely one of how to establish and maintain reasonable minimum wage rates in the face of widespread unemployment, efforts to spread available work, and drastically reduced demand for new machine tools.[47]

The NRA Code of Fair Competition proposed by the machine

[46] U.S. Bureau of Labor Statistics, "Employment and Earnings Statistics."
[47] RG 9, Machine Tool and Forging Machinery, File 103–116, "Labor Provisions."

tool builders provided a $.40 per hour minimum wage, but excluded from the minimum all work which paid less than $.40 per hour on July 15, 1929. This exception was protested by the Director of the Women's Bureau of the Department of Labor on the ground that it virtually meant that the real minimum wage would be $.35 an hour rather than $.40. A proposed exemption for "casual and incidental" labor and "learners" was also opposed at the same time.

All minimum wage experience indicates that the allowance of a learning period tends to jeopardize the enforcement of the minimum rate. It complicates pay roll inspection and leads to employment as learners of persons with ample experience in other establishments. It results in evasions of the law such as those practiced by employers who discharge a "learner" at the completion of the learning period and employ another "learner" in his place, or who classify their own experienced employees as learners. The Conference of State Labor Administrators in 7 States recently adopting a minimum wage legislation, recommended the elimination of any provision for a learning period in the administration of minimum wage laws, and it was the thought of the Conference also that this should apply to codes under the National Recovery Act.

The learner provision in this code is especially undesirable in that the length of the learning period is not defined.[48]

The proposed wages and hours provisions of the Machine Tool and Forging Machinery Industry Code were provided by the Machinery and Allied Products Institute, and the MAPI representative was asked to aid in answering questions regarding these articles. Under NRA rules labor complaints had to be referred by NRA to local Compliance Boards except where labor was represented on the Supervisory Authority. When the machine tools Committee on Code Presentation acting as Supervisory Agency was informed of the latter requirement it concluded that

. . . some more practicable way should be found to get complaints to come to our Supervisory Agency so that they would be handled more expeditiously, less expensively and with perfect fairness to all concerned.[49]

[48] *Ibid.;* Memorandum for Deputy Administrator Muir, NRA, October 19, 1933 from Mary Anderson, Director, Women's Bureau, U.S. Department of Labor.

The forty hour week and $.40 minimum hourly rate were opposed by organized labor, including William Green of the American Federation of Labor, who urged that available work be "spread" by establishing a thirty hour week with a $.50 minimum. Their concern was not merely with the machine tool or machinery industries but that the machine tool code (Approved Code No. 103, November 8, 1933) would set a pattern for codes for the consumer goods industries.[50]

The code required that each member of the industry report to the Supervisory Authority action taken to adjust wage rates. A sample format was proposed covering the following items for the second week in June 1933 and the second week of January 1934: (1) number of hourly employees; (2) average hourly wage rate; (3) number of salaried employees receiving less than $35 per week; and (4) average salary rate.[51]

The NRA's Labor Advisory Board objected to the use of average salary increases as evidence that the industry had effected an equitable wage adjustment.

> The average has no definite meaning if it is computed for a group larger than the individual plant, and even then it is obvious that it will conceal downward movements in the wage rates of individuals. The concealing power of the average is increased manifold when its scope is widened to include the whole industry.[52]

Reports from 138 firms for the week of November 12, 1934 showed that these companies employed 11,901 workers at $.40 or more per hour or $23.30 per week, the average hourly rate being $.61 per hour. Only 346 employees receiving less than $.40 were employed at a weekly average of $13.70. There were 1,989 salaried employees receiving from $15 to $35 per week or an average of $22.63. Thirty-four salaried employees were reported as having received less than $15 or an average of $12.91. During the first

---

[49] RG 9, *Ibid.*, Minutes of First Meeting of Supervisory Agency in Washington, D. C., November 13, 1933.

[50] Broehl, Jr., *Precision Valley*, p. 139.

[51] RG 9, Minutes of Second Meeting of Supervisory Agency, January 11, 1934.

[52] RG 9, File 103–16, Memo to J. R. Howland, Asst. Deputy Administrator, NRA, March 14, 1935 from the Labor Advisory Board re: "Equitable Adjustment Report—Machine Tool and Forging Machinery Industry."

week in February 1935 there were 15,562 workers receiving $.40 or more and an average of $25.32 per week. Four hundred and forty-one employees received less than $.40 per hour or $13.70 per week. There were 2,374 salaried employees receiving between $15 and $35 or an average of $23.43 per week. Seventy-four salaried workers received less than $15 per week or an average of $12.51.[53]

Summary

The physical volume of machine tool production and shipments declined between 1919 and 1939, but the value of shipments rose by about one-fourth. This increase was partially due to the fact that machine tools were heavier, more complex, more expensive to build, and more productive. Many machine tool builders also increased their prices on the assumption that higher prices were the only, or most likely, source of increased profits. Some tool builders, however, believed that it was more important to reduce costs to a minimum and reduce prices and profits per unit in order to secure a larger volume of sales. In general, the machine tool industry during this period followed a policy of minimizing price competition and trying to increase its profit margins over those which had been secured prior to World War I. This policy appeared to be effective in raising prices except in the recession of 1921-1922 and the depression from 1932 to 1936. It probably had some negative effect on machine tool demand. There is no definite evidence that it increased or reduced net profits of the industry as a whole or affected the number of business failures during the postwar recession or the depression of the thirties. Senator Flanders recently recalled in this connection that during 1921-1922 that "we experimented with lowering prices and found that it was useless as a stimulant to the machine tool business." He also recalled that about 1935 General Motors announced new designs and the purchase of machine tools to produce them.

I thereupon visited K. T. Keller, President of Chrysler, and tried to get him to tell me how soon a new and improved machine tool would have to pay for itself to interest his company in ac-

---

[53] RG 9, Supervisory Agency Report, *Employment Hours and Wages,* November 30, 1934, and March 6, 1935.

quiring a tool. He told me in effect that no rapid pay-off of the cost would interest his company at that time.[54]

This experience probably illustrates that where the machine tool user did not feel that new machine tools were needed to increase volume; to produce work of a type or quality not within the capacity of existing machines, he was not likely to be greatly influenced by theoretical computations as to how rapidly the new machines would pay for themselves through reduced costs. On the other hand, if he felt new machine tools were needed, price and production costs were important in determining what machines would be purchased.

Machine tool builders' profits (or losses) varied widely between the high and low points in the business cycle and between different firms. In general, it appears that the more successful and efficient firms obtained a very adequate ratio of net profits after taxes as compared to net worth during periods when the industry was operating at or near capacity. These profits were sufficient for the companies to accumulate substantial reserves for use in a depression. Small and less successful companies had to operate on smaller margins. A large proportion of the investment by the machine tool industry was financed from retained earnings rather than new investment.

One of the major reasons for the fact that machine tool demand was frequently well below the machine tool industry's capacity was the long average life of most machine tools and the tendency of machine tool users to retain machine tools even though better tools were available. Machine tool replacement policies varied between industries and were dependent on tool age, wear, improvements in tool design and construction, and upon the financial condition and policies of individual firms. The tool user was likely to concentrate most of his purchases in the periods when major changes in product design or rising demand required additional machines. He was also influenced by the cost of new machines in relation to labor cost.

Machine tool builders and the NMTBA devoted a great deal of time and effort during the early twenties to compiling and analyzing available statistical data reflecting fluctuations in business activity for their own industry, major machine tool using industries, and

---

[54] Letter from Sen. Ralph E. Flanders to the writer of August 11, 1967.

other industries in an effort to understand what had happened in the past and to provide a basis for predicting what was likely to happen in the future. Public statements by NMTBA staff members and machine tool builders during this period indicate a degree of optimism regarding the value of statistical projections as guides to management decisions which, in retrospect, is difficult to understand. The fact that a good many tool builders were unwilling to incur the expense and trouble required to provide all the statistical data desired by the NMTBA suggests, however, that they doubted the practical value of the statistical services.

Little evidence was found to indicate that the improvements made by the NMTBA, other business organizations, or the federal government in statistical reporting and economic analysis during the twenties had any significant effect in predicting the timing, severity, or duration of the major depression to come or in stimulating action to moderate its impact. It seems certain that the political situation and the effects of laissez faire theories of economics would have prevented effective action in the twenties even if the business statisticians and economists could have developed adequate statistical tools and agreed upon the significance of their data.

It also seems clear that most of the measures advocated by the machine tool builders had little chance for general acceptance by machine tool users or by the federal government. It is unlikely that, even had they been accepted, they could have prevented the depression, though they might have protected the machine tool industry from some of its effects. They would have required exceptional foresight and courage on the part of machine tool users, special tax concessions and subsidies by the federal government, large scale spending for defense, etc., during a period when the government's role was confined largely to providing information and well-intentioned advice. The main effects of the NMTBA's efforts during the twenties appears to have been to reduce price competition and to raise prices. This probably increased the profits earned by the more successful machine tool builders during the period between 1922 and 1929 or 1930, but also had some negative effect on machine tool demand.

The NMTBA, the machinery trade journals, and later MAPI attempted to stimulate interest in improving equipment replacement policies and practices followed by major machine tool users; to prove that most machine tools should be replaced sooner than was usually the case; and that replacement should be accelerated rather than retarded in depressions. Nevertheless, it seems unlikely that these efforts had much practical effect on machine tool sales during this period. This problem was closely related to the cost accounting systems used and to existing restrictions in tax laws. These were not under the control of the machine tool builders, although they attempted to exert some influence on them through publicity and personal contacts with members of Congress, government officials, and businessmen. While many technical improvements and refinements were introduced during the twenties and thirties, these were not sufficient to greatly accelerate tool replacement generally, although they were probably significant in determining the gains made by some individual tool builders.

The financial crash of 1929 preceded by from three to six months a substantial reduction in machine tools production, shipments, or employment. No information was found on machine tool orders which would indicate whether these declined significantly prior to the crash in the stock market. It is beyond the scope of this study to examine in any detail the causes of the financial crash or why it was followed by a general economic disaster. The machine tool industry did attempt to determine what was happening and what it could do alone, through government assistance, and through cooperative efforts under government sanction. None of these efforts had more than a very limited effect and eventual return to capacity operation was mainly the product of external forces—mechanization in the U.S.S.R. and Japan, and the threat, preparation for, and fact of another major war.

The Commerce Department encouraged the formation of a broader organization of machinery builders than the NMTBA and other existing trade associations. This proposal was, at least partially, implemented in the fall of 1933 by the creation of the Machinery and Allied Products Institute (MAPI) as a device for coordinating and pooling the efforts of the various machinery industry organizations on common problems.

Following the passage of the National Recovery Act in June 1933, an NMTBA Committee drafted a "Code of Fair Competition for the Machine Tool and Forging Machinery Industry." This attempted to translate rules of acceptable business practices such as were stated in the NMTBA's "Code of Ethics" into a legally enforceable "code" which could be applied to all machine tool builders whether they were members of the NMTBA or not. This code had limited effect since the NRA Act was invalidated before the code's value could really be tested.

Machine tool industry wage levels were usually competitive with other metalworking industries. The major exception was some automobile manufacturers in the twenties. These firms were rapidly expanding and hiring many machinists ranging from the apprentice level to highly skilled tool and die makers, setup men, etc. The machine tool builders were usually able to retain their more highly skilled and experienced men during short periods of inactivity by reducing hours, and using them in preparing for introduction of new models, experimental work, maintenance and repair, or production of repair parts and components for inventory. In the case of a major depression, these measures were not adequate and drastic reductions in the work force occurred in addition to the reduction in average hours. Machine tool builders took it for granted that the laws of economics made it inevitable that many employees, including particularly those with less skill and experience, would have to be "laid off" or discharged as soon as management found, or anticipated, that reduced demand would make it unprofitable to continue production at current levels. What happened to such employees was not considered the responsibility of the employer.

6

Managerial Problems, Policies, and Practices 1919-1939

This chapter describes the machine tool industry's efforts to improve and standardize cost accounting systems, to reduce the effects of price competition, and to maintain the more favorable profit ratios achieved during World War I. It summarizes the reaction of some machine tool builders to the increased overhead costs resulting from the application of scientific management techniques. The adoption of a Code of Ethics for the industry, introduction of industry self-government under the National Recovery Act, and the attempts of individual firms to limit competition are also discussed.

Status of Cost Accounting

NMTBA President A. E. Newton in May 1919 reviewed the NMTBA's accomplishments in the field of cost accounting and indicated that machine tool builders generally now had good information on their costs; that tool prices were being set with due attention to costs; that tool buyers had been convinced that machine tool price lists were really firm and not subject to bargaining, and that it could be taken for granted that tool builders would not soon again resort to selling tools below cost.[1] Newton reported to the NMTBA, in May 1920, that costs of building machine tools had been rising more rapidly than prices, and that prices could not be reduced despite a slight decline in new orders. He added that tool

[1] *Machinery*, 25:924–925, June 1919, Report on NMTBA Convention, Atlantic City, May 12–13, 1919.

builders still had plenty of unfilled orders and predicted that within a few months new orders would again be at "full volume."[2]

Machine tool builders needed to know what their costs were currently rather than merely at the end of the year. Profit margins should be sufficient to allow machine tool builders to make a profit despite drastically reduced demand but there was little indication as to how this was to be achieved except through price maintenance. There also did not appear to be much concern as to the implications of this policy in periods of high demand and production.

The NMTBA published a revised version of the cost system prepared by Miller, Franklin, Basset and Company (the last revision had been distributed in 1912). The introductory letter to this report stated that

> . . . the value obtained by the use of uniform costs within an industry has been so frequently demonstrated that it is hardly necessary . . . to dwell upon the advantages to be gained by manufacturers as a whole in the use of uniform costs to secure the elimination of misguided and therefore unintelligent competition.

The letter warned that it was unsafe for one firm to base its prices on the prices set by another firm which was believed to have an adequate cost system since many factors such as equipment, location, and methods of distribution might be quite different. While a uniform cost system provided that all members of the industry should base their costs on the same principles and elements, it did not guarantee that their costs would be the same. The revision did not change the principles outlined in the previous editions but recommended changes in methods to provide greater accuracy, bring out inefficiency, and supply "a foundation whereby the executive can better control the broader policies of the business through specially prepared reports."[3]

The automobile industry had influenced the machine tool industry's production control procedures and had produced a need for changes in forms and procedures used in cost accounting. In some cases, a single form could be used in both cost accounting and production planning and control. The use of cost accounting

---

[2] *Ibid.*, 26:922–923, June 1920, NMTBA Convention, Atlantic City, May 20–21, 1920.

[3] Miller, Franklin, Basset and Company, *Uniform Cost System* (New York: National Machine Tool Builders Association, April 1920), p. 5.

records for production control made it even more important that
the reports and records be as accurate as possible.

Accounting policies and procedures, while improving, were still
far from uniform. There were many points of possible difference in
treatment of costs that could not be presented in a report. It
recommended that the NMTBA establish a permanent cost finding
advisory bureau which would patrol NMTBA members to discover
variations from the uniform and discuss how changes should be
made to secure uniformity. "Only by establishing a point of control
between manufacturers, whereby all will be visited and aided
periodically, will real uniformity in cost finding be ultimately obtained."[4]

It thus seems obvious that the ultimate objective was uniformity
of "cost finding" rather than just the adoption of good cost accounting systems by machine tool builders. It also seems apparent, however, that a considerable proportion of the NMTBA membership
was not yet convinced that standardization was necessary nor willing
to accept the changes, cost, and policing that were required to
achieve uniformity. The system proposed was probably very similar
to those already used by the leading machine tool builders and other
machinery producers.

Possibly the most important section of the report was that
covering overhead costs. Until a few years earlier, it had been
customary to charge to the product all overhead expenses regardless of the current level of operation. In this way apparent unit costs
rose rapidly as volume declined and fell as production levels rose.
The Miller, Franklin, Basset report urged that the product be
charged with only a normal rate of expense based on a representative period of operation. Selling prices were to be based on such
"normal" costs but the cost records were also to show losses due
to idle plant capacity in periods of poor business.[5]

New Cost Accounting Report

In January 1921, five regional conferences of NMTBA members
and representatives of Scovell, Wellington, and Company were
held to discuss cost accounting systems and practices in the machine

[4] *Ibid.*, pp. 8–9.
[5] *Ibid.*, pp. 65–71.

tool industry. Questionnaires were also sent to NMTBA members by Scovell and Wellington, and the latter reported its findings to the NMTBA meeting in Cleveland at the end of February 1921. The Scovell-Wellington Report indicated that most machine tool builders were handling material and labor costs in a reasonably satisfactory manner, and consequently that "their discussion of better or more uniform methods of accounting for the industry would be concentrated upon . . . the development, distribution and application of overhead or burden."[6]

The Executive Committee of the NMTBA had recommended unanimously that interest on investment be included in calculating cost of manufacture. This accounting device was considered by the tool builders to be necessary to ensure that the overhead of different departments or of different machine tools would be correctly stated. Interest was to be calculated on all the assets employed in manufacture—land, buildings, equipment, and inventories. The effect was to increase the overhead charged to work done on large and costly machines, in comparison with work done with less expensive equipment. The Scovell-Wellington report added that virtually all businessmen insisted on including in costs interest on borrowed money or bonded debt despite the fact that "charges of this kind are incorrect in principle, and most objectionable in practice. . . ."

It was more important to apportion overhead to departments or production centers in the case of large shops than with small ones. A small shop, and particularly one making a single product, could use a single overhead rate or perhaps two or three rates, but where operations were more complex, varied overhead rates were essential if costs were to be reasonably accurate. Tool builders were warned to exercise great care in calculating overhead rates. When a shop was normally busy, all overhead would be "earned" and the total amount "earned" might exceed current overhead expenses; but, when operating part-time, a portion of the overhead would be unabsorbed and be charged directly to profit and loss.

The report emphasized the need to compare "actual hours" with "standard hours" and said that many shops with strong management had daily operation reports, which were summarized at

[6] *American Machinist*, 54:Part 2:726–731, April 28, 1921, "Cost Accounting for the Machine Tool Builder."

frequent intervals, accounting for all idle machine time. While all idleness was not avoidable executive attention was needed to minimize lost time. Greater emphasis was placed upon the importance of using cost accounting as a major and versatile tool of management rather than merely as a device for fixing prices than did the Miller, Franklin, Basset Report of the preceding year.

The report recommended that depreciation rates take into account obsolescence in case equipment had to be replaced before it was worn out. It also attempted to show how various charges should be added to manufacturing cost in order to arrive at a correct selling price. While a tool builder could not expect to "collect all his Federal Income Taxes from his customers" he should attempt to secure a margin of profit which would cover taxes and leave a reasonable sum for dividends to investors. The report reminded NMTBA members that where only "normal burden" was included in costs during periods of slow business, there would be a considerable amount of unearned burden and that

> . . . this feature of the business, so far as it is reasonably associated with good management, should be reflected in the selling price, and must be included, if the manufacturer is to continue in business. It is like the idleness of a seasonal business that must be covered during the months the business runs, only that the machine tool industry has long stretches of activity and then a slump that may continue for months.

Nevertheless, at each regional meeting, someone was present who had neglected the amortization privilege or whose claims had been rejected because poorly presented. Many such rejected claims were later approved when properly presented.[7]

NMTBA General Manager E. F. DuBrul warned NMTBA members that the "Amortization Section" (of the Federal Internal Revenue Service) was inclined to fix a base below which they considered the price of machine tools abnormal, and that they might attempt to settle amortization claims on this arbitrary basis. He insisted that the proper price for the taxpayer to take, both as salvage and as value in use, was the price that a second-hand dealer would pay the taxpayer for the tools:

[7] *Ibid.*, 56:Part 2:672–674, May 4, 1922, NMTBA Spring Meeting, Atlantic City, April 25, 1922.

Now, it is an unchangeable principle of economic law that no commodity can have two prices at the same time in the same market; and in accordance with this law of single price, the same basis should be taken for valuing amortizable equipment that may be retained in use. It cannot have a greater value in use than it has on the market. Whether the Tax Unit will accept this point of view or not remains to be seen; but whether accepted or not, it is the only logical basis that can be taken, in justice and with common sense.[8]

Dubrul also urged NMTBA members to accept and act promptly upon the recommendations regarding uniform cost accounting made in the Scovell-Wellington Report. It was better, he emphasized, to make such changes in a dull period than to wait until business was good and there was not time to make the changeover.

In October 1924, DuBrul reviewed the NMTBA's efforts toward establishment of "rational cost-finding methods" in the machine tool industry and the "formulation of a plan of accounting that discloses the true costs of producing machine tools." He concluded that there was still much to be done along those lines and that most machine tool builders were not making adequate allowance for the effects of enforced idleness. DuBrul insisted that unused capacity was a liability rather than an asset, and suggested three ways such facilities could be brought into use: (1) by creating new designs which would make old types of machines obsolete, (2) by making products other than machine tools, and (3) by mergers within the industry to concentrate production in fewer shops and sell the remaining shops for other use.

DuBrul described the association's publicity work since 1920 directed at those who might be considering entering the machine tool industry. This publicity emphasized the low profits, fluctuating demand, high costs, and idle capacity which were said to be characteristic of the industry. Similar information was distributed to machine tool buyers in an effort to make them more sympathetic to the machine tool builders' problems, and presumably, therefore, more willing to pay prices for machine tools that the tool builders considered fair. This publicity was also intended to counter demands from prospective buyers for lower prices based on reductions in

8 *Ibid.*, p. 674.

costs of materials or labor. It seems unlikely, however, that such appeals to machine tool buyers had much practical effect.[9]

After World War I, increased emphasis was placed upon the economic problems inherent in machinery building at a fraction of available plant capacity. A Committee on Waste established by the Federated American Engineering Societies reported probable waste to be about 40 or 45 per cent. It also indicated, however, that most of such waste in the machinery building industry could not be charged to restrictive practices by labor as frequently alleged by spokesmen of employer groups. It emphasized that primary responsibility for taking steps to reduce or eliminate waste rested on management: "Efficient planning and guidance of production is the duty of management; better employment service and policies lie within the power of management and not of the employees." NMTBA members were urged to do everything possible to reduce waste in their plants including equipment, time, material, and organization.[10]

Reaction Against Scientific Management

As cost accounting, personnel management, production control and other phases of management became more sophisticated, the cost of management increased both absolutely and relatively to direct costs of manufacture. It is not surprising, therefore, that there should be a reaction against this trend. Efforts were made to simplify the elaborate record keeping and reporting associated with scientific management and to critically examine the need for various control procedures. An interesting example of this type of reaction was described by Ralph E. Flanders, Manager of the Jones and Lamson Machine Company and President of the NMTBA before the American Society of Mechanical Engineers in 1924.

During the preceding twelve or fourteen years Jones and Lamson had concentrated primarily on improving control of manufacturing operations and had adopted most of the techniques of "Scientific Management." As a result, operations were made more

---

[9] *Machinery*, 31:189–191, November 1924. NMTBA Convention, Lenox, Massachusetts, October 8–10, 1924.

[10] *Ibid.*, 28:193–194, November 1921. National Machine Tool Builders' Convention, New York, October 18–20, 1921.

profitable, and machine time and labor costs were reduced despite higher wages.[11] It was then discovered, however, that while manufacturing costs had been reduced, overhead had greatly increased and that, consequently, the net reduction in costs and gain in profits was much less than was expected. Direct labor costs were very small; material costs were much higher, but manufacturing overhead was still larger. When business declined even moderately, profit margins threatened to disappear completely.

It was decided to apply some techniques of scientific management to the overhead problem. Departments were established by major product, and a separate department was established to handle special machines and service operations including production of replacement parts for machines no longer being built. Everything of an irregular nature was thus put into one department and the work of the other departments was made as routine as possible. Departments were also physically rearranged to make the flow of work as efficient as possible and to simplify supervision.

Simultaneously, efforts were made to redesign, standardize, and simplify the firm's products and to make it possible to use the same components in more than one machine. This permitted longer production runs and reduced the size of stocks required. The variety of machines manufactured was also reduced, but this was done in such a way as to cover the broadest possible segment of the lathe market. Standardization meant that, in some instances, a component was used which was heavier than required in the particular machine, but the economies of larger volume production and savings in inventory resulted in net savings.

It was decided to eliminate the perpetual inventory system previously used for stock control, and to operate stockrooms on a self-service basis without stockkeepers. A physical inventory of raw and finished stock was taken six times a year, and it was claimed that this method was more accurate and less subject to error than the perpetual inventory method.

With minor exceptions work from raw material to finished machine was kept in one department and control of work in process depended largely on the foreman's ability to see what was happening throughout his department. Foremen were given full authority

[11] Ralph E. Flanders, "Design, Manufacture and Production Control of a Standard Machine," ASME, *Transactions*, 46:691–738, No. 1933, 1924.

to run their departments according to their production orders and schedules. Since the latter were based on approximately 80 per cent of full production capacity the foremen had some idle time which was filled from work in the "special" or other departments, and particularly work on repair parts for which it was difficult to predict demand. Performance was measured in terms of the established schedules.

It was also concluded that most of the detailed bookkeeping involved in accounting could be dispensed with to reduce overhead without losing the principal benefits of cost accounting. No doubt it was considered that the most important of these was to provide a basis for setting prices.

Flanders explained that while they used a straight hourly rate basis for wages, the plan would also be adaptable to a premium payment system, and was particularly suited to the group-bonus scheme. The latter conclusion was based on the fact that the organization was divided into small groups each having a definite work assignment with all the work under its own control.

Flanders summarized the principal features of Jones and Lamson's plan of management as

1. Standardization of product.
2. Separate equipment and organization for each major product.
3. Departmentalization by product rather than process.
4. A recurrent production schedule or program.
5. Concentration of plant.
6. Minimized transportation.
7. Disturbing and difficult factors confined to purchasing.
8. Visual control of the work itself, instead of remote control by records.
9. Control by orders instead of by records.
10. Automatic control of inventories.
11. Cost determined by analyzing total expense rather than by totalling innumerable details.
12. A plain job for every man and full responsibility with it.
13. Don't try to overcome difficulties—avoid them.

An extended discussion of the paper included several statements approving of Jones and Lamson's efforts to simplify management and reduce overhead, and strong disagreement with some of the methods used.[12]

Walter M. Kidder, Consulting Production Engineer, New York, suggested that while the methods described by Flanders appeared ideal in the case of Jones and Lamson, who had (a) ample floor space, (b) adequate plant facilities, (c) able foremanship, and (d) workmen of native intelligence and above average disposition to team work, they were not suitable where all or most of these factors were lacking.

> Anyone who is familiar with the contrast in each of these points between a representative Vermont machine shop and the majority of those situated elsewhere, particularly in cities, will understand why Jones and Lamson succeeded and why copyists of their simplified and emasculated routine are liable to fail.[13]

Kidder pointed out what he considered to be various weaknesses and dangers in the simplified form of management adopted by Jones and Lamson including

1. Shop organization by product rather than by process required greater capital investment.
2. Straight wage payments of labor did not provide incentive for high output and superior workmanship.
3. Visual control of production was not suitable if the product was varied or foremen of only average ability.
4. The simplified method depended entirely on the judgment and diligence of foremen.
5. Lack of records made it impossible to analyze the causes and personal responsibility for spoilage or loss.
6. Lack of cost records eliminated a way of finding areas for reducing costs.

Luther B. Burlingame, Industrial Superintendent of the Brown and Sharpe Manufacturing Company, reported that they were using almost identical methods in some lines of production but that in others production was organized by process or type of machine used. Piece work or incentive systems of wage payment were, he sug-

[12] *Ibid.*, pp. 717–718.
[13] *Ibid.*, pp. 719–721.

gested, generally preferable and gave a fairer return to the worker than straight hourly or daily rate systems.[14]

E. P. Bullard, Jr., President of the Bullard Machine Tool Company, was highly critical of the system described by Flanders:

> Overhead has a faculty for creeping in unexpectedly in many disguises. In this paper it appears, first, in the title, which smacks strongly of overhead of a high degree. It also appears in the standard drawings with established tolerances, material specifications, jigs, tools, and fixtures for production of this kind, which imply planning, time study, costs, and records, all of which call for overhead.[15]

Bullard emphasized the difficulties involved in balancing and scheduling production in such a way that capital equipment was used efficiently and the various components were ready for assembly when needed. He compared the stockroom to a bank and expressed incredulity that no record was made of stock withdrawals. Flanders appeared to assume that inventories of raw, in-process, and finished parts would remain constant and, therefore, that the cost of complicated machines was equal to total payroll, material purchases, and expenses of the producing department. Bullard objected that such a stable situation would not exist and, consequently, the described method would not give reasonably accurate or comparable results. He also contended that taking physical inventory and establishing reasonably fair and accurate values for materials and parts would actually be about as expensive and require about as much time as the perpetual inventory system but would not provide current information when needed as would the perpetual inventory. He concluded that while it was undoubtedly desirable to control overhead, the methods outlined by Flanders would not reduce overhead to the extent supposed.

Flanders replied that

> . . . the particular scheme described should not be regarded as a panacea for all kinds of manufacturing problems. It does not apply to cases where the product cannot be controlled as to design, or where it is subject to the whims of fashion. Neither does it apply to businesses made up of a large number of separate

---

[14] *Ibid.*, p. 722.
[15] *Ibid.*, pp. 727–728.

items never assembled into one uniform mechanism. It does apply, however, to a large range of manufacture of machinery of ordinary size in all sorts and varieties. It is only on the particular work to which it does apply that the author urges its adoption in any form.

He denied any intent to criticize management engineering, but rather to suggest that the management engineer had been asked to provide control schemes for firms manufacturing such a wide variety of products, models, and sizes that efficient operation and management was impossible. The solution lay with greater product specialization and standardization.[16]

Flanders explained that the system described had been successfully applied when production was at a very low rate. Under it overhead had increased by only about 25 per cent—in relation to productive hours—over that when output was three or four times as great. The number of inspectors required was about the same as in the earlier system, but the number of foremen had been cut by about one-third.

The test performance of men or foremen, Flanders indicated, was simply whether they kept up to schedule and in this way contributed to the orderly production of a specified number of machines each week at a reasonable cost. He also noted the concern expressed over the rudimentary cost figures kept by Jones and Lamson, and contended that the continued compilation of detailed cost figures, where such figures had been available over a period of years, was of little value in reducing the cost of manufacture. Such savings were particularly small in comparison with savings possible through a direct attack on overhead costs. "Why worry about the cents when the dollars are melting away?"

Flanders repeated that he would not hesitate to cut out a function even though it might later prove to be needed, but that this did not mean throwing out their whole production control mechanism. He conceded that they probably could not have secured as good results from their simplified plan of management if they had not previously had a more elaborate system.

He challenged the assumption that the system of departmentalization by product would require more equipment, result in higher

16 *Ibid.*, pp. 731–732.

costs, and lower equipment utilization, and said that their experience had actually been the reverse of this. Machine utilization had been improved although it had been necessary to add certain special machines.

Flanders expressed pride in the quality of Jones and Lamson foremen and workmen but added that

> . . . if the author were manager of a plant under similar conditions in regions which are supposed to be less Elysian than his native soil, he would expect this scheme of production to make things as much easier with unpromising material as it does with that of a higher grade.[17]

He added that the plan adopted had resulted in such considerable savings in floor space that had it been adopted five years earlier, the firm could have saved "many tens of thousands of dollars on now unneeded shop structures, built when costs were at their highest."

Personal contact between management and foremen and between foremen and workers had been restored. Moreover, there was a closer personal relationship between the worker and his work since it was now possible for a worker to see the entire production process from raw material to finished machine. Flanders said that he was well aware that constant changes were occurring which required changes and adjustments on the part of business management.[18]

It seems probable that Jones and Lamson first went considerably farther than most tool builders in applying the principles and techniques of scientific management to its manufacturing operations and had then drastically simplified its methods. Its initial efforts had resulted in increased production efficiency, much better knowledge of its operations, and reductions in direct costs. As long as business was good and production at or near capacity there was little pressure on management to examine critically its own methods or become alarmed at the growth of overhead costs. When demand began to decline, however, it became necessary to find all possible ways to reduce costs in order to prevent the complete disappearance of profits and possibly disastrous losses because of the high fixed overhead. Why not then apply the methods which had been so

[17] *Ibid.,* pp. 733–736.
[18] *Ibid.,* p. 737.

successful in reducing direct costs of manufacture to the problem of excessive overhead? When this was done, it was decided that many of the management procedures and controls had outlived their usefulness and could be eliminated or greatly simplified.

Adoption of a Code of Ethics

Following World War I, and the "Big Slump" of 1921, there was a growing public discussion and interest among businessmen in business ethics. In October 1922, Henry M. Lucas, President of the Lucas Machine Tool Company called attention to the efforts of the Rotary to promote better business ethics and proposed an investigation of the success of other associations which had adopted written codes of ethics, as a basis for deciding whether the NMTBA should adopt such a code. This proposal was approved and Lucas was named as Chairman of the Investigating Committee. The committee reported favorably at the NMTBA Convention in the spring of 1923, and announced that it was working on a code for the machine tool industry. The draft code was forwarded to NMTBA members, and was discussed at the NMTBA Convention in October 1923. Much of this discussion was apparently designed to educate members on the need for such a code. Some members favored immediate adoption of the draft, but the committee requested that it be returned for further consideration.[19]

Early in May 1924, a Code of Principles of Business Conduct was presented to the U.S. Chamber of Commerce meeting in Cleveland. The NMTBA Committee decided to recommend that the machine tool builders adopt this code with certain modifications to apply the principles to the machine tool industry in lieu of the committee's draft code. This recommendation was approved by the NMTBA membership. Ernest F. DuBrul later said of the NMTBA's decision to drop the committee's draft code:

> The tentative code previously presented had 42 clauses, each one dealing with some abuse that somewhere or other had cropped out in our industry. Some members had cynically complained that 42 commandments were entirely too many. The Chamber's Code has 14 principles. So our next step was to get

[19] *Machinery*, 29:189–190, November 1922, NMTBA Convention, Lenox, Massachusetts, October 3–5, 1922.

the Association to adopt the Chamber's principles, in October 1924, and to instruct the Committee to prepare annexes to each of these principles setting forth the specific practices that our industry had found destructive of the various principles. Classification of our 42 Commandments showed that every practice condemned by them could be listed appropriately as a practice destructive of one of the principles formulated by the Chamber.[20]

DuBrul added that it took two or three years to educate a trade association's members on the value of a code and the need to put it into active practice rather than "having it framed merely as a collection of interesting pious maxims." Discussions of objectionable business practices caused many firms to abandon "some pet practice that was inherently bad." In order to make the code effective, a Committee on Trade Practices consisting of five members was established to pass upon cases of alleged violations of the code. DuBrul claimed that the very fact of the committee's existence was instrumental in suppressing most of the bad practices and that only two cases were presented to the committee within three years.

The NMTBA Convention at Lenox, Massachusetts, on October 7, 1924, prefaced its adoption of the U.S. Chamber of Commerce's "Principles of Business Conduct" with the following words:

> As our industry represents the highest types of attainment in the mechanical arts, it should likewise typify the highest ideals and standards in our business practices and relations. Recognizing that safety in business lies in the fine regard for the rights of others, and that like good standards in physical manufacture, good standards of business conduct are a protection and insurance against waste and loss. . . .

NMTBA members were asked to subscribe individually to the "principles."

The code covered the duties and obligations of the machine tool builder to his customers, dealers, employees, investors, competitors, the public, and to his own firm. It described and illustrated various forms of conduct which were either considered objectionable or to be commended. It also declared certain rights of machine tool builders. The duties cited included those of providing good service,

[20] Ernest F. DuBrul, *The Machine Tool Industry's Code of Business Principles* (General Management Series: No. 78). New York: American Management Association, 1928.

full performance, fair prices, equal treatment, and up-to-date knowledge of tools and customer requirements of machine tool customers. It was the duty of the machine builder to treat his dealers fairly and to offer security, fair wages, opportunity for advancement, good working conditions, and equitable settlement of disputes to his employees. Investors were entitled to a fair return on their investment, to security, to stability of returns, and to be assured that managers would have adequate knowledge to protect the investors' interests. Competitors were entitled to fair competition, to expect cooperation through the industry's trade association in exchange of information and other efforts for the common benefit, and protection against copying of machine tool designs. The public should be able to expect that the machine tool builder would always act with integrity and with knowledge of, and concern for, the public interest. Managers had a duty to their firms to be efficient, knowledgeable, and alert to ways of assuring the security of the firm's investment and returns.

The tool building firm, on the other hand, had a right to a fair profit, to security, and to continuity of business. It should be treated fairly by customers, dealers, employees and competitors alike. The business community was so interdependent that it could not function effectively except on the basis of mutual confidence. The latter was not possible if contracts could be broken without mutual agreement of the parties. It was expected that contracts would be mutually beneficial, but whether they were or not was to be carefully considered before contracts were made rather than after.

The NMTBA Code warned tool builders against indulging in various pricing policies and practices considered objectionable. Prices were to be maintained at a level which would cover all costs of manufacture and sale, a reasonable profit, etc., and should reflect their "utility" or value to the tool buyer. How the latter was to be assured in a competitive market was not indicated. It was also not explained how the machine tool builder was to determine a machine's potential utility to the customer without very extensive knowledge of the customer's business, prices, costs, and future plans.

The importance of having and using full knowledge of all cost factors, based on an adequate accounting system, as a basis for prices was emphasized in various ways. Not only were overhead and depreciation on fixed assets to be considered along with direct materials and labor but there should also be an allowance for obsolescence in design of the tools manufactured. How this factor was to be arrived at was also not indicated.

Tool builders were urged to insist that their agents, distributors, and employees conduct themselves in conformity with the NMTBA Code. Individual executives or employees were to be held responsible for their conduct and should not claim that unethical actions were due to pressures from a board of directors, creditors, etc.

Machine tool builders were said to be obligated to pay adequate wages and salaries both as a matter of fairness and as a matter of self-interest in order to attract and retain competent employees. The chronic problem of instability of employment, however, was said to be mainly due to, and within the control of, the machine tool industry's customers rather than the machine tool builder. Machine tool builders were urged to study this problem and to tell their customers about it. Apparently it was hoped that tool users would, if properly educated, have both the foresight and the money or credit necessary to finance purchases of new equipment during periods of slow business thereby benefiting from somewhat lower prices and better service.

Specific types of competitive practices which were identified by the NMTBA as objectionable included:

1. Attempts to discredit a competitor.
2. Failures to promote mutual education through the collection and exchange of facts and dissemination of information which might discourage overexpansion.
3. Copying designs.
4. Threatening suits for patent infringement for purposes of intimidation.
5. Tampering with or misadjusting a competitor's machine to discredit it with a customer.
6. Combining to maintain prices, dividing territory, or trying to put a competitor out of business.
7. Failing to maintain a friendly attitude toward competitors, or accepting unverified reports reflecting on their honesty.
8. Failing to cooperate and provide advice and counsel on questions affecting the whole industry.

The following selling practices were declared contrary to the code:

1. Selling the customer something not suited to his needs.

2. Quoting unrealistic delivery dates (presumably as a way of getting orders which might otherwise go to a competitor).
3. Giving performance guarantees without adequate knowledge of the work to be done, specifications to be met, etc.
4. Misrepresenting materials, workmanship, or performance.
5. Selling repaired or rebuilt machines as new or new machines as repaired or rebuilt.
6. Granting demands from some customers for free service, discriminatory, or excessive credit terms, preferential prices, etc., not offered to all buyers.
7. Accepting used machinery as trade-in at too high a price.
8. Encouraging "speculative stocking" by dealers.

Machine tool builders were warned against conducting any trade association activity in an illegal manner.

Adequate effort to improve tool designs was essential to meet competition and stay in business. Tool builders were warned, however, against creating unnecessary sizes and styles in machines because this would increase the firm's investment and reduce stock turnover. The dangers of inventory losses due to obsolescence where speculative stocks of tools were built up in anticipation of orders were also pointed out. Tool builders were urged to improve their manufacturing practices; to join in reasonable standardization of tool holding and work holding elements as means of reducing waste to tool users; and to build machines in conformity to standard safety codes.[21]

Ralph E. Flanders, President of the NMTBA, summarized his views on the general principles which should guide the machine tool builder as follows:

> It is the duty of the industries in general, and of the machine tool business in particular, to manufacture and distribute only such things as are of use and beauty, serviceable to the truest need of mankind; that these products should be produced and distributed with the greatest efficiency, avoiding waste of both labor and materials; that the returns from business should be based upon the serviceability of the product and the efficiency of its manufacture, rather than accrued from sharp practices of any kind.[22]

[21] *Ibid.*
[22] *Machinery*, 31:189–191, November 1924, National Machine Tool Builders' Convention, Lenox, Mass., October 8–10, 1924.

Flanders also emphasized the advantages of "equitable and harmonious relations" between management and labor, that management should strive to reduce business fluctuations thereby protecting workers, and that tool builders should set a high standard in their personal affairs.

In our personal habits we will avoid extravagance and display, not only as personally unworthy but as socially dangerous. We will find our personal satisfactions in rational and fitting ways, and particularly in the successful management of a socially useful business.

This statement probably reflected the Puritan influence of Flanders' own Vermont background and training. It seems likely, however, that many other tool builders did look upon their trade as an essential and highly skilled art rather than merely as a business whose success or failure could be measured purely in terms of profit and loss without regard for the methods used to make a profit.

The establishment of industry codes of ethics—usually accompanied, or followed closely, the creation of a trade association, but in the machine tool industry it did not occur until about twenty years after the NMTBA was established. To a degree, the codes were modeled after the professional codes and were part of an effort to make business a profession. John M. Clark summarized the general situation with regard to business codes as follows:

. . . the written codes set a higher standard than the unwritten and lay more emphasis on the obligation of service, but they also lay a deal of emphasis on protecting the interests of the trade itself. There are large sections dealing with rights rather than duties, and serving notice on various groups with which the trade has dealings, as to what the trade considers to be its due, and what treatment it will insist on. The written codes, like the unwritten, are made of decidedly mixed elements.[23]

It seems likely that most machine tool builders adhered fairly closely to most and perhaps all of the principles stated in their code and had done so prior to its formal adoption. Nevertheless, the mere fact that a written code was considered desirable or necessary and so many specific objectionable practices were listed is evidence

[23] John M. Clark, *Social Control of Business*, 2nd Ed. (New York: McGraw-Hill Book Company, 1939), p. 217.

that enough firms resorted to tactics considered unethical or unwise that collective action was considered desirable.

Laws of Manufacturing Management

During the twenties there was also an effort to codify management theories, principles, and techniques in a code of "Laws of Manufacturing Management", covering such subjects as the division of labor, leadership, incentive pay, delegation of authority, specialization, transfer of skill, and profits. Despite the interest in the development and application of various methods of improving management during the first two decades of the twentieth century, no body of commonly accepted principles had been developed. This situation was contrasted with that in such fields as mathematics, physics, and chemistry, each of which had established bodies of laws.

These fundamentals of the older sciences are recognized as having always existed, as being natural, or God-made. They have been formulated for use by putting together the discoveries and results of the work of many scientists, investigators and engineers. They are taught to all engineering students, and are universally applied in engineering work. The result of conformity to the truth they express has been mastery over the forces and resources of nature.[24]

Such laws were sufficiently reliable and generally applicable to satisfy many of the practical needs of engineers. If similar basic principles relating to management could be discovered and formulated, management would be put on a much firmer and more "scientific" basis. L. P. Alford suggested that there was sufficient evidence of the existence of fundamental laws of management, and that there were probably a rather large number of such laws.

Alford called attention to the fact that most of the principles

[24] L. P. Alford, "Laws of Manufacturing Management," American Society of Mechanical Engineers, *Transactions*, 48:393–438, No. 2014, 1926. An economist reviewing this history prior to publication described these "laws" as "silly and pretentious." The author is inclined to agree that the "laws" probably had little practical value and lacked both the precision and general applicability normally associated with "scientific laws." They appeared, however, seriously intended; to have been so accepted, and had some influence on the NRA Code developed for the machine tool industry in the thirties.

usually considered basic to manufacturing management such as the division of labor were actually very old, and offered as evidence a quotation from Xenophon written about 370 B.C. describing the division of labor already customary in the manufacture of sandals.[25]

Alford formulated about forty laws which he divided into twenty-five categories. For example, under one category "Laws of Specialization" were included,

1. Law of Division of Work or Specialization of the Job.
2. Law of Division of Effort or Specialization of the Individual.
3. Law of Transfer of Skill or Specialization of Tools and Machines.
4. Law of Simplification or Specialization of Product.

The most significant of these laws from the viewpoint of the machine tool builder was the third regarding which Alford quoted from Dexter Kimball's "Principles of Industrial Organization."

> Transfer of skill is in fact the basic idea in all tool construction. It is embodied in the first stone ax, and all succeeding improvements in tools of production were, essentially, advances in transfer of skill.

> *   *   *

> The greatest inventions carried transfer of skill to the point where the skill of the worker became an adjunct to the tool or machine.[26]

Alford also cited a "Law of Profit" based on the assumption that business was a service which would be rewarded by a fair and reasonable profit and quoted from the NMTBA "Guide for Applying Code of Ethics" that: "The reward of business for service rendered is a fair profit plus a safe reserve, commensurate with risks involved and foresight exercised."[27] It is not likely that codification of these laws proved of much value to the machine tool industry. During the thirties, however, machine tool industry leaders tried

---

[25] *Ibid.*, pp. 397–398. No doubt this historical trail could be followed at least another 1,000 years further, since a similar division of labor was practiced by the Egyptians. For an example taken from the tomb of Rekhmire at Thebes, c. 1450 B.C. see Vol. II of *A History of Technology*, ed. by Charles Singer, E. J. Holmyard, *et al*, New York: Oxford University Press, 1956, p. 162.

[26] *Ibid.*, pp. 399–401.

[27] *Ibid.*, pp. 402, 414.

to give some of the laws a formal legal basis by incorporating them in the NRA Code of the machine tool industry.

Further Efforts to Improve Cost Accounting

The NMTBA continued its efforts to improve the industry's cost accounting methods even when business was relatively good and its members less concerned about costs. In 1928, a new staff cost consultant visited a number of machine tool builders. This cost expert, Albert E. Grover, also read a paper entitled "Some Important Points on Machine Tool Cost Accounting" before a meeting of the Grinding Machine Group of the NMTBA in October 1928.[28] That these efforts were reasonably successful and that the NMTBA's contribution was being recognized is suggested by the following quotation:

> During 1929 some progress has been made in improving management methods, and particularly cost methods. The outstanding example is the work of the National Machine Tool Builders' Association under the direction of its general manager and his staff cost consultant. Much progress has been made in getting uniformity of cost methods so that true comparisons are really possible. By this means the plant management can tell with some assurance whether it is efficient as compared with its competitors. Other branches of the field would do well to take steps toward the same goal.[29]

NMTBA efforts to improve cost accounting in the machine tool industry and to secure adoption of a uniform cost accounting system continued after the crash of 1929. Its efforts in this and related fields were supplemented by those of the Machinery and Allied Products Institute (MAPI) after its establishment in 1933. Such voluntary efforts, however, were only partly successful and consequently, most machine tool industry leaders were initially sympathetic with the National Recovery Act.

[28] RG 151, U.S. Department of Commerce, Bureau of Foreign and Domestic Commerce, "File 721–N, Conventions—NMTBA—1927–1928."

[29] ASME, *Transactions*, 52:1–2, 1930, MSP–52–1, "Progress in Machine Shop Practices," Report of Executive Committee of Machine Shop Practice Division of ASME.

Open Price Policy

Herman H. Lind, NMTBA General Manager, and Executive Officer of the NRA Machine Tool and Forging Machinery Industry Code Authority, confirmed that the machine tool industry had maintained a firm price policy for many years by which a price was fixed for a given machine and adhered to while the particular price list was in effect. Lind added that in times of depression weaker firms were sometimes forced to deviate from the firm price policy in order to reduce their stocks or obtain funds. Prices in the machine tool industry had never been uniform between competitors; there were wide variations in style, method of operation, and attachments in the same type of machine, and it was necessary to vary prices in terms of productivity, patented features, and consumer acceptance.[30]

Lind explained that it was very difficult to prove a charge of selling below cost due to the fact that material and labor costs were a small part of total cost while engineering costs, patents, service, selling, and administrative costs added a heavier burden than in the case of consumer products.

> There is no known method of determining whether a competitor's price is high enough to continue him in business for any length of time. In general, the industry suffers from too low a price level because of this fact.

Lind reported that there had been no revisions of prices to meet prices in competitor's lists when these were received, and no cases where a member had withdrawn announced prices before their effective date.

The open price policy was also defended by Lind in a statement presented at a public meeting of the Code Authority on February 28, 1934. He recalled that President Roosevelt, early in the depression, had appealed to industry to maintain wage scales, sustain buying power, and maintain the existing standard of living. Lind suggested that there should be some provision to restrain buyers, and particularly those operating on a large scale, from putting

[30] RG 9, NRA, Code Authority Files, Machine Tool and Forging Machinery Industry; Letter from Lind to General Hugh S. Johnson, NRA Administrator, Feb. 26, 1934.

undue pressure on vendors to reduce their prices or discriminate in a particular buyer's favor in order to secure an order.[31]

Lind urged that prices should be firm as well as open since if prices could be changed without notice to competitors such changes could be used as a subterfuge for price cutting. If the seller was required to give a reasonable notice of price changes, his competitors were given an opportunity to adjust their prices. This eliminated one of the principle incentives to price cutting.

It was apparently felt that there were enough "chislers" in the machine tool industry, together with those who were too weak to withstand pressure tactics on the part of tool buyers, for it to be possible to maintain fair prices voluntarily. The National Recovery Act permitted industry to establish rules of fair business conduct with the government acting as arbiter in their formulation and referee of their operation. The firm open price policy was said to be the most important rule and the only honest way of doing business. This policy was considered fair to everybody, would create business confidence, and should be made a universal practice.

Lind suggested that buyers should also be organized under a Code of Fair Competition which would construe "as an unfair trade practice to divulge, or even to intimate to any supplier the prices, terms, and conditions offered to him by the supplier's competitor or competitors." How this provision would apply or why it would be needed if the Open Price Policy were effective and prices were available to all competitors was not explained. Possibly it applied to bids for special machines not covered by price lists.

Cost Accounting and Pricing Under the NRA

Article VIII of the Machine Tool and Forging Machinery Industry's Code "Accounting and Costing" required the Supervisory Agency to establish "a practical system of cost finding" as a basis for the determination of a fair price for each unit manufactured by any member of the industry. It specified that the cost accounting system should be drafted to provide "sound methods of dealing with cost problems peculiar to the Industry;" that it was subject to NRA approval, and that it was to be used by the industry "with

[31] RG 9, "The Open Price Policy," February 28, 1934.

such variations therefrom as may be required by the individual conditions affecting any member of the Industry" also subject to NRA approval.

Article IX provided that after the cost system specified in Article VIII was approved by the NRA, no member should sell any product at less than his cost of manufacture. It permitted, however, any member of the industry to dispose of obsolete products at less than cost provided that he immediately notified the Supervisory Agency, and through it all direct competitors, in writing of the description and quantity of equipment sold.

A Cost Committee established by the Supervisory Agency developed a cost accounting formula to be used in setting prices. It consisted of three parts, namely, (1) cost classification, (2) rates for depreciation, and (3) cost restrictions.[32]

A survey of the machine tool industry made by the NMTBA and covering a period of eleven years from 1921 through 1931 had shown an average utilization of plant capacity of about 65 per cent and this was to be considered "normal volume." The committee recommended that there be at least two overhead rates including one for machining and one for assembly operations. Other overhead rates were to be established for each department where equipment values or operating expenses covered a wide range. Suggested cost classifications conformed to those outlined in the "Manual of Standard Accounting and Cost System," Fourth Edition, issued by the Machinery Builders' Society in September 1933. Depreciation rates recommended were based on the experience of many machine tool plants over a period of years and were contained in the "Manual of Cost Procedures for the Machine Tool Industry" issued December 1, 1933. It was recommended that appraised value be based on the relative productive capacity of existing equipment as compared with modern equipment.

Recommended cost restrictions—items to be excluded from cost —included (a) interest on borrowed money or capital in any form, (b) unusual expenses, and (c) depreciation on idle facilities.

The cost formula probably represented about the minimum which

[32] RG 9, "Proposed Cost Formulas for Machine Tool and Forging Machinery Industry" by Sub-Committee on Cost Plan Appointed by the Supervisory Agency.

the members of the Supervisory Agency, NMTBA, and most machine tool builders felt would provide any assurance against abuses of the selling-below-cost provisions of the machine tool industry's code. It was a logical end product of years of effort by the NMTBA to improve and standardize machine tool builders' cost accounting practices. It did not, however, meet with the unqualified approval of either the NRA or all tool builders and dealers.

M. S. Massel recommended to the NRA Consumers' Advisory Board that before the cost formula's selling-below-costs provision was approved, the problem of price restriction should be reconsidered.

> The main drive of the N.R.A. was an increase in goods and services for everyone. . . . If prices in any industry are low, it would seem that demand and supply are out of harmony. Regulating the price would be tantamount to attempting to cure by changing a symptom.[34]

Massel objected that high-cost manufacturers would be squeezed out of the market, that the cost formula would require all firms to establish expensive departmentalized accounting systems, and that inclusion of employee services would handicap such humanitarian activities. He also objected to the proposal to base depreciation rates on appraised value and suggested that the depreciation rates allowable for Federal Income Tax purposes be used instead. Since profits or losses were dependent upon volume of business as well as upon unit prices, a firm might be in a worse position if it maintained or increased its prices, than if prices declined while volume remained constant or increased.

There were also objections to the cost formula because it excluded interest on investment and "unusual expenditures" from costs, and to the proposed treatment of depreciation on idle facilities. J. R. Howland, Acting Assistant Deputy Administrator, NRA, insisted that inclusion of interest on investment, unusual expenses and depreciation on idle facilities as suggested was very difficult, largely a matter of personal judgment, and not subject to any

---

[34] RG 9, Memorandum from M. S. Massel to Consumers' Advisory Board, November 14, 1934, "Cost Formulas for Machine Tool and Forging Machinery Industry."

formula "which will guarantee sound and equitable use by all parties."[35]

A. E. North, Secretary and Treasurer, the Bullard Company, objected to the provision that "direct material" cost should include cost of transportation on the ground that this resulted in unnecessary clerical effort, and suggested that transportation expenses be charged directly to shop expense. He also objected to the recommendation that not less than two burden rates be used—one for machining and one for assembly work—on the ground that they had found that only one rate was needed. They used rather expensive equipment in their assembly departments and overhead for these departments did not differ materially from some machining departments using relatively large and expensive machines.[36]

C. R. Rosborough, President, Moline Tool Company, pointed out that the item "direct materials" in the proposed Uniform Cost Formula did not specify whether the actual cost, replacement cost, or the lower of actual cost or replacement cost was to be used and suggested that this be specified. He also suggested that the proposal that the appraised value to be used for equipment depreciation should be proportional to productive capacity as compared with modern equipment was inadequate and should be supported by a complete set of index numbers for buildings and machinery based on costs in different years in order to make it possible to adjust actual cost to replacement cost. Rosborough also stated that Moline had found a single overhead rate per productive hour satisfactory and gave sufficiently accurate information on product costs. J. R. Howland, NRA, agreed that the basis for figuring materials costs was important and must be corrected before the proposed formula was acceptable. He expressed doubt whether much restriction could be placed on depreciation other than that it be *no greater* than allowed by Internal Revenue for income tax purposes.[37]

A meeting of the Machine Tool and Forging Machinery Industry Supervisory Agency in Cleveland on February 15, 1935, resulted in agreement on two main points: (1) the changes suggested by

[35] RG 9, Letter from S. Owen Livingston, Gallymeyer, and Livingston to Dexter A. Tutein, NRA, November 20, 1934, and reply of November 22, 1934.

[36] RG 9, Letter from North to Tutein, November 30, 1934.

[37] RG 9, Letter from Rosborough to Tutein, November 30, 1934; Letter from Howland to Rosborough, December 3, 1934.

the government would make the formula considerably more elementary than that proposed and less desirable from the industry's standpoint, and (2) while the major tool companies were already using cost formulas as complete as that proposed by the industry, there were many small companies which were not using cost formulas as detailed as the one which was proposed by the NRA representatives. The more complex formula was particularly desired by the builders of special tools who looked upon the "selling below cost" provisions of the code as the only market control of value to them since they did not benefit from the price listing provisions. It was also emphasized, however, that enforcement of compliance with the provisions of the code relative to sales below cost was at best a difficult matter and likely to be of doubtful value in view of the possible variations in interpretation of a cost formula. It was decided at this meeting, to inform the industry of the points on which the industry's proposal was unacceptable to the NRA. However, by the time this formula was ready for final presentation, NRA policy on cost accounting and the prohibition of sales below cost had changed and no action was taken on the formula beyond the preliminary review.[38]

Probably the most controversial aspect of the Machine Tool and Forging Machinery Industry's Code provisions relating to the filing and exchange of price lists under the open price policy was whether prices applied only to the firm filing them or also applied to builders of competitive machines as well. Lind and others appeared to feel that where a particular manufacturer filed prices on his standard product, these prices were applicable to another firm which might offer a similar machine even though this was not a "standard product" of the competing firm. Robert S. Denvir, NRA Assistant General Counsel, and Charles J. Stillwell, Vice President, Warner and Swasey Company, objected that prices filed by a member were "his own prices" and applied only to "his standard product."[39]

A machine might, according to Stillwell, agree in every respect

[38] RG 9, Extract from Code of Fair Competition; NRA, "History of the Code of Fair Competition for the Machine Tool and Forging Machinery Industry."
[39] RG 9, Memorandum to John L. Murrie, Assistant Deputy Administrator, from Robert S. Denvir, Assistant Counsel, July 19, 1934, "Machine Tool and Forging Machinery Industry—Interpretation of Standard Products, etc."; Letter from Herman H. Lind to John R. Howland, September 1, 1934; Letter from Charles J. Stillwell to J. R. Howland, October 19, 1934.

with a standard product of another manufacturer and yet not be a standard product of the firm which built it. Stillwell was concerned, however, regarding situations in which a machine tool builder who had filed price lists covering certain standard machines might attempt to justify a substantial price reduction by leaving off some nonessential part whose value did not correspond to the price reduction.

Under the Open Price Policy, prices could be changed but sufficient advance notice, through filing of new price lists with the Code Authority, had to be given to allow the Code Authority to notify competitors of the proposed changes and to permit competitors to make changes in their own prices to meet the new prices. In the machine tool industry, the effect of filing and exchange of price lists was restricted by the fact that many machine tools were not "standard" machines but rather were built specially to meet the user's needs. Also one manufacturer might build as a special tool a machine equivalent to the standard product of a competitor. While it was not considered practical to file price lists for special machines, there was opportunity for considerable differences of opinion among tool builders, the Code Authority and NRA officials as to whether prices should be filed in particular instances.

The Supervisory Agency continued to urge approval of a definition of the term "standard machine" as

> Any machine to which a manufacturer applies a designated number, or size, or name, that will indicate to an informed person a specific machine; or

> Any machine of style, type or design that is accepted by the Industry as competitive to an established product of any other member of the industry, and on which prices have been filed with Supervisory Agency.

It was also specified that

> The addition to or elimination of any special feature from a standard machine shall not be considered as removing the machine from the classification as standard product. Deductions allowing for eliminating a feature, or charges added because of adding a feature shall be in reasonable relationship to the saving in cost or the added costs.[40]

[40] RG 9, Minutes of Sixth Meeting, Supervisory Agency, May 23, 1934.

NRA Counsel James R. Garfield commented favorably on the proposed definition though he appeared confused as to whether it was intended to cover all special machines.

There may be cases of really special machines which, though competitive to the established product of another part of the Industry, embody newly patented principles or otherwise are so special in nature as to not constitute a standard product. . . . Even if such situations might arise, it is doubtless still within the intent of Article X that prices with respect to such special machines should be established, announced, quoted and effective until changed as provided under the terms of Article X.[41]

At the Supervisory Agency Meeting of August 23, 1934 a more critical opinion of NRA Assistant Counsel, Robert S. Denvir, was read:

A competitive product manufactured by a member of the industry, which product is not a standard product of said member, cannot be classified under this article as a standard product on the ground that another member has classified the product of similar style, class and design as a standard product of his make. Each member shall establish his own standard product and file prices on same but in no sense are the prices to be binding on any other member of the industry, as the second sentence of said article provides. "Such prices" referring to the phrase "his own prices" in the first sentence shall be the prices to all customers, meaning all his own customers or all customers to whom he quotes.

The use of the term "special feature," without a definition of same, is objectionable because it is too broad and ambiguous.

It is my opinion that an amendment to the code will be necessary to accomplish the aim of the industry in curbing the practice mentioned in their letter, which they are trying to curb through the submitted interpretation.[42]

Thus according to Denvir's interpretation, the price filing features of the code could be used to prevent discriminatory pricing on the part of a given firm. The same price had to be offered to all customers, but prices filed by one firm were not binding upon an-

[41] *Ibid.*
[42] RG 9, Seventh Meeting, Supervisory Agency, August 23, 1934.

other even though a machine might be substantially identical with that sold by the first firm which had filed a price list showing the machine as a standard product. The Supervisory Agency, however, was not inclined to accept this viewpoint as final nor did it favor applying for an amendment of the code. Instead, it requested the Supervisory Agency's Executive Officer to continue his efforts to secure a satisfactory interpretation without amendment of the code.

At the next meeting of the Supervisory Agency, Lind reported that the proposed definition of "standard product" had been "favorably received" by NRA headquarters but that it had been suggested that all members of the industry be given a chance to express their views of it. The proposed definition was therefore submitted to the members of the machine tool industry by letter.[43]

This poll showed 166 firms approving the suggested definition and twenty-five filing objections. These results and objections were given to the Supervisory Agency with suggestions for amending the definition, and were discussed with NRA officials. The Supervisory Agency, on February 15, 1935, passed a motion adopting the following revised definition:

(1)   A Standard Product is any machine, or any accessory or attachment to which a manufacturer applies a designated number, or size, or name, that might or should indicate to an informed person a specific type of machine, accessory or attachment, or

(2)   Any machine, accessory or attachment which is offered to a customer as competitive in style, type or design to an established product, on which product a price has been filed with the Supervisory Agency by any member of the Industry.

(3)   Any machine, or any accessory or attachment which is sufficiently different in style, type or design substantially to distinguish it from one which might or should indicate to an informed person a specific type of machine accessory or attachment, or from an established product on which a price has been filed with the Supervisory Agency, and which is manufactured for a customer according to special or particular specifications, shall not be included in the classification of a Standard Product.

(4)   The addition to, or elimination from any machine of any special feature shall not, *ipso facto*, be considered as excluding any machine from its classification as a Standard Product. Deductions allowed for eliminating a special feature shall be in reason-

[43] R.G. 9, Minutes of Eighth Meeting, Supervisory Agency, October 1, 1934.

able relationship to the actual saving in cost or addition to cost, as the case may be.[44]

The principal change in the definition as finally approved from that originally proposed was in the second paragraph where the phrase "offered to a customer" replaced the words "accepted by the industry." In both cases, however, the intention of trying to control price competition seems clear enough. By 1935, however, business was improving and many machine tool builders appeared to feel the NRA was not worth the cost and was mainly of value to "big business." The discussion was ended, so far as the NRA was concerned, in May of 1935 when the Supreme Court declared the National Recovery Act to be an illegal delegation of legislative power to the President.

Restraint of Trade

It has already been noted that the NMTBA and individual tool builders attempted at various times to discourage or eliminate price competition although, in most cases, they were not entirely successful. In addition, even where price competition was restricted, there was competition of other types and there were individual attempts to control such competition. In Civil Action No. 10664 in the U.S. District Court for the Eastern District of Michigan, Southern Division, June 22, 1951, it was charged that starting in about 1933, the defendants (Associated Patents, Inc., Brown and Sharpe Manufacturing Company, The Carlton Machine Tool Company, DeVlieg Engineering Company, DeVlieg Machine Company, Charles B. DeVlieg, the Lodge and Shipley Machine Tool Company and the MAC Investment Company) had violated the Sherman Anti-Trust Act by restraining trade in machine tools by use of a patent pool [Associated Patents, Inc. (API)]; allocating to themselves exclusive rights to manufacture and sell specified types of tools. The agreements were based on three patents developed by Charles DeVlieg including a "backlash eliminator," power transmission mechanism, and automatic positioning device. Any improvements made by any of the participating companies were to be turned over to API.

[44] RG 9, Minutes of Ninth Meeting, Supervisory Agency, February 15, 1935. Supervisory Agency Bulletin No. 25.

On June 20, 1955, the court found that the API agreement imposed unreasonable restraints on the parties including:

(a) The parties were restricted in their manufacture of machine tools by being unable to obtain licenses permitting them to incorporate features covered by the subject matter patents or improvements thereon on machine tools not included in their respective fields of use.

(b) Outside parties were restricted in their manufacture of machine tools by being foreclosed from obtaining licenses on the subject matter patents or improvements thereon for any of the types of machine tools included within the fields of use exclusively reserved to API members.

(c) Each of the parties was restricted in the licensing of improvement patents it developed by the requirements that all improvement patents be assigned to API.

(d) Invention and technological development have been discouraged by the limitations imposed on the members' rights to use and license improvement patents developed by them.

The API agreement was declared by the court to be illegal and void.

A different type of conspiracy to violate the Sherman Act was alleged in Civil Action No. 24,530 in the U.S. District Court for the Northern District of Ohio, Eastern Division filed January 2, 1947. This was a complaint against the National Acme Company (NAMCO) of Cleveland and two alleged coconspirators, The Birmingham Small Arms Tools Limited (B.S.A. Tools), a British firm, and Pittler Werkzeugmaschinenfabrik Aktiengesellschaft (Pittler) of Germany. The complaint alleged that starting in 1930 (in the case of Pittler) and 1932 (in the case of B.S.A. Tools), NAMCO entered into agreements with its coconspirators to control manufacture of multiple-spindle automatics and divide world markets among the parties to the agreements. Under the agreements, B.S.A. Tools and Pittler agreed to manufacture NAMCO automatics for sale in their assigned marketing areas and to refrain from manufacturing or selling any other multiple-spindle automatics to compete with the NAMCO automatics. They agreed that they would not compete with NAMCO in the United States and would also pay NAMCO a specified amount on each tool sold. NAMCO was to provide B.S.A. Tools and Pittler all information necessary to manufacture NAMCO automatics and to give them a discount on any automatics manufactured by NAMCO itself but sold in the marketing areas of the other parties. This was to take care of such cases as a customer insisting on the American-made machine or B.S.A. Tools or Pittler being unable to supply the tools ordered. B.S.A. Tools and Pittler were to be sole agents for NAMCO tools in their assigned areas. Any inventions or improvements were to become the property of NAMCO.

Pittler, under a contract of 1930, was assigned the sole right to manufacture NAMCO multiple-spindle automatics in Europe, and the sole right to sell NAMCO automatics in Europe and Russia, except for England, France, Belgium, Spain, Portugal, and the town of Couvet, Switzerland. It was given a nonexclusive right to sell NAMCO automatics manufactured by Pittler in the excepted countries. This contract was extended until September 30, 1940 and was to be extended automatically for another five years unless one party notified the other of its desire to cancel one year before the termination date.

A similar understanding was worked out with B.S.A. Tools in about 1932 and included some modifications to the contract between NAMCO and Pittler whereby the latter relinquished its manufacturing right for England to B.S.A. Tools. Pittler was to receive a commission on multiple-spindle automatics manufactured by B.S.A. Tools and be given a monthly list of all multiple-spindle automatics sold by B.S.A. Tools. The latter's territory was to include Great Britain, Ireland, and all parts of the British Empire except Canada. Effective January 1, 1933, NAMCO assigned Pittler the sole right to sell multiple-spindle automatics manufactured by NAMCO or Pittler in Japan and its colonies in China, Manchuria, and Manchoukuo.

It was alleged that, in September 1939, NAMCO notified Pittler of its desire to terminate the contract the following year and to negotiate a new agreement. Such an agreement was alleged to have been signed in April 1940. It redefined Pittler's territory. Among the provisions was one specifying that Pittler would continue its efforts to secure permission of the German government to make payments to NAMCO due under the terms of the agreement between NAMCO and Pittler. (Payments had been stopped by German laws restricting transfer of funds from Germany.) The contract of 1930 was to be continued for a period of five years from September 30, 1940 and to be automatically extended for an additional five years unless one of the parties notified the other of its desire to cancel one year prior to the expiration date.

The agreements between NAMCO, B.S.A. Tools, and Pittler were alleged to have the following effects:

1. Interstate and foreign trade were unreasonably restrained.
2. NAMCO refrained from exporting and prevented the export of multiple-spindle automatics from the United States except as permitted by the Agreements.
3. B.S.A. Tools and Pittler refrained from exporting multiple-spindle automatics to the United States.
4. The principle world markets were divided between NAMCO, B.S.A. Tools, and Pittler.

The court was asked to perpetually enjoin the defendant from combining or conspiring to restrain trade in multiple-spindle automatics, and that the contracts and agreements between NAMCO and its coconspirators be ordered terminated. This action also resulted in a "Consent Decree" enjoining the defendants from engaging in the restrictive agreements.

Summary

Following World War I, the machine tool industry attempted to avoid, so far as possible, the effects of the expected postwar slump in demand and resisted pressure to reduce prices. It tried to retain the gains it had made in profit ratios on the ground that prewar profits had not been sufficient for many machine tool builders to build up adequate reserves to carry them over the low spots in the business cycle. Greater interest was taken in the improvement and standardization of cost accounting mainly as a basis for establishing and maintaining prices at a profitable level. These efforts produced considerable improvement in the methods used and in the understanding of the problems involved but there is little evidence that they accomplished their main objectives of stabilizing profits and protecting machine tool builders against the effects of major business fluctuations.

The NMTBA played a leading role in developing and installing better cost accounting systems during the twenties. In this area, as in the design and construction of machine tools, the machine tool industry was influenced by developments in the major machine tool using industries such as the automobile industry. The changes in accounting proposed by the NMTBA were similar to the methods already used by leading machine tool builders and were intended to secure reasonable conformity by all firms.

The NMTBA tried to discourage other firms from entering the machine tool industry by emphasizing the low profits and uncertain demand characterizing the industry. It also attempted to make machine tool users more aware of the machine tool builders' problems, more sympathetic, and more willing to pay higher prices for machine tools.

One of the usual and almost inevitable results of the introduction of the principles of "Scientific Management" in manufacturing was a substantial increase in the amount of record keeping, reporting, coordination, and supervision required. The proportion of cost represented by overhead as compared to direct costs of labor, materials, and equipment almost invariably rose rapidly. Frequently, it seemed that most of the savings in direct costs were lost through higher overhead and were only reflected to a very limited extent in lower selling prices and higher profits or wages. This trend appeared particularly characteristic of industries such as machine tool building where production runs were usually comparatively short. As this situation began to be recognized, it was natural that machine tool builders would turn more of their attention to the problem of overhead costs.

Concern over the high cost of "overhead" as compared to direct costs of production resulted in a reaction against the features of scientific management which, in addition to causing large amounts of paperwork, required additional supervisors and foremen, and tended to separate the worker from the work and bosses from their workmen. This reaction was toward simplification of management, elimination of nonessential paperwork, greater emphasis on standardization and simplification of products, and concentration of production. These efforts were not industry-wide by any means, however, since there was not either full agreement as to the problems involved or their solution.

Amortization of capital equipment was also a major cost accounting problem of special interest to machine tool builders both directly and indirectly as it affected tool users' replacement policies. The NMTBA's emphasis on full amortization of equipment and insistence that the value of a machine tool for tax purposes should be the amount that a secondhand dealer would pay for it, seems inconsistent with machine tool builders' argument that profits should be based on total investment rather than net worth. It seems unlikely that most machine tool builders would have been willing to use the secondhand value for equipment in calculating costs and establishing prices. This would be particularly true where special machines were involved which might be highly productive for their intended use but have little resale value. The main effect of using the secondhand value for tax purposes would be to greatly increase deductions in the first years of a machine's life and decrease the amount to be taken in later years. This would be an advantage so long as tax rates and earnings were stable or declining, but would have a reverse effect if tax rates and earnings rose significantly over the life of the machine.

Development of a Code of Ethics for the Machine Tool Industry was not an isolated or unique event but rather part of a general movement following World War I carrying forward the organization of American business begun near the end of the nineteenth century. It was promoted by the efforts of the Rotary and the U.S. Chamber of Commerce whose Code of Principles of Business Conduct was used as a trunk to which examples of objectionable conduct from the machine tool business were grafted as illustrations of conduct to be avoided. A Committee on Trade Practices was established to pass upon code violations but it appears that the mere threat of publicity or just a reminder that specific conduct was objectionable was usually sufficient to secure conformity. This was true during the latter half of the twenties when the industry was generally prosperous, but was probably less true of the earlier thirties when the survival of many firms was at stake. At any rate, there was an effort to give many of the same ideas the force of law by incorporating them in the NRA Code for the Machine Tool and Forging Machinery Industry.

The Code of Ethics gave about as much attention to the rights of machine tool builders as to their obligations in relation to customers, dealers, and employees. Some of these "rights" seem very difficult to interpret as, for example, the provision that the right to a "reasonable profit" should reflect the machine tool's "utility" to the tool buyer. The machine tool industry code was intended to apply not only to machine tool builders but also indirectly to tool users, dealers, and employees even though these groups were not asked to formally subscribe to the code. The code probably reflected fairly closely the practices normally followed by most machine tool builders and was directed mainly at the exceptional cases. The latter, however, were frequent enough that the code was considered desirable.

The effort to codify "Laws of Manufacturing Management" was not aimed solely or even primarily at the machine tool industry. Nevertheless, many of the principles stated were closely related to the design, construction, and applications of machine tools and other capital equipment in manufacturing. Some of the so-called "laws" such as the "Law of Profit" were restatements of sections of the NMTBA and other Codes of Ethics. During the thirties, as in the case of the Code of Ethics, there was an effort to incorporate some of the Laws of Manufacturing Management into the NRA Code for the Machine Tool and Forging Machinery Industry and thus give them official sanction.

The NRA Code for the Machine Tool and Forging Machinery Industry included provisions requiring establishment of a standard cost accounting system, and prohibited machine tool builders from selling their products at less than their cost. A cost formula was developed specifying the elements to be included in computing costs and excluding certain items such as interest on borrowed money or capital in any form. There were various objections to the proposed cost formula including an objection to the selling below cost restrictions from a member of the NRA Consumer Advisory Board and from some machine tool builders. By the time the objections were reconciled or overruled, NRA policy had changed and no further action was taken on the cost formula. The selling below cost provision was the major restriction in the code applying to builders of special machine tools, whereas standard tools were covered by provisions for "Open Pricing" including filing and publication of price lists and prior announcement of price changes.

The definition of the term "Standard Product" and particularly the question of whether a price filed by one tool builder on a standard machine was binding on other firms producing competitive machines even though they did not consider them standard products, or only on the firm filing the price list was probably the most controversial aspect of the Open Pricing Policy in the NRA Code. The question was resolved affirmatively by NMTBA members and the Supervisory Agency, but not until shortly before the National Recovery Act was declared invalid. Even had the list prices not been considered binding on other firms, the publicity required on price changes would tend to restrict price competition.

In addition to the voluntary efforts to control competition on an industry-wide basis, and the efforts to impose compulsory restraints under the NRA, there were at least two instances where individual firms entered into restrictive agreements subsequently declared to be violations of the anti-trust laws. One of these involved operation of a patent pool by domestic firms to restrict competition within the United States. The second case covered agreements between a U.S. firm and British and German companies to control manufacture and divide markets for NAMCO automatics world-wide. These agreements were apparently effective within their limited areas and were found to be illegal restraints of trade, but no evidence was found that other similar agreements were in effect or characteristic of the machine tool industry.

7

Foreign Trade and Competition

This chapter describes the efforts of U.S. machine tool builders to expand or, at least, retain foreign markets; to protect themselves against foreign competition; and government policies and programs intended to aid these efforts.

Threat of Foreign Competition and Promise of Foreign Markets

As previously noted, U.S. machine tool builders had been worried about the potential threat of foreign competition before World War I had ended. There was no agreement, however, as to how serious this threat was or as to what should be done to maintain or expand foreign markets for U.S. machine tools. One question was the relative cost of foreign machine tools compared to those of U.S. tool builders. It was reported that while wage rates were lower in Great Britain than in the United States in 1920, unit costs of production were as high because of lower productivity. British tool builders were attempting to adopt mass production methods to reduce costs. France was having fewer labor troubles than most European countries; wages were about three times prewar levels; there were fuel and labor shortages; and despite a program of industrialization, reconstruction was proceeding slowly.[1]

European countries were buying machine tools and other manufactured goods from Germany because of the depressed value of the Mark. Belgian recovery had been faster than that of other countries and had been aided by surplus machine tools bought from the United States Government. Further exports were restricted by ex-

[1] Carl F. Dietz, "Recent Impressions of Industrial Conditions in Europe," *Machinery*, 26:611–613, March 1920.

change rates unfavorable to European buyers and could not return to normal until the United States was ready to buy at least as much from Europe as it sold to European countries.

The threat of German competition was discounted on the theory that labor policies, demands for labor participation in management, union activity, and socialism would increase costs and lower productivity to the point that Germany could not compete for export business.[2]

American machine tool builders, however, became more concerned over German competition during the early twenties and complained of German imitations of American tools appearing in the U.S. and foreign markets. The NMTBA sought information as to methods by which tool builders could protect themselves from this threat.[3]

A. J. Wolfe, Chief of the Division of Commercial Laws, Bureau of Foreign and Domestic Commerce, advised that

1. Since the designs of the machine tools in question were not covered by patent there could be no question of patent infringement.

2. There might be grounds for bringing the cases before the Federal Trade Commission on the grounds of unfair competition, providing it could be shown that the American manufacturers were being injured through fraud or misrepresentation.

3. It did not appear likely that a cause of action could be found under German Law in view of the fact that the German Law of June 7, 1909, was narrower than French and U.S. laws and was limited to specified acts of unfair competition.

The NMTBA was advised to present all the facts to the Federal Trade Commission which would take action if the allegations made were well founded.[4]

---

[2] Dietz, "European Conditions Affecting the American Machine Tool Trade," *American Machinist*, 53:75–77, July 8, 1920; *Machinery*, 26:922–923, June 1920, "Report on NMTBA Convention, Atlantic City, May 20-21, 1920."

[3] RG 151, Bureau of Foreign and Domestic Commerce, Letter from Ernest F. DuBrul, NMTBA to W. H. Rastall, Bureau of Foreign and Domestic Commerce, December 17, 1924 and related correspondence.

[4] *Ibid.*

DuBrul concluded that there wasn't much to be done, although he described a circular which had been issued by a German firm advertising their drills as "System Cincinnati Bickford" and stating that their machines had all the features of the American prototype. DuBrul advised Cincinnati-Bickford to send photostats of the material to the Federal Trade Commission with a complaint alleging unfair competition.

The American Machinery Commissioner at Berlin, reported sixty-four different American machine tools which had been copied by from one to twelve different German firms. There was a good deal of variation in the quality of the copies and prices (in Germany) were 25 to 40 per cent lower than for the corresponding U.S. tools. It was suggested that American firms could obtain some protection from copying by securing foreign patents. An active sales campaign in the area around the copying firm in an effort to prevent it securing profitable business was also recommended. Another suggestion was formation of a Webb-Pomerene Corporation to engage in export trade and to prosecute those in Germany who infringed legitimate patents.[5]

W. H. Rastall said that this report was excellent but doubted that it could be used and particularly questioned the practicability of the proposed Webb-Pomerene Corporation.

> . . . you could find that the centrifugal forces exceeded the centripetal; in other words, the things fly to bits, and entirely apart from any Webb-Pomerene organization there is already enough difficulty in holding the machine tool manufacturers of this country together on any subject whatever.

Rastall said they (the Industrial Machinery Division of the Commerce Department) were reluctant to distribute copies of the report because they did not want to give publicity to German copies of American machines. He also referred to a movement to get other countries to give more favorable recognition to American patents, but pointed out that many countries required that patented items be locally produced within a relatively short time and there were many cases where it was not practicable for American firms to

[5] RG 151, Special Report No. 54, American Machinery Commissioner (Pilger) at Berlin, Germany.

establish German plants. No reference was made to the possibility of licensing German firms to produce U.S. tools for sale in Germany.[6]

An NMTBA Bulletin stated that a number of complaints of German copying of machine tools, trade marks, and trade names had been received and discussed with the Department of Commerce, which suggested that the matter should be handled through firms of German-American attorneys. The NMTBA offered to try to organize collective action of this sort if all NMTBA members, who had been adversely affected, would present their complaints to the NMTBA. Such collective action would hold the costs for legal fees and other expenses to a minimum. No evidence that this approach was attempted was found.[7]

By the spring of 1926, DuBrul was apparently about convinced that there was little tool builders could do to protect themselves or much chance of meeting German prices. Patent protection was considered hardly worth the cost of obtaining it because German firms could evade the German patent laws by making minor changes. The best available protection seemed to be through use of trade marks and trade names.[8] Nevertheless, DuBrul suggested that Rastall present his findings regarding ways by which machine tool builders could protect themselves to the next NMTBA Convention. Rastall accepted the invitation although he expressed some doubts as to how much concrete action had followed similar efforts in the past:

> You will remember that I have appeared before your conventions on a number of occasions and many of the gentlemen present have been kind enough to say pleasant things about the subjects I have discussed. Following all this, ordinarily, nothing happens. Notwithstanding which I have felt that these efforts are worthwhile because there is a very definite advancement to be noted in the interest your members and other machinery manufacturers are taking in the export business.

He urged more positive action on the part of tool builders and the NMTBA such as the formation of a Webb-Pomerene Corporation, a less formal cooperative group to look into the matter of legal pro-

[6] RG 151, Memorandum from W. H. Rastall to Charles E. Herring, American Commercial Attache in Berlin, January 11, 1926.

[7] RG 151, NMTBA Bulletin, "Unethical and Illegal Practices Among German Machine Tool Builders," October 17, 1925.

[8] RG 151, Letters from DuBrul to Rastall, February 18, 20, and March 3, 1926.

tection against copying, and appointment of an NMTBA Committee to work with the Bureau of Foreign and Domestic Commerce.[9]

DuBrul suggested on March 3, 1926 that a preliminary meeting be held in Washington of "men whose own pocketbook nerves have been touched" and who could be expected to take an interest in a Webb-Pomerene Corporation and the Department of Commerce's efforts to promote foreign trade. A little later, Rastall reported a case in which one tool firm had succeeded in suppressing "copyists" by use of a "protect" lodged through the State Department. He concluded ". . . that if we work with this thing long enough we will be able to accomplish something worthwhile." Rastall recommended that the preliminary meeting not be given publicity outside the NMTBA, but suggested that firms from other industries be invited to join the group in an effort to determine what legal protection American firms could secure under German law.[10]

The projected meeting was held on November 12, 1926. Those attending appeared surprisingly optimistic regarding possibilities for legal action and concluded that:

> German laws gave ample protection not only against infringement of patents, but against the unfair use of trade marks, trade names, and copyrights, and also against other practices not specifically covered by any of the foregoing bodies of law.[11]

Alleged German copying of American tools continued to be a matter of concern, but the Bureau of Foreign and Domestic Commerce does not appear to have had a great deal of specific information as to individual instances of copying of machine tools, whether American tool builders had licensed German firms to use their designs, etc. Some concrete suggestions such as one made by Pilger, Machinery Commissioner at Berlin, that U.S. firms establish a joint "American Manufacturer's Protective Association" in Germany were dismissed by Rastall as "not very practical" though desirable.[12]

Pilger also suggested that consignment business be expanded but Rastall again disagreed stating that

[9] RG 151, Letter from Rastall to DuBrul, February 27, 1926.
[10] RG 151, Letter from Rastall to DuBrul, December 14, 1926.
[11] RG 151, NMTBA Consecutive Bulletin No. 468, Administrative Series No. 130 "Unethical German Competition," November 17, 1926.
[12] RG 151, Letter from Rastall to DuBrul, January 20, 1926.

I usually feel that we should adopt the policy here of encouraging machinery manufacturers to conduct their export business on a basis that is clean and wholesome, making sure that such export business as is executed is really attractive. I feel that it would be most unfortunate if our manufacturers allowed their export business to drift in directions that result in unsatisfactory transactions, and consignment business is rather dangerous in this sense.[13]

Rastall had expressed much the same line of thought in an article during the summer of 1925. This article was published and reprints sent to a large number of firms on the Department of Commerce and Industry's Export list. It was generally cautious in tone and urged that most export sales of machinery should be virtually on a cash basis. It was favorably received by many U.S. firms, but copies were also sent to U.S. Consulates abroad where the reaction was much less favorable. W. L. Schurz, American Commercial Attache in Rio de Janeiro wrote Rastall on October 28, 1925, that

. . . No importers in Rio can be found who know of exporters of machinery receiving cash in New York. . . . Firms dealing in every type of industrial machinery have been interviewed and it has been impossible to locate a single firm which receives payment in less than 90 days sight. Local firms doing business on these and on more liberal terms include such well known houses as Niles Bement Pond, Pratt & Whitney, Worthington Pump, etc.

He concluded by repeating the warning that insistence on cash business could only result in U.S. firms losing out to German and other foreign competition.[14]

Undoubtedly trade under the conditions suggested by Rastall would be very desirable if it could be secured in reasonable volume. Rastall apparently felt that it was better to risk the possible loss of most of our foreign trade, rather than resort to dangerous competitive practices and risk loss or elimination of profit margins. It seems highly doubtful, however, whether the advice offered by the Commerce Department during this period—supposedly to promote foreign trade—was actually of much practical value to American

[13] RG 151, Also Special Report No. 33, "Exporting Machinery on Consignment," December 22, 1925.
[14] RG 151, "Machinery—General—1925," File 221.

firms or likely to stimulate export trade. It was, nevertheless, in harmony with the viewpoints expressed in the machine tool industry's published Code of Ethics and corresponded to the usual practices of the industry in earlier periods when competition had been less severe.

The following excerpts from a pamphlet issued by the Industrial Machinery Division of the Bureau of Foreign and Domestic Commerce appear representative of the Commerce Department's advice to American machinery builders during this period.

To a considerable degree the problem of increasing American machinery sales abroad is that of marketing standardized products of superior quality and relatively high price, in competition, if that word is appropriate, with foreign products whose designs frequently do not embody the same excellence, whose materials are not selected with such good judgment, if indeed such materials are obtainable, and whose workmanship is not so good, especially if judged by standards of accuracy and appropriate finish as distinguished from paint and unnecessary polish. It introduces also the problem of advertising, which can be employed effectively in many instances.

. . .

Export business can be secured on terms that are clean and attractive, but to sell without proper preparation is only to sell trouble. Bungling methods, neglect of foreign customers, in fact, all the long list of export sins, accumulate "bad will" against the day when a serious effort is to be made. Also these failures create a handicap for other Americans who are at work overseas. Manufacturers should keep out of foreign trade until prepared to handle it properly. These remarks should not be interpreted to mean that foreign trade is especially difficult, for, properly approached by competent people, it is easily handled and clean business. Americans can handle the trade as well as anyone else, as is demonstrated by the volume of our machinery sales abroad.[15]

Foreign Visitors to Machine Tool Expositions

The Commerce Department tried to assist the NMTBA in various ways such as in promoting the Machine Tool Expositions, but such

[15] U.S. Department of Commerce, *Developing Machinery Markets Abroad* (Rev. ed., Washington: Government Printing Office, 1928).

aid was not always welcomed or even accepted. The NMTBA Convention and the Exposition Committee for the 1927 Exposition had serious doubts as to some of the specific ideas suggested by Rastall and others. The machine tool builders doubted that they would have much time to show foreign visitors around their plants during the period immediately prior to and following the Exposition. They also were skeptical of the value of a tour for foreign visitors in relation to the expense.[16]

Rastall suggested that the NMTBA request a firm specializing in foreign tours to quote a price to visitors which would cover all costs so that the machine tool industry would need only pay for "some little entertainment that would not be of great consequence." He added that if a good number of foreigners "of the right kind" could be attracted to the Exposition "your membership would find time to give this group of real customers adequate attention. It seems to me they would find nothing else more important." He concluded that:

> . . . Many of these Europeans are bound to come anyway, so it would seem to resolve itself merely into a question as to whether your exposition managers arrange to do the thing in a first-class way.[17]

Roberts Everett, NMTBA Exposition Manager, indicated that the NMTBA planned to maintain virtually a "hands off" policy with regard to foreign visitors but would not object if a tourist agency organized a tour on its own initiative. Rastall called the Exposition to the attention of the U.S. Lines which apparently pursued the matter aggressively. The NMTBA subsequently sent out memorandums to its members taking a rather pessimistic view regarding foreign visitors but suggesting that particular firms interested in foreign trade might do something through their own channels abroad to attract visitors. The NMTBA clearly showed a desire to "manage their own show" and Rastall rather reluctantly conceded that the machine tool builders were the best judges of what was to their best interests.[18]

---

[16] RG 151, Letter from E. F. DuBrul to W. H. Rastall, December 21, 1926.
[17] RG 151, Letter from Rastall to DuBrul, December 27, 1926.
[18] RG 151, Letter from Roberts Everett to Rastall, January 18, 1927. Letter from Rastall to W. L. Cooper, American Commercial Attache in London, June 7, 1927.

Whether the Exposition Committee's apparent coolness or indifference in this instance was due to lack of interest of NMTBA members in foreign trade at this time, to a desire to discourage Rastall's meddling in NMTBA business, or possibly a combination of these and other factors is not known. It seems certain, however, that a majority of the association's members were much more interested in the domestic market than in stimulating sales abroad. This is also borne out by the fact that when an NMTBA Bulletin was sent out asking association members interested in foreign trade to indicate whether they would care to join together in sending a man to Europe, only three replies were received.[19]

Interest in foreign trade increased sufficiently by 1929 that the NMTBA's attitude toward foreign visitors to the Machine Tools Exposition, then being planned, was radically changed from that displayed in 1927. DuBrul asked Rastall for suggestions and stated: "Our first concern, of course, is the foreign visitors who may be induced to come over to the show." DuBrul added that they were planning to write various trade commissioners abroad but would like any further ideas Rastall might have. Rastall indicated various ways by which foreign visitors might be attracted to the Exposition; pointed out the efforts of the Commerce Department, State Department, and tourist agencies to this end; and called attention to the desirability of having visitors visit both machine tool builders' plants and those of tool users.[20]

P. E. Bliss, President of the Warner and Swasey Company, reported that many machine tool builders were getting an increasing volume of foreign business. He urged that the federal government establish requirements that patents granted to aliens must be "worked" in this country within a reasonable period unless the foreign governments granted similar protection to U.S. firms. He also felt that group action to enforce patent rights in foreign countries was worth further consideration, and suggested that the Commerce Department might take the lead in arranging for meetings with foreign machine tool builders.[21]

Rastall indicated his intention to attend the NMTBA Spring Con-

[19] RG 151, "NMTBA Bulletin" December 23, 1927.
[20] RG 151, "Convention—NMTBA—1929–1931," File 721.
[21] RG 151, Letter from P. E. Bliss, President, Warner and Swasey Company to W. H. Rastall, April 30, 1929.

vention but said that since he was not "on the program" he wouldn't be able to speak on foreign trade or the patent situation though he considered them important subjects deserving the continued attention of machine tool builders. He called attention to the fact that U.S. firms were exporting about $1,000,000 per day of industrial machinery.

> The importance of this item will strike you even more favorably if you will remember the economic forces which this large volume of machinery releases. Also, as you suggest, the copyists are still copying.

> A foreign patent is of little value unless its owner is prepared to conduct such litigation as is necessary for its protection. Most machinery manufacturers find such litigation a rather difficult undertaking and it would seem that through group action of some sort steps could be taken which would result in great improvement in the present situation.[22]

Rastall was subsequently put on the convention program to discuss foreign trade.[23]

Trade with the U.S.S.R.

By the middle of the twenties, some American machine tool builders had begun to take a serious interest in promoting trade with the Soviet Union. The U.S.S.R. appeared to offer a very promising market for machine tools and other production machinery needed to expand its metalworking industries. The principal limiting factor was the ability of the U.S.S.R. to either pay cash for the machines it wished to buy or to obtain adequate credit. American companies, however, were impressed with the fact that the Soviets were meeting their credit obligations promptly.

Since the Soviet Government had not been recognized by the United States the Commerce Department urged caution in the extension of credit. The Soviet Government controlled the U.S.S.R.'s foreign trade including the Amtorg Corporation which was practically a part of the Russian Commissariat of Foreign Trade. The

---

[22] RG 151, Letter from Rastall to Bliss, May 4, 1929.
[23] RG 151, Letter from DuBrul to Rastall, May 8, 1929 enclosing Convention Schedule.

Allied American Corporation was one of the foreign firms authorized by the U.S.S.R. to handle transactions with the U.S.S.R., but
the Amtorg Corporation had a priority in handling Soviet business.
Robert S. Alter, American Tool Works Company, had dealt with
the Allied American Corporation, and in cooperation with other
firms, had sent a representative to the U.S.S.R. to promote business.
Little if any business had been secured by machinery manufacturers
through the Allied American Corporation but Amtorg had done
better. Both companies were very anxious to do business on a credit
basis; total credits had amounted to millions, and payments had
apparently been made promptly at maturity.

It was urged that great care be used in dealing with either the
Allied American Corporation or Amtorg:

> . . . credit transactions with them are unsafe because credits
> have been asked regardless of the commodity represented, and
> you will know that, although shoes and collars may be considered
> as merchandise for resale and because of this resale feature there
> may be a justification for a request for credit in most countries,
> machinery usually represents a capital investment and it is diffi-
> cult to see how a 90-days credit would materially assist the ma-
> chinery user.

> But in the present instance all credits are probably unsafe be-
> cause a suit has been filed in the Federal Court by Wulfshon &
> Company, which it is anticipated will have the effect of determin-
> ing the status of the Amtorg Trading Company and its relation-
> ship to the Russian Soviet Government. If the Court should de-
> cide that the two are identical, it would then imply that all of
> the assets of Amtorg could be attached to satisfy American
> claims against the Soviet Government and such a decision would
> probably put an end to all credit transactions of this sort. Such
> a decision would also have its effect on the business of the Allied
> American Corporation.[24]

The Soviet Government, however, was anxious to obtain capital
equipment needed to build up its industries and, from time to time,
made various overtures to U.S. officials abroad and to U.S. businessmen directly.[25]

Soviet efforts to stimulate this type of business included invita-

---

[24] RG 151, Letter from W. H. Rastall to E. F. DuBrul, March 19, 1925.
[25] RG 151, "Machinery, Russia 1926, File 221 Russia."

tions to U.S. machine tool builders to exhibit their latest machines at an exhibition in the U.S.S.R. by Orgametal, Inc., another Soviet corporation. The Commerce Department urged great caution in accepting such an invitation and suggested various dangers such as the possibility that the machines might not be set up properly, that they would depreciate more rapidly than normal and should be sold at an early date and replaced by later designs, that there was the danger of copying, and that American Companies would not get any protection from patents, trademarks, or copyrights.[26]

Rastall in a letter to DuBrul, NMTBA General Manager, concluded with regard to the Orgametal Exhibition

> I hope you will find some way of conveying to the members of your association an accurate picture of the conditions now existing in Russia and the peculiar factors involved in doing business there.[27]

Robert S. Alter, Vice President and Foreign Manager, the American Tool Works Company, wrote Rastall that Amtorg had told them about German cooperation with Orgametal and German efforts to sell machinery in the U.S.S.R. He asked that Rastall help in supplying information requested by Amtorg for a Convention in Moscow, and send a copy to Amtorg. A handwritten note added that Alter and his wife were leaving for an extended European trip; that they were taking machine tools to demonstrate in the U.S.S.R., arrangements having been made with Amtorg, and added that he didn't want their competition to know of the trip.[28]

Rastall supplied material providing much of the information desired by Amtorg but declined to send a copy to Amtorg. The material furnished supported the view that U.S. machine tool production was far superior to its competitors in quality as well as quantity.[29]

A letter from R. F. Ingram, Sales Manager, Landis Tool Company,

---

[26] RG 151, Letter from J. E. Andress, Barnes Drill Company to W. H. Rastall, November 1, 1927 and related correspondence including a letter from Rastall to Andress, November 11, 1927.

[27] RG 151, NMTBA Bulletin No. 543, December 30, 1927, regarding Orgametal Exhibition. Letter from Rastall to E. F. DuBrul, January 12, 1928.

[28] RG 151, Letter from Alter to Rastall, February 10, 1928.

[29] RG 151, Letter to Alter, February 13, 1928.

to Rastall, forwarded a clipping from the London Times of January 24 on German-Soviet trade and stated that

All this is interesting and has been the subject of discussion among our Group during the last few weeks. We all realize that in doing business with Russia there is a risk and will always be a risk until things modify more than they have up-to-date. However, a great deal of trade has been carried on with Russia thru mixed companies licensed to import into Russia and up-to-date, everyone has been paid. However, there is always more or less danger that something may arise that will prevent collecting of outstanding accounts and this is a chance we all take. I guess the only way to look at it is that if we do enough business before this happens, we could then check up and see how much of the profit we had lost on the total business done up-to-date.

We are glad to have this information and while we are doing business with Russia, we are proceeding cautiously and we shall hope that their development over there will be toward normalcy so that the risk is diminished rather than increased.[30]

C. H. Carswell, Treasurer, Reed Prentice Corporation, explained that his firm had made a few small sales to Amtorg since January 1927 on the basis of cash against documents in New York, but that Amtorg was negotiating with them for the sale of equipment on a basis of part cash and part notes of three, six, and nine months duration. He added that Amtorg had informed them that a great many machine tool builders were granting deferred settlements of this kind, and that they were wondering if the situation of Amtorg had changed since Rastall's earlier letters.[31]

Rastall replied that

There has been the usual gradual evolution, more and more American machinery is going to Russia, and in a number of instances credit has been extended. Furthermore, so far as we have been able to learn, the Soviet authorities have met all obligations of this character punctually in this country as well as other countries. Also, from this point of view it might appear that they are building a credit structure that deserves consideration. You will

[30] RG 151, Letter from R. F. Ingram to Rastall, March 9, 1928.
[31] RG 151, Letter from C. H. Carswell to Rastall, June 13, 1929, refers to letters from Rastall of January 7, and 24, 1927.

probably also want to remember that credits extended in connection with such business are credit pure and simple.

It is our understanding that in connection with these transactions creditors have no security whatsoever and in case of difficulty would have no recourse of any sort. In these respects such credits differ radically from the normal domestic transaction.[32]

Other letters of the same period seem to indicate that a good many machine tool builders were willing to take their chances in doing business with the U.S.S.R., although they would like government assistance, and that Rastall appeared to such firms to represent a very conservative point of view with regard to both Soviet trade and foreign trade generally.

Foreign Trade as a Compensating Factor

Interest in the possibility of expanding foreign trade was increased by the fact that while domestic orders declined drastically in 1929–1931, foreign business remained at the 1929 level during 1930 and 1931 with the result that the relative importance of foreign business increased very substantially. During 1929, foreign machine tool sales (cutting type only) amounted to $18,862,000 or a little more than 10 per cent of total machine tool shipments of $185,000,000. In 1930, foreign shipments declined only slightly to $18,043,000 while total shipments dropped to $96,000,000. Foreign shipments again declined slightly in 1931 to $17,571,000 while total shipments fell to $51,-000,000, their lowest point since 1922. Thus the percentage of exports to total shipments rose from 10 to almost 35 per cent. By 1932, however, it was evident that the depression was virtually world-wide in character, and that it was unlikely that sufficient foreign trade could be found to compensate for the loss of domestic business.[33]

Nevertheless, greater efforts to stimulate foreign trade seemed worth while. The main questions related to the form these efforts should take; where they were most likely to be effective; and the

[32] RG 151, Letter from Rastall to Carswell, June 21, 1929.
[33] RG 151, NMTBA Reports.

respective roles of the machine tool industry, financial institutions, exporters, and the federal government.

One controversial question regarding foreign trade was whether prices lower than were listed for domestic customers should, in some cases, be offered to attract or retain foreign business. The major argument favoring such sales was that they made a higher level of operation possible and that part of the normal overhead should not be charged in establishing selling prices for export. The Bureau of Foreign and Domestic Commerce urged that export prices include full overhead, and took the position that tool users needing machine tools were not influenced very significantly by lower prices. This viewpoint was not shared by some of those closest to foreign markets who were convinced of a need for flexibility in foreign sales and that price was a very significant factor.[34]

The NMTBA established a foreign trade committee with Perry E. Bliss, President of the Warner and Swasey Company as Chairman. W. H. Rastall, Chief of the Industrial Machinery Division of the Bureau of Foreign and Domestic Commerce, was asked to cooperate with the group and supply it with a variety of information. He agreed to work with the NMTBA Committee, and indicated that reciprocal tariffs or trade agreements were areas which would require attention. He recalled that in 1929, the United States had enjoyed a large and profitable export trade in which most machinery was paid for in cash before it left this country and urged that an effort be made to recapture this "normal" business as soon as possible. Rastall's view appeared to be that either the foreign tool customer or dealer should pay for tools before they left the United States or that they should be handled by an exporter who was willing to pay for them, "without recourse" to the manufacturer in the event the foreign customer failed to accept or pay for the machines. Unfortunately for the machine tool builder, as both domestic and foreign demand fell and competition increased, it also became much more difficult to arrange export sales on terms so favorable to the tool builder.[35]

Germany, which had been an important machine tool customer,

[34] RG 151, Letter from William L. Cooper, U.S. Commercial Attache, London to W. H. Rastall, October 27, 1932 and previous correspondence between Rastall and the Commercial Attache in Paris.

[35] RG 151, Letter Rastall to Bliss, March 1, 1933.

deliberately restricted imports to encourage expansion of its own machine tool industry as part of the industrial base for their armaments program. Russia cut back its machine tool purchases from the United States drastically during 1932 for a variety of economic reasons including limited exports to pay for foreign purchases and limited credit. There were probably also political and diplomatic motives involved including the desire for diplomatic recognition by the United States. France also attempted to reduce imports including machine tools and Great Britain launched a "Buy British" campaign.[36]

Financing Soviet Trade

Another restriction on trade with the U.S.S.R. was imposed by the Johnson Act of 1934 which prevented countries which had defaulted on their debts from selling securities in the United States. This act also prevented the Export-Import Bank from discounting Russian Trade Acceptances.[37]

The U.S.S.R. was, nevertheless, a major machine tool customer during the depression years, and U.S. machine tool builders were happy to have such business and were interested in obtaining more. One of the major problems, however, continued to be that of financing. On January 12, 1932, J. E. Andress, President, Barnes Drill Company, informed Rastall that he had been urging members of Congress to support Washington conferences on the Russian situation as a means of working out better methods of financing Russian business. He also urged acceptance of Russian exports of raw materials not produced extensively in the United States.

Andress charged that the United States had loaned Germany $400,000,000 and that Germany in turn had loaned an equal amount to Russia. German machine tool builders benefited from a 70 per cent government guarantee on their foreign trade acceptances, and had been able to secure most of the recent Russian machine tool orders "with the result that our government is in a measure financing the present program and German manufacturers are getting the benefit."

[36] W. G. Broehl, Jr., *Precision Valley* (Englewood Cliffs, N.J.: Prentice-Hall Inc., 1959), p. 147. See also Appendix Table 6 for Value of Exports.

[37] RG 151, Memorandum of Meeting of Foreign Trade Committee, Washington, D. C., June 27, 1934.

Andress urged the need for quick action to get a better share of the Russian machine tool business. He indicated that we should not care how the Russians ran their government and noted that most other countries had recognized the Soviet Government. Despite dire predictions, the Russian program of development and industrialization was continuing, and the Russians were still paying their bills promptly with the result that almost all of their trade acceptances had been cleaned up.

Andress said they would be "keen to take on more business" on the same terms as in the past—part cash with the remainder in three, six, or twelve months as necessary—but that the Russians were asking for eighteen months credit, and most manufacturers were not able to assume such long-term credit risks without government support. He referred to the fact that most of the machine tool industry's capacity—estimated at about $200,000,000 per year —was idle, and concluded that this situation was unnecessary and could have been avoided had the industry been able to secure more of the Russian business.

Andress concluded with a reference to the coming presidential election:

> . . . I hope you good Republicans will commence to "shell out," for unless our party doesn't very quickly do something in a very definite way to encourage business activity and employment— which can only be accomplished through expanding credit—I fear that it is going to be hard to get votes this fall.[38]

Rastall replied that Congress had made "great progress" on the economic measures in which Andress was interested, and expressed his belief that this legislation would have good results. He indicated, however, that while Andress might be disappointed that there had been no change in the Russian situation, there was a "great deal of misinformation on this subject being passed about . . . " and that they might have an honest difference of opinion regarding the Russian credit situation. Rastall disassociated himself from Andress' interpretation of the connection between United States' loans to Germany and German credit to Russia which he said "seems to be a distortion of the situation."[39]

[38] RG 151, Letter from Andress to Rastall, January 12, 1932.
[39] RG 151, Letter from Rastall to Andress, January 20, 1932.

While no information was found indicating what percentage of machine tool firms were actively seeking Russian business, it seems certain that many machine tool builders were conscious of the fact that, in the past, their industry had been able to operate at anything like capacity only in wartime and during periods of rapid industrial expansion. Russia was in such a period and was anxious to obtain large numbers of machine tools. The primary obstacles were financial and political. Andress and other tool builders recognized that Russian purchases of machinery would utimately have to be paid for by Soviet exports—presumably mainly raw materials—but there is no indication that they had figured out what these exports could be except that they should be largely noncompetitive with domestic industries.

The Soviet Government was undoubtedly anxious to obtain as much capital equipment as possible with the foreign exchange it could get from its limited exports. It would have liked to buy additional machine tools and other machinery but was limited by its ability to pay for them or to obtain adequate long-term credit.

Henry S. Beal, General Manager, Jones and Lamson Machine Company, writing to Rastall in July 1932, called attention to the fact that the current Russian orders for machine tools represented perhaps the largest order for high production machine tools ever placed, and said that this business belonged naturally to the United States. He attributed the fact that American machine tool builders were getting only a small part of the Russian business largely to credit guarantees provided by the English and German Governments to their manufacturers.

Beal emphasized the importance of the Soviet business if machine tool builders were to be able to keep their plants operating, and asked whether it would be possible to get supplementary credit from the Reconstruction Finance Corporation (RFC), or to obtain other federal financial support. He expressed hope the Secretary of Commerce Robert P. Lamont would take a personal interest in the matter and would arrange a conference between machine tool industry representatives and RFC officials "of sufficient importance to give the problem consideration."[40]

The tool builders were encouraged that some progress was made

[40] RG 151, Letter from Henry S. Beal, Jones and Lamson Machine Company, to W. H. Rastall, July 1, 1932.

in the subsequent meetings with RFC officials although it was apparent that the government was not willing to share the credit risks on Soviet trade. Machine tool builders, however, did not feel the matter should be dropped even though Secretary of the Treasury Ogden Mills had predicted that any discussion of including Russian "paper" in the rediscount scheme being considered would "kill the whole deal" so far as Congress was concerned.[41]

A conference was also held with representatives of the Amtorg Corporation who had indicated that they thought they could arrange tool orders amounting to from $3,000,000 to $4,000,000 on terms of 20 per cent cash with the balance average credit for about eighteen months. The tool builders had assured Amtorg that their insistence on part cash or an early trade acceptance was due to the machine tool builder's inability to finance business in any other way.

Secretary of Commerce Robert P. Lamont had mentioned a plan suggested by a New York acquaintance which "would of course solve this problem completely," but if such a plan could not be worked out, United States recognition of the U.S.S.R. appeared to the tool builders to be the most desirable step to put business with the U.S.S.R. on a legitimate basis. It is not clear what the first plan referred to was, but apparently nothing came of the suggestion. Beal said that the machine tool builders preferred to work with the administration rather than try to exert political pressure on Congress, and asked for Lamont's advice on the best way of achieving their objective of a "legitimate business with Russia."[42]

Other correspondence of this period between the machine tool builders and Commerce Department officials confirmed that the machine tool builders were anxious to do everything possible to obtain additional Russian business and that this included political support for United States diplomatic recognition of the U.S.S.R. as a way of legitimizing trade with the Soviet Union and easing the credit problem.

Similar views were more strongly expressed by Fred L. Eberhardt, President, Gould and Eberhardt. Gould and Eberhardt had

[41] RG 151, Letter from Henry S. Beal to Frederick S. Feiker, Director of the Bureau of Foreign and Domestic Commerce, July 13, 1932.

[42] RG 151, Letter from Henry S. Beal to Secretary of Commerce Robert P. Lamont, July 19, 1932.

sold over $500,000 worth of machine tools to Russia through Amtorg during the preceding seven years. This trade had been particularly welcome during the two preceding years. Payment had been made through trade acceptances of varying maturities and final payments had been promptly met.

They were working on their last Russian order, for about $140,000 and expected to complete it within three months. Payment was to be by trade acceptances of from six to twenty months. Eberhardt said that acceptance of this order had depended on their ability to finance it, that their banks had given them no direct credit or assistance and had questioned whether they should take the business. There had been no compulsion that they accept the order but they were faced with a "Hobson's Choice" in that nonacceptance would have forced them to further reduce their work force and break up their organization.

Eberhardt referred to the British and German Governments' credit guarantees of 60 and 70 per cent respectively supporting their Russian trade. This had made it possible for the British and German machine tool builders to outmaneuver American firms on both prices and terms. He also referred to "the 12 months moratorium extended Germany last year, . . . Together with the monies advanced by the U.S. bankers . . . " as a virtual subsidy to Germany which hurt the efforts of U.S. manufacturers to secure foreign business.

Eberhardt urged prompt action to work out United States' differences with the U.S.S.R. and establish relations with them on a basis that would encourage American banks to "give some credit value" to Russian trade "paper."[43]

F. C. Ropes of the Russian Section of the Bureau of Foreign and Domestic Commerce supplied information on the British Credit Guarantee Scheme and the German credit guarantee of 1931, and confirmed the fact that European Governments' support had made it possible for their nationals to accept more Soviet business than they could have otherwise taken and which American firms would have liked to have had. He took exception, however, to the implication that U.S. recognition of Russia would necessarily improve Soviet credit, and stated that Soviet credit depended upon the relationship between its existing foreign debts which were estimated at

[43] RG 151, Letter from F. L. Eberhardt to Secretary of Commerce Roy D. Chapin, August 12, 1932.

about $500,000,000 and the funds it could reasonably be expected to secure to cover such debts. Britain, Germany, and other countries were trying to reduce the amount of credit outstanding and were tightening up restrictions on further credits except where old credits were paid off. He concluded that there was no possibility of a United States-Soviet Conference until "Russia has taken certain steps, which Moscow has steadfastly refused to take. The question is one which we have consistently referred to State."[44]

The Commerce Department's position was that it could only provide information on matters of credit and contracts with Amtorg which would help the individual manufacturer to make up his own mind. Possible recognition of the Soviet government was outside the scope of the Commerce Department but it was happy to put visiting manufacturers in touch with the proper men. It denied knowledge of any prospect of change in official U.S. relations with Russia, and doubted that the United States would be prepared to offer credit guarantees.[45]

The NMTBA Board Members considered themselves obligated to include the "Russian business" as a topic for discussion at the NMTBA Convention because of (1) the bad condition of the industry, (2) the cessation of Russian orders, and (3) the activity carried on by some individuals within the association. They desired, however, to keep discussion at the convention under control, wished to come to Washington to discuss the matter with Feiker and meet Secretary Chapin, and, if Chapin were willing, also desired an interview with President Hoover as planned by former Secretary Lamont.[46]

Feiker suggested that the proposed visit be put off until after Labor Day and assured Beal of his desire to cooperate by arranging that the NMTBA Group should meet the proper officials who could explain the existing situation, but added that: "The position of the Administration is clear and fixed, and I do not see any prospect of a change."[47]

Feiker added that "at the moment I feel there is opportunity for machine tool men themselves to get together." He also suggested

[44] RG 151, Memorandum from Ropes to Rastall, August 16, 1932.
[45] RG 151, Letter from Feiker to F. L. Eberhardt, Gould and Eberhardt, August 20, 1932.
[46] RG 151, Letter from Beal to Feiker, August 22, 1932.
[47] RG 151, Letter from Feiker to Beal, August 27, 1932.

that this be attempted at the NMTBA's October Convention and that they consider four points which he considered firmly established.

1. There was no immediate opportunity to secure a change in the official attitude toward recognition.

2. There appeared to be no agreement among machinery manufacturers as to whether they should do business with Russia.

3. There was propaganda from those trying to promote Russian business "to agitate factors in our political situation which, . . . have nothing to do with the business transactions involved."

4. Russia appeared to have reached the limit of her ability to purchase from any nation on the terms which had prevailed in the past and was looking for new ways to finance purchases either by new credits or by floating loans which were "somewhat doubtful in character."

Beal sent Feiker a draft of a letter which the NMTBA group proposed to send to the new Secretary of Commerce, thanked Feiker for his courtesy, and added that

I realize that this is rather a difficult and delicate affair. There can be, I think, no question of the importance of Russian business to the machine tool industry, but, as made plain in the letter, we realize that it is only part of the problem. I realize that your Bureau is serving the country as a whole and that it is sometimes difficult for you to be helpful in a cause which is unpopular. . . . [48]

Beal explained that the draft letter reflected conversations between Gaylord, Lind, Heald, and Beal; was not intended as an official act of the NMTBA, but was preparatory to the association's convention on October 11 and 12, 1932. The letter included the following statistics on Russian imports of machine tools, reflecting the declining U.S. share of Russian machine tool purchases.

The draft letter suggested that, had United States machine tool builders been able to maintain the percentage of Russian business they had in 1929 (approximately 50 per cent), they would have been able to give "a great deal of additional employment and at the same time been able to reduce greatly the heavy losses which our industry has incurred." Amtorg had indicated to the NMTBA group

[48] RG 151, Letter from Beal to Feiker, September 28, 1932.

	U.S.	Germany	England	Total	U.S. per cent of
	(Dollar	Values	in Thousands)		Total Russian
					Purchases
1929	$ 8,990	$ 8,550	$ 500	$17,950	49.5%
1930	10,750	20,950	1,100	32,800	32.7%
1931	9,650	33,750	3,150	46,550	20.7%
1932	2,150	10,000	6,000	18,450*	11.6%
(9 mos.)					
*Estimated					

that the main reasons that business with this country had been drastically reduced were (1) the matter of terms, and (2) our unwillingness to trade with them including our refusal to recognize them diplomatically and our unwillgness to accept imports from them.

We realize that the Amtorg officials in pointing out these facts are probably carrying on a propaganda towards recognition of their government by this country which they now seem to desire. We wish to make most plain that we would consider it presumptious for us to make representations as to what our government should or should not do in this case because we appreciate we have not complete information available. We do feel, however, that it is only legitimate and proper that we should express forcibly to you our point of view as to the desirability of Russian business for us.[49]

The draft letter emphasized the economic importance of the machine tool industry, that it had suffered from wide fluctuations in demand, that Germany and England had been important markets, and that Russia was a natural market since it was entering a developmental period.

Feiker's reply again challenged the theory that there was any relationship between trade with Russia and diplomatic recognition and suggested:

 . . . we shall get nearer the truth if we recognize certain basic economic factors like government guaranteed credit, the falling off in Russian purchasing capacity caused by the low price level and shortage of certain export commodities, and perhaps the

[49] *Ibid.*

shifting in the Russian requirements in accordance with the progress in the industrialization plans . . .

He questioned whether, even in the event of recognition, there would be sufficient public support of economic measures such as were adopted by Germany and England to encourage trade for them to be adopted. Feiker added that even governmental credit guarantees would not result in a substantial increase in exports to Russia and in Russian purchasing power unless there was a substantial improvement in prices on Russian exports. The Soviet Government was said to be adjusting its purchases to its capacity for meeting its obligations, in order to protect its credit position. Feiker suggested that the letter to Chapin be modified to include "nonrecognition factors."[50]

Beal replied that the points raised were probably sound but that their group wished only to request full consideration of their viewpoint, and that ". . . our letter is actuated by the belief on our part that the Administration has not appreciated the degree of feeling that there is on this subject on the part of American manufacturers."[51] Beal enclosed the NMTBA group's transmittal letter to Secretary Chapin in which he stated that

> In the last two or three weeks I have run across several individuals and organizations who feel very much as we do on the subject of cultivating Russian business. I feel quite confident that these individuals and associations will become more and more vocal in expressing their point of view to the Administration.

In the fall of 1932, there was also some interest in trying to stimulate Russian trade through consignment shipments. The Bureau of Foreign and Domestic Commerce, however, reported that there was little or no evidence of consignment business.[52]

Tool builders were no longer able to obtain part cash on Soviet orders and by 1933 were taking orders based on trade acceptances of twelve months or longer. Between 1933 and 1935 many machine tool builders and the NMTBA became worried about the dangers

---

[50] RG 151, Letter from Feiker to Beal, October 5, 1932.
[51] RG 151, Letter from Beal to Feiker, October 7, 1932.
[52] RG 151, "Machinery–Russia–1932," File 221.

of trade with the U.S.S.R. and particularly where tool builders had designs which could easily be copied.[53]

Machine Tool Sales to Japan

During the twenties, Japanese purchase of American machine tools was a relatively minor factor in our foreign sales of tools, and in 1929 amounted to about $570,000 or only 3.0 per cent of our exports of machine tools. The situation remained almost unchanged in 1930, and in 1931, exports to Japan dropped drastically to less than 1 per cent of our export business. In 1932, however, Japan began to buy more significant quantities of U.S. machine tools amounting to $802,000 or about 13 per cent of our export sales. This upward trend continued in 1933, when Japan bought $1,030,000 worth of U.S. machine tools or 23.5 per cent of our exports. Their total purchases more than doubled in 1934 to $2,194,000 although their percentage of our exports declined to 18.2 per cent. Japanese tool purchases declined to $1,636,000 in 1935, representing 9.4 per cent of our foreign business, but then rose sharply in 1936 to $2,-606,000 which represented a small percentage increase to 10.5 per cent of our machine tool exports.

Under strong stimulus of their armaments program, Japanese purchases of machine tools rose rapidly in 1937 to $8,977,000. In 1938 they almost doubled to $18,502,000 despite the fact that our total shipments of machine tools fell drastically. Japanese purchases of machine tools remained at about the same level in 1939 totaling $18,063,000.[54]

Exports versus Total Shipments

Both foreign and total machine tool sales dropped drastically in 1932 to $6,190,000 and $22,000,000 respectively. Foreign sales fell still further in 1933 to $4,388,000 while total shipments rose very substantially in 1934 to $12,000,000 and $50,000,000. The same trend continued in 1935, 1936, and 1937 when exports amounted to $38,-000,000 of a total of $195,000,000, the highest dollar value since

[53] Broehl, Jr., *Precision Valley*, p. 129; NMTBA, Newsletter, No. 51, November 30, 1935.

[54] *Ibid.*, pp. 152–156.

World War I. Total shipments dropped rather drastically in 1938 to $145,000,000 despite the fact that exports rose to $65,000,000.[55]

There was another facet of international trade which has not been mentioned. So far as the machine tool industry is concerned, it appears comparatively insignificant in the period prior to World War II but was to become important following the war. This consisted of the establishment by U.S. machine tool builders of subsidiary machine tool firms in other countries and the granting or acceptance of licensing agreements covering the manufacture of particular machines by another firm. Such devices made it possible for U.S. firms to compete, on more nearly equal terms, with foreign machine tool builders and, in some cases, to reduce costs to a point where the foreign subsidiary or affiliate could also compete for the U.S. machine tools market.

The foreign subsidiaries not only benefited from lower labor costs, lower duties, and reduced shipping costs, but also by the fact that they were close to the foreign markets and could provide better service to the tool user. Licensing agreements provided additional income from sales of foreign built machines which it might not be possible to obtain otherwise.[56]

Summary

Many of the larger machine tool builders saw foreign markets for machine tools as a promising counterbalance to fluctuations in domestic demand. To a limited degree these hopes were rewarded as in 1927 when exports increased substantially while domestic sales declined from the 1926 level, or in 1930 when exports remained virtually at their 1929 level while domestic shipments fell precipitously. Also in the late thirties, exports rose much more rapidly than did domestic sales and gave some machine tool builders enough orders to bring them back to profitable near-capacity operation sooner than would have been possible without this business.

U.S. machine tool builders were also concerned regarding the threat of foreign competition to our export sales and, to a much

[55] *Ibid.*, and NMTBA Report of Shipments.
[56] Robert Stanley Himes, "A Study of the Machine Tool Industry With Emphasis on the Problem of Stability," Ph.D. Dissertation, The American University, 1962, pp. 182–184.

lesser degree, to domestic sales. These fears were aimed primarily at German machine tool builders who were admired for their efficiency, enterprise, and hard work; criticized for illegal or unethical copying of American machine tools; and envied for the support they received from their government through guarantees of credit for export sales. There was less concern about British competition even though the British government also provided credit guarantees, since prices of British tools were generally higher. When Germany deliberately restricted imports of machine tools to encourage further development of its own machine tool industry and Britain embarked on a "Buy British" campaign, major attention was concentrated largely on the U.S.S.R. as a market for machine tools despite U.S. government efforts to discourage or at least lend no support to this trade.

In general, the interest of the U.S. machine tool industry in foreign markets appears to have varied inversely to the level of domestic demand. Also most export business was confined to comparatively few firms though the number of firms attempting to develop export markets probably increased during the period between World Wars I and II. Machine tool builders appeared to be willing to take some risks to stimulate export sales even though they also wished to have federal government assistance in financing export trade. No use was made during this period of the Webb-Pomerene Act approving establishment of combinations of competing firms for joint efforts in foreign markets.

It was not always easy, and sometimes not possible, to convince all potential customers of the superior quality and performance of American tools and production methods. Foreign firms sometimes offered machines which were either identical with an American machine or which had been modified in some way to better adapt them to the needs or practices of particular users. Also foreign buyers sometimes took many American firms' lack of care with regard to finish as evidence of careless workmanship which might carry over to functional parts of the machine offered for sale. Similarly, while an American design was standardized for the domestic market, it might not be compatible with other equipment in foreign shops. The foreign buyer was also at a disadvantage in trying to obtain adequate assistance and repair parts.

Though some of the advice given by the Commerce Department

during the twenties and thirties was constructive as well as merely well-intentioned, it did not appear very practical as a guide for obtaining additional foreign business. U.S. machinery builders who were unable to get enough domestic business to keep their shops operating at a profitable level during peacetime had to work hard and sometimes take considerable financial risks to obtain a significant increase in export business.

PART III

THE MACHINE TOOL INDUSTRY
AND
THE SECOND WORLD WAR

8

Mobilization Requirements versus
Machine Tool Capacity

This chapter discusses World War II industrial mobilization planning as related to the machine tool industry, the determination of requirements, and the expansion of industrial facilities with particular reference to the major tool-using industries, and the reasons for the limited success of efforts to prepare for war production. It describes the efforts to expand machine tool production after the United States entered the war and results achieved. It is also concerned with the balance between machine tool requirements and productive capacity, under conditions of partial mobilization and full-scale war.

Prelude to War

During the thirties when Germany and Japan were building up their armed forces, including large modern air forces and, in the case of Germany, the technical base upon which a missiles program could be built, the United States lagged far behind in its military establishment. This was probably true not merely in the size of the army and navy and the quantity of military hardware on hand, but in terms of the effort devoted to military research and development, in planning for war, and in efforts to develop an industrial base for war.

One reason that the United States was not even more poorly prepared both in military equipment productive capacity and in the machine tool industry was that other countries, including future enemies, bought substantial quantities of tools and military equipment from the United States. Consequently, the United States was able to maintain larger industries than would otherwise have been possible. In the case of machine tools shipped to Japan, Russia, or France, these tools would not have been saved for the U.S. defense industry, but, in all probability, would not have been produced at all. The U.S. machine tool industry would certainly have been smaller and would have been able to employ and train fewer employees. Presumably this indirect benefit to the American defense program should be balanced against the direct value of the tools to potential enemies. It is quite likely that most of the tools would have been purchased from other countries if not from the United States. In addition, it seems certain that the machine tool industry, together with representatives of other industries, would have opposed any earlier or more drastic controls on exports in view of the important role this business played in rebuilding the industry.[1]

Armed Services' Machine Tool Replacement Policies

The replacement policies followed by the army and navy were a significant factor determining machine tool demand. These policies were directed at keeping government-owned industrial facilities in as good shape as possible with available funds, but the funds provided were far from adequate. In the summer of 1938, it was estimated that the average age of machine tools in navy establishments was about twenty years, and that, if the then current rate of expenditure was maintained, the average age would be reduced to fifteen years within five years or by 1943. F. H. Colvin, Editor Emeritus of the *American Machinist*, wrote to Charles Edison, Assistant Secretary of the Navy, in August 1938 that he hoped it would be possible to obtain sufficient funds to reduce the average age of medium and small machine tools to not over seven and one-half years.[2] Colvin's recommended target for modernizing the naval machine ships was based on the belief that many types of machine

---

[1] RG (Record Group) 80, Navy Department, Office of the Secretary, General Correspondence Files, JJ 40/L8–3 (411213–3), ANMB, *Report on Machine Tools*, December 13, 1941. Harry C. Thomson and Lida Mayo, *Ordnance Department: Procurement and Supply* (Washington: Government Printing Office, 1960), p. 192.

[2] RG 80, JJ 40/A9–10. Letters from Asst. Sect. Charles Edison to F. H. Colvin, July 28, 1938 and from F. H. Colvin to Charles Edison, August 3, 1938.

tools had been so greatly improved during the depression that most tools produced prior to 1930 were obsolete, would be inefficient to use, and would waste manpower and time in the event of an emergency.[3]

During the years prior to World War II, the War and Navy Departments and Army-Navy Munitions Board (ANMB) recognized that machine tools would be an important factor in event of war and attempted to plan for control of the machine tool industry in wartime. They also tried to anticipate machine tool requirements, to allocate machine tool productive capacity between the departments, and to modernize their own facilities. Unfortunately, these efforts, based on existing military planning, greatly underestimated the scale and nature of the war to come.

Not only did military planning misjudge the scale and nature of World War II, but the remaining steps necessary to translate plans into requirements for military materials, etc., were not carried through. Other problems were divided responsibility, bureaucratic inertia, and political opposition to increased defense spending. There were also difficult technical problems which seemed to defy satisfactory solution. These included the fact that the designs of many weapons were changing so rapidly it seemed impossible to stabilize designs and programs long enough to develop comprehensive requirements for machine tools or to take orderly steps to assure that needed tools would be available.

During the pre-emergency period, the ANMB Machine Tool Committee was in close contact with the machine tool industry and collaborated with the NMTBA in preparing a machine tool catalog, to standardize nomenclature, and provide a standard system for reporting requirements. A study of machine tool production capacity was made including an attempt to forecast what types of machine tools would be critical in event of an emergency. This proved reasonably accurate. Machine tool plants were designated as "reserve facilities" to be shared by the procuring services rather than being allocated to a single service.[4]

---

[3] Irving Brinton Holley, Jr., *Buying Aircraft; Material Procurement for the Army Air Forces* (Washington: Government Printing Office, 1964), p. 159; Ralph Elberton Smith, *The Army and Economic Mobilization* (Washington: Government Printing Office, 1959), pp. 61–63.

[4] RG 80, ANMB, *Report on Machine Tools*, December 13, 1941; Smith, *Economic Mobilization*, p. 56.

The NMTBA established a Defense Committee to cooperate with government departments late in May 1940. The committee conferred with Secretary of the Treasury Morgenthau, Mr. William S. Knudsen, National Defense Advisory Commission (NDAC), and representatives of the army and navy on June 3, 1940. The Armed Services' representatives presented estimated machine tool requirements for 1941 totalling $202,505,000, and Secretary Morgenthau urged aggressive action to accelerate tool production. The machine tool industry representatives took a deceptively simple position, that said in effect: "Tell us what machine tools will be needed and we will produce the tools." Unfortunately, it was not easy to supply the kind of information the machine tool builders wished and in the form wanted—essentially firm orders for delivery of specific machine tools at specified rates over a period of several years, with suitable provisions for adjusting prices to reflect changes in production costs, priorities for needed materials, etc.

Estimating Requirements for Machine Tools

One of the most difficult problems facing the machine tool industry, the federal government, and defense contractors prior to World War II and during the early war years, was the problem of determining requirements for machine tools far enough in advance to allow time for the tools to be produced before they were needed. This was an extension of the peacetime managerial problem of estimating demand for machine tools. Most machine tool builders would have liked to have been able to base their production plans, plant expansion, recruiting, and materials purchases entirely on firm orders and to have these far enough in advance to permit orderly expansion of essential and efficient production. Moreover they were strongly influenced by the fact that the industry had been operating at a fraction of its capacity and were inclined to be skeptical of generalized estimates of future requirements not yet backed up with Congressional appropriations and government contracts.

In peacetime, it took a lengthy period to develop military programs, get the programs approved, translate the programs into budgetary requirements, obtain Congressional appropriations, and place contracts for military equipment. Contracts then had to be let to prime and subcontractors (and in some cases to sub-subcontractors) who had to work out plans for producing the items contracted for, determine what tools would be needed, when the tools would be needed, what tools were already available or could be diverted from nondefense work, whether suitable used tools were available from used tool dealers or other sources, and lastly what new tools must be purchased. The problem was particularly difficult when the item to be produced was new or designs were drastically modified and there was no comparable production experience to draw upon. These processes could be accelerated and simplified in wartime, but it still took many months to get a new weapon into production or drastically increase production.

The problem of developing comprehensive machine tool requirements covering a reasonable period was further complicated by the fact that there were many types of machine tools and a variety of models, sizes, accessories, etc., within most of these types. While some tools might be interchanged to perform various operations, economy, efficiency, and technical considerations combined to limit the degree of flexibility tool users had and particularly so where maximum production with limited manpower was needed.

Widely varying estimates of machine tool requirements were developed. Some of the differences were due to differences of definition of what was meant by machine tools. In other cases, data were derived from different sources and for varying time periods. It seems clear that the basic problem of machine tool supply was solved before all the arguments over machine tool requirements were settled. The more generalized estimates, while of possible value within the government for purposes of programming and budgeting, were of little direct value to machine tool builders. The tool builder needed to know what tools he should produce in terms of specific models and sizes, but the government agencies could seldom tell him this before the contracts were placed for the components to be produced with the machine tools.

The Planning Committee of WPB in April 1942 concluded, after considering machine tools as a limiting factor in the industrial facilities program, that an overall analysis of machine tools as a limiting factor in the munitions program was not possible because of the many variable factors involved, changes in specifications, improved production techniques, and price considerations. Professional statisticians in the Office of Production Management (OPM) and the Bureau of the Budget, however, were convinced that deficiences in machine tool requirements statistics were at least partially responsible for what they considered to be the failure to deal adequately with the tools problem.[5]

Competing Demands

There was a general tendency for defense contractors to prefer new machine tools of the latest design rather than make do with used tools which were not only less desirable but, as tools became scarce, might cost as much as new tools. There was also a tendency to order general purpose tools with all the accessories available even though a simpler tool and a few accessories might be adequate for the work currently under contract. These tendencies grew out of the contractor's desire to be in the most favorable position possible for further defense business and for peacetime production in the event the emergency ended.

There was strong competition for machine tools not only among the various programs of the army and navy, Maritime Commission, and some types of civilian production, but also with the requirements of allied nations. Basic decisions regarding the latter had to be made at the highest military and political levels and could not be settled merely on the basis that all U.S. defense requirements came first. There were such awkward questions as whether, following the fall of France, the probability that the United Kingdom would also be successfully invaded or its industry completely destroyed was so great that we could not afford to ship more machine tools to Britain.

In the spring of 1941, the Tools Section of OPM learned that Great Britain planned to ship machine tools to Canada to equip a new turret lathe plant. The Machine Tool Control of Canada was

---

[5] RG 80, Memorandum from Isador Lubin, White House Staff to Under Secretary James V. Forrestal, November 10, 1941, enc. Memorandum from Stuart Rice, Bureau of the Budget to Lubin, October 25, 1941; RG 179, Memorandum from Norman J. Meiklejohn, OPM, to Stuart A. Rice, "Machine Tools as Related to National Defense," November 18, 1941; RG 179, WPB, Policy Analysis and Records Branch (PARB), Draft of Special Study No. 35, pp. 240–242; *Minutes of the Planning Committee of the War Production Board,* March 19, 1942, p. 21 and April 6, 1942, p. 37.

warned by OPM that if machine tools were shipped to Canada for this purpose, its supply from the United States would be cut off and that the United States could not divert any machine tools from its program for Canada to start a turret lathe plant. The Machine Tools Section had no knowledge of whether other tools had already been shipped from Great Britain for this project. U.S. policy in this case was probably influenced both by the current tool shortage and the machine tool industry's opposition to construction of competitive plants in Canada.[6]

Expansion of Aircraft Production

U.S. aircraft production rose to over 14,000 in 1918 only to fall to a little over 300 in 1920. It then rose gradually to a peak of about 6,200 in 1929 before suffering a drastic decline to a little over 1,300 in 1933 after which the 1929 production (in number of units) was not reached again until 1940. During the thirties, military aircraft were a small percentage of the total units produced, although in dollar value, they were much closer to civilian aircraft since military aircraft were much more expensive per unit. The dollar value of 1939 output was about 2.5 times that in 1929. In any case, aircraft production between World War I and World War II was comparatively insignificant compared to production of any of the major industries, and the aircraft industry was a minor user of machine tools. Most tools used were standard general purpose machines. In 1939, capital investment per employee in the aircraft industry was about $800 as compared to $2,600 per employee in Chevrolet automobile plants. Output per employee was about $4,400 in 1937 as compared to over $15,000 for the automobile industry.[7]

There was only one branch of the aircraft industry in which there was something approaching mass production. This was aircraft engine production where there was a greater measure of standardization in design, longer model life, and a higher degree of concentration in production than in the production of finished aircraft

---

[6] RG 179, OPM, Machine Tool Priority Committee, *Minutes,* March 5, 1941.

[7] Holley, Jr., *Buying Aircraft,* pp. 6–7, 27–28; W. S. Woytinsky and E. S. Woytinsky, *World Population and Production* (New York: The Twentieth Century Fund, 1953), p. 1171; U.S. Bureau of the Census, *Historical Statistics of the United States* (Washington: Government Printing Office, 1960), p. 466.

or most other components. Thus, in 1929, two firms produced 56 per cent of the aircraft engines and in 1934, these firms produced 72 per cent of the total engines.

The trend in military aircraft was toward a higher percentage of bombers, multiengined planes, and higher performance aircraft. In November 1938, the Assistant Secretary of War directed the Chief of Staff to prepare plans for an Air Force of 10,000 planes within two years. Since this represented over ten years production at the current rate of production, this constituted a major expansion. He also requested budgetary plans for seven government-owned contractor-operated aircraft plants with an average capacity of 1,200 planes per year. This request worried the aircraft builders who were afraid that if this program was met in two years, there would not be enough orders to keep plants operating and that the government-owned plants would force some private plants out of operation.[8]

The aircraft builders preferred to work longer hours and, if necessary, expand their own plants. By the time the expansion program was approved by Congress in April 1939, air corps policy had shifted to emphasize keeping existing plants fully utilized rather than to expand capacity. This shift was probably greatly influenced by the aircraft manufacturers' opposition to government-owned facilities. While the argument was going on, there were no additional appropriations for aircraft contracts and there was talk of having to "stretch out" existing contracts to keep the aircraft plants going. A survey was also made which indicated that aircraft output could be increased by as much as 50 per cent by relatively small expenditures and, on this basis, it was decided to drop the President's plan for providing government-owned stand-by capacity.

The aircraft production ceiling was raised, however, so that the aircraft manufacturers began to worry about production problems rather than keeping their plants filled. The air corps expected that the main production problems would be air frames, engines, and propellers, and planned to use educational orders to work out ways to solve these problems and prepare for production of cargo and training planes. Collector rings and oleo struts were soon added to the list of production problems, and by the summer of 1939, dozens

[8] Holley, Jr., *Buying Aircraft*, pp. 175–185.

of other components were added. By this time, it was too late to use educational orders. As the aircraft builders were offered large contracts, they began to make major additions to their plants.

The contractors estimated production schedules tended to be based on highly optimistic assumptions including the assumption that all machine tools would be available as needed, that designs would be frozen, and that government furnished equipment would be on hand as required. Unfortunately, such ideal conditions seldom developed or continued for very long.

Air corps officials claimed after the fact that they were able to determine army aircraft requirements "efficiently and effectively" before the outbreak of war in September 1939, but this was too flattering an estimate of the situation. Even in September 1939, the estimates appear to have been based on appropriations rather than upon national defense needs. The "tooling-up" problem was made more difficult because estimated requirements were changing rapidly and even though, in general, they were increasing, there was a good deal of confusion regarding what was included at any particular time.

The President's request for production of 50,000 planes in 1942 was intended as an incentive to an all-out effort to meet army and navy requirements plus those of our allies, but the apparently clear objective was largely lost in the appropriation and procurement process. It was also feared that even if the program were somehow achieved, many of the planes would be obsolete before they were actually needed.[9]

The machine tool problem in 1940 and 1941 was aggravated by the fact that a shortage of aluminum forging capacity caused aircraft builders to resort to machining parts from solid billets, greatly increasing the machinery required and the workload on tool rooms. Part of the difficulty was due to the slowness of aircraft builders in supplying the detailed drawings and specifications needed before forging dies could be started. Changes in design also required changes in the forging dies.[10]

There was also a furor over the so-called "Reuther Plan" to produce 500 fighters per day in the excess plant capacity of the automobile industry. This included arguments over how many automobile industry machine tools were suitable for aircraft produc-

[9] *Ibid.*, p. 235.
[10] *Ibid,* pp. 250–251.

tion. One automobile industry spokesman estimated that not over 10 per cent of the industry's tools could be used for aircraft production.[11] This claim was eventually proven to have been much too pessimistic, since by June 1942 almost 70 per cent of the Detroit machine tool pool was being used on war contracts.[12]

Machine tools were identified in 1940 and 1941 as the major obstacle to more rapid acceleration of aircraft production. One alleged reason for the shortage of tools was that the ANMB placed too low an estimate on the importance of aircraft with the result that too low a priority was placed on tools and essential materials needed for aircraft production. There were also conflicts between aircraft contractors for the various aircraft programs which were assigned different priority ratings.[13]

In September, 1941, Brigadier General Oliver C. Echols, Air Corps Material Division, declared machine tools to be the most critical item delaying aircraft production but confessed that he was not sure of the reasons for the situation:

> I do not know today whether we are unable to get tools because the machine tool industry is too small to produce the machines required for the program, or whether orders for machine tools are not placed early enough to give the industry time to manufacture them in order to meet requirements. I believe that both are factors in our present unhappy situation.[14]

Established manufacturers of major aircraft components also usually preferred to expand their own plants with or without direct government assistance rather than to subcontract part of the work to other firms. This was particularly true when there was a fear that the subcontractor after securing the necessary production "know-how" would seek prime contracts for the same items. The aircraft prime contractors were also reluctant to place orders for important components with any but the most reliable of the established producers even though a new producer might have the necessary capacity and ample production experience on other items.

[11] *Ibid.*, p. 311; *New York Times*, December 23, 1940, k:1 and December 24, 1940, 1:1, December 29, 1940, Sec. x, 4:6.

[12] Holley, Jr., *Buying Aircraft*, p. 323.

[13] J. Carlyle Sitterson, *Aircraft Production Policies Under the National Defense Advisory Commission and Office of Production Management, May 1940 to December 1941*, CPA, May 30, 1946, pp. 109–124.

[14] *Ibid.*, pp. 109–110.

These preferences or prejudices tended to limit the use of converted facilities, subcontracting to new suppliers, etc., and so tended to increase requirements for new machine tools to expand existing facilities or for new plants.[15]

By December 1941, it was thought that the aircraft facilities expansion program was completed; that any future increases in production could be accomplished by conversion of existing facilities. The conversion of major existing plants had been talked about and there had been a great deal of industrial surveying and planning before the war, but little had actually been accomplished. Pearl Harbor, however, quickly changed this outlook and stimulated further major expansions of aircraft production facilities, although conversion of existing facilities had not been completed or production begun. One of the new projects was a $173,000,000 plant for the Dodge Division of Chrysler Corporation which was even larger than the Ford Willow Run Plant.[16]

Under the conditions of a major two-front war, the first and overriding consideration in facilities expansion was the time element rather than cost. It required an average of about thirty-one months to build a new plant and achieve full production with fighter plane plants being built in as little as twenty-four months while the B-29 plants required forty months. It also required just about as long to convert existing automobile factories to production of aircraft engines. The main problem was that such conversions required many special machine tools, jigs, fixtures, and other accessories which required about as long to procure as it took to build a new plant. Where such tooling was not essential, the conversion time was considerably shorter.[17]

The Ford B-24 bomber plant at Willow Run was the outstanding attempt to apply full mass production methods to aircraft production. This project was only partially successful mainly because it did not seem possible to stabilize plane design long enough to take full advantage of the mass production technique. There were also production difficulties because of the special characteristics of the basic metals used which differed significantly in machining characteristics from the steel used in automobiles, unfamiliarity with draw-

---

[15] Holley, Jr., *Buying Aircraft*, p. 318.
[16] *Ibid.*, p. 320.
[17] *Ibid.*, pp. 326–328.

ings and specifications supplied by the Consolidated Aircraft Company, and dependence upon Consolidated. This experience did not really prove or disprove the belief that aircraft could not be mass produced.[18]

Aircraft production in terms of units produced approximately doubled each year from 1939 through 1943 during the major tooling-up period. The increase in other terms such as value or weight was much greater since the proportion of multiengined planes and of more powerful engines for greater carrying capacity and speed was also increasing. Production continued to increase through 1944 before major cutbacks began. The trend can be illustrated by the relative growth in engine horsepower produced. Thus, the output of the largest class of engines—over 1,600 horsepower—increased by almost forty-three times between 1940 and 1944; the next smaller class—between 1,000 and 1,599 horsepower—increased about six times between 1940 and the peak year of 1943; and the smallest engines increased by only a little over three times between 1940 and 1943. The first jet engines appeared in 1944 and a significant number were produced (over 1,200) in 1945 but not in time to be of value in World War II.[19]

During the period from 1939 through 1944, the aircraft industry grew almost from infancy to the leading position in manufacturing output. Because of the increase in capital equipment required to accomplish this, the special production problems involved, and the high priority assigned to expansion of aircraft production, this industry was the dominating influence on machine tool requirements during World War II. The dramatic cutbacks in aircraft production starting in 1945 and after the end of the war were a major factor in the decline of machine tool demand prior to the Korean War. The rapid transition from propeller-driven to jet aircraft and development of missiles, however, at the end of the war provided new demand for machine tools.

Machine Tool Requirements for Ordnance Production

The aircraft industry was, of course, not the only industry with expansion problems requiring a large number of machine tools.

[18] *Ibid.*, pp. 521–529.
[19] *Ibid.*, p. 549.

Between World Wars I and II, the Army's Ordnance Department and the Navy's Bureau of Ordnance tried to keep their own production facilities in good condition; to obtain adequate information on industrial facilities which could be used in event of war; and to obtain funds for "Educational Orders" which could be used to discover and solve production problems before the need for quantity production arose. None of these efforts was entirely successful and the net result seemed wholly inadequate in terms of World War II requirements.

The ordnance planners prior to World War II were convinced that there would be critical machine tool shortages in the event of full mobilization and that every effort would have to be made to use existing machine tools. Their surveys of facilities, however, at least partially disclosed how inadequate these facilities would be. For example, a survey in the fall of 1939 of the Birmingham Ordnance District disclosed that none of the contractors surveyed had the machine tools needed for production of any of the items ordnance proposed to produce in the district. Bids on educational orders also revealed that the shortage of suitable machine tools was much greater in the northern industrial areas, such as Philadelphia, than had been expected a few months earlier.[20]

The educational orders program was considered by ordnance officials to have been a success in 1939 and the first half of 1940 even though it had received funds too late and in too small amounts. The Winchester Repeating Arms Company estimated that an educational order had saved it a year in getting into production on the M-1 rifle. Its main accomplishment was probably to indicate what might have been accomplished had the program gotten underway sooner and on a larger scale.

Some progress was also made during the thirties in modernizing equipment at Frankford Arsenal, but little new equipment was provided for the six army ordnance arsenals, and a large part of their equipment was considered obsolete. The arsenals were also not sufficiently advanced in production techniques to serve as models for new plants for ordnance production. It also appears that, in general, procurement planning for ordnance production did not get serious attention until late 1939. American ammunition makers

[20] Thomson, *Ordnance Department,* pp. 18–20.

were standardized on production machinery developed for the Frankford Arsenal and by 1940, the British also adopted this machinery. This made possible equipment pooling and transfer of equipment and spare parts between plants as needed.[21]

The munitions program of 1940 resulted in requirements for thousands of new machine tools including replacement of many standard tools with special purpose tools. The machine tool shortages grew worse during the last half of 1940 and early 1941, and in mid-March 1941, General Charles M. Wesson, Chief of Ordnance, reported to Under-Secretary of War Patterson that the ANMB policies giving first priority to navy and air corps projects was making it almost impossible for ordnance contractors to get deliveries of machine tools. He concluded that unless prompt remedial measures were taken to improve deliveries of machine tools, the already critical situation would become "calamitous." Patterson was unwilling to support a general increase in ordnance priorities for machine tools which would hurt other important programs. He requested specific information on particular tools needed and the ordnance districts were requested to compile this. The Office of Production Management (OPM) attempted to increase tool production, encourage subcontracting, and locate machine tools not in use. A new ANMB Directive late in August 1941 slightly improved ordnance's priority position, but machine tool deliveries were still considered unsatisfactory by those in charge of ordnance production.[22]

In January 1942, after the President had announced his new production goals for 1942, the Artillery Division estimated that 200,000 pieces of artillery would have to be produced in 1942. Machine tools were identified as the principal bottleneck in meeting this goal and it was considered best to give the relatively few new tools available to a small number of "strong companies" on the assumption that this would provide the added capacity and bring better and quicker results than by dividing the tools among a larger number of firms. Increased pressure was put on contractors to subcontract work they could not handle with available machine tools. Machine tool panels were also set up in each ordnance district to help contractors solve their machine tool problems, and machine tool

21 Ibid., pp. 22, 192.
22 Ibid., pp. 38–39.

distributors were asked to serve on these panels. The panels reviewed contractors' estimates of requirements for machine tools and suggested alternatives including subcontracting and use of substitute types of tools. They also provided information regarding where used tools could be obtained. These panels succeeded in some cases in drastically cutting the estimated requirements for new machine tools, but there is no way of determining how seriously the substitutions made affected the quality of work produced, labor costs, and other factors.[23]

Production problems were not confined by any means to machine tool shortages. For example, in some cases, as soon as adequate machine tools were secured and put into production, it was discovered that scarce materials had become the limiting factor. This apparently was true by 1942 in the tank program which required large amounts of high grade steel plus nickel, copper, aluminum, and rubber. The tank plants also required powerful cranes to move equipment around the plant as well as heavy machine tools to do the work of cutting and shaping major components. The locomotive builders had much equipment which could be used, but still had to obtain many additional machine tools and rearrange their production lines. Chrysler's experiences with expanding tank production in 1942 were reminiscent of Ford's problems with B-24 production at Willow Run. K. T. Keller said regarding them that

> . . . the job experienced all the standard hardships of World War II production. The first design was scrapped before we could begin. Despite the early start made, the value of priorities for machine tools and equipment quickly melted away like snow on a hot day. Frantic calls for increased production alternated with drastic cut-backs. Disappearance of critical materials held it up. Sudden changes in design upset ability to deliver and broke the planned flow of operations. We never once had all of the machine tools and equipment that our schedules called for.

Shortages of machine tools attributed to low priorities also appeared to be a major problem in production of tank transmissions in 1941, but this problem was at least partially solved in 1942.[24]

[23] *Ibid.*, pp. 87–92.
[24] Thomson, *Ordnance Department*, pp. 240–242, 246–247, 251, 281–282; (Industrial College of the Armed Forces) Lecture by K. T. Keller, March 17, 1948.

Conversion of automobile plants to tank production caused many problems including those of developing suitable jigs and fixtures and finding additional machine tools suitable for tank parts which were normally much larger and heavier than automobile parts. There were problems in finding subcontractors to produce many components. It was also necessary to expand heavy truck production facilities, and this effort encountered problems in obtaining both needed machine tools and an adequate steel supply.

Tools for Shipbuilding Program

During 1940 and 1941, machine tool shortages were considered a critical factor limiting expansion of construction of cargo ships for the Maritime Commission and naval ships. In October 1940, Admiral Land, Chairman of the Maritime Commission, wrote to William S. Knudsen, Director-General OPM, that there was a serious problem with reference to priorities for machine tools for new shipbuilding facilities. Late in November 1940, Admiral S. M. Robinson, Bureau of Ships, requested that first priority be given to machine tools.[25]

Admiral Land again warned Knudsen on March 19, 1941, that machine tools and engines for ships were the bottlenecks which would make it impracticable to make any deliveries of emergency cargo ships during 1941 and 1942 except those already contracted for or about to be contracted for. The actual or threatened shortages of machine tools for shipbuilding continued for several months, and in September 1941, the Bureau of Ships prepared a list which showed machine tools as a delaying factor in the construction of thirty-one destroyers, twenty-two submarines, sixty minesweepers, and one floating workshop. It also listed sixty-four contractors who were unable to meet navy requirements due to shortages of machine tools. Admiral Robinson told the Supply, Priorities and Allocation Board (SPAB) that 1,500 additional machine tools were needed to remove the principal obstacle to completion of the navy's shipbuilding program.

Late in November 1941, William H. Harrison reported to Donald M. Nelson and to SPAB that the tools available together with those

[25] Charles H. Coleman, *Shipbuilding Activities of the National Defense Advisory Commission and Office of Production Management, July 1940–December 1941,* (Washington: U.S. Civilian Production Administration, July 25, 1945), pp. 102–105.

to be delivered in the following four to six months would satisfy the shipbuilding programs as then planned, but that completion of naval ships could in some important instances be advanced if machine tools could be delivered ahead of schedule.

The U.S. shipbuilding industry needed to expand rapidly its output during the war years, but the development of time-phased requirements for naval and commercial vessels was slow in coming. The magnitude of the ultimate requirements was great enough to make it highly desirable for the industry to make an aggressive effort to standardize and simplify ship design and construction methods, and to equip their facilities with modern machine tools, accessories, and work-handling equipment. Considerable progress was made in this direction during the war, but not enough to make the commercial shipbuilding industry competitive with the shipbuilding industries of other leading countries following World War II, or to provide an important continuing demand for machine tools.

Production Objectives

The President's production objectives announced in January 1942 following Pearl Harbor provided dramatic targets and a strong incentive for the defense agencies and industry, but there were many uncertainties as to what was included and whether particular objectives were realistic. The process of translating the large round numbers of various items of major war equipment into specific requirements first resulted in requirements without any relation to productive capacity, materials available, etc. These were later modified and reduced in an effort to make them realistic. Machine tools were considered to be one of the major limiting factors which made necessary reductions in the War Munitions and Construction Programs.

The initial objectives for 1942 were fixed at 60,000 planes plus necessary spares; 8,000,000 tons of merchant ships soon raised by the President to 9,000,000 tons; 500 heavy tanks; 25,000 medium tanks; and 19,500 light tanks (this was later adjusted to call for 46,523 "tank-type units" which included self-propelled artillery units), plus other weapons and material needed to supply a balanced force. These objectives made it clear that many more new machine tools would be needed plus much more drastic efforts to use existing productive capacity to best advantage. Determination of specific machine tools requirements necessitated detailed decisions as to what was to be produced and firm information on the design of the items to be produced.[26]

The 1942 objectives were confirmed and slightly modified by the President in May 1942. The presidential objectives also provided for still higher levels of production in 1942 including 100,000 aircraft, 75,000 tanks, 35,000 antiaircraft guns, 4,000 antitank guns, and 500,000 machine guns. A goal of 10,000,000 tons of merchant ships for 1943 was quickly raised to 15,000,000 tons. It was estimated that the total program for 1943 would require expenditure of $110 billion and it was concluded that this objective was unattainable. The overall objectives were subsequently reduced by the President to about $45 billion for 1942 and $75 billion for 1943 war production. The 1943 program objectives were further revised and restudied until in December 1942 a "Must" Program for 1943 was approved. Nevertheless, there were still fears that portions of the program could not be completed in 1943 because of machine tool shortages and shortages of some aluminum semifinished products.[27]

Expansion of Machine Tool Production

There were three basic ways of increasing machine tool production to meet defense needs. These were (1) increased production from the existing machine tool industry, (2) bringing new firms into machine tools production, and (3) increased subcontracting or "farming-out" of parts and components production. Production of the existing machine tool industry could be expanded to an undetermined degree by fuller use of existing equipment through greater use of multiple shift operation, longer working hours, longer production runs on standardized machines and components, or by adding new facilities. The latter approach required that additional machine tools be diverted to machine tool production and thus had the immediate effect of reducing tool deliveries to defense contractors. Increased use of existing facilities seemed the preferable course wherever practicable but offered its own problems. These

[26] U.S. Civilian Production Administration, *Industrial Mobilization for War* (Washington: Government Printing Office, 1947) Vol. I, pp. 273–282.
[27] *Ibid.*, pp. 290–292.

included the problems of recruiting, training, and supervising new and largely inexperienced employees, and also the fact that it was rarely possible to balance production in a way which would keep all machines and departments busy through a second and third shift.

By the middle of 1941, the capacity of the machine tool industry had been expanded by about 10 per cent and a major question was whether further expansion of capacity of plants producing critical machine tools should be pushed more vigorously.[28]

There was evidence that a number of the plants on OPM lists as potential sources of machine tools were reluctant or unwilling to take on machine tools orders which might interfere with their less critical business, and it was doubtful whether, under the existing voluntary system, these facilities could be converted to tool production. It was also true that existing machine tool firms were concerned about the problems of readjustment at the end of the emergency if there was excess machine tool capacity or too many tools on hand.

The Defense Committee of the NMTBA met with Robert A. Lovett, Under Secretary of War for Air; Ralph Bard, Assistant Secretary of the Navy; and service representatives on July 23, 1941 to discuss the machine tool situation. Committee members agreed that, in some cases, the amount of shift work could be increased but insisted that there were many complicating factors and that statistical data were often misleading. They also pointed out that some contractors who did not appear to be making adequate use of shift work due to lack of supervisory personnel or other factors, were doing very well in respect to subcontracting which also required much time for supervision and coordination.[29]

During the summer and fall of 1941, there was frequent criticism from the army and navy, ANMB, White House, Congress, and other sources that machine tool production was not being expanded rapidly enough; that adequate plant utilization was not being

[28] RG 80, Office of Procurement and Material, Machine Tools Section, 1942U to 1941W. Memorandum from Ferdinand Eberstadt, ANMB to Under Secretary James V. Forrestal, June 28, 1941; Letter from John D. Biggers, OPM, to Forrestal, July 16, 1941, enclosing comments on Eberstadt memorandum prepared by Mason Britton and Howard Dunbar, OPM.

[29] RG 80, JJ 40/L8–3, Memorandum from Captain E. D. Almy, USN, for Navy Under Secretary James V. Forrestal, July 23, 1941.

achieved through multiple-shift operations and other methods; that the machine tool builders were not doing as much as they should; and that the OPM was not being aggressive enough. There was not complete agreement within the government—and probably not within the machine tool industry either—as to what the facts were regarding plant utilization or what conclusions should be drawn from them. Under Secretary of War Robert P. Patterson wrote to Navy Under Secretary James V. Forrestal on July 16, 1941, relaying charges made to him regarding the number of men employed on night shifts and suggesting that the ANMB send a letter to John D. Biggers of OPM urging that pressure be put on tool manufacturers. Captain E. D. Almy, USN, defended the machine tool builders and OPM although he had joined in past criticism. He now felt that the machine tool industry generally was making very good progress, that it would be unfair to pressure the industry as a whole, and that effort should be concentrated on the companies which were not doing as much as they should. He suggested that NMTBA officials be invited to Washington for a conference with Forrestal and Patterson, and expressed his conviction that the NMTBA would do "anything possible within their powers to meet our wishes."[30] Nevertheless, Forrestal warned the NMTBA that while progress had been made in expanding machine tool production, still greater effort was needed.

Clayton R. Burt, Chairman of the NMTBA Defense Committee, reported that total machine tool output in August 1941 had reached a new high of $64,300,000 as compared to $57,797,000 in July and $40,870,000 in August 1940. While the machine tool industry was interested in increasing its total output, it was aware of the fact that the most important problem was to meet defense requirements for certain "critical" types of tools. Burt insisted that while the industry had about $53,000,000 of unfilled orders on hand representing about seven months production at the current rate, some types of critical tools were in good shape. He then summarized the status of facilities expansion and production for a number of major types of tools to show how much effort had already been expended by the tools industry, and its continuing efforts to expand production, meet re-

[30] *Ibid.*, Memorandum from Almy to Forrestal, July 18, 1941.

quired delivery dates and priorities, and minimize the need for diversion of tools from one contractor to another.[31]

Government Plant Proposed

Another method of expanding machine tool production suggested early in 1941 and later revived was for the army or navy to build one or more machine tool plants to produce critical tools just as they maintained arsenals and shipyards. This proposal was criticized as being inconsistent with previous planning for war procurement including efforts to expand private output of machine tools. It was charged that such a plant could only produce a few specialized types of tools, that it would require many of the large tools critically needed for arms production, and that such a plant could not be in production for at least a year. Some planners thought the idea had merit for future long-range planning, but the army and navy agreed to postpone action first for three months and then at least until the end of 1942.[32]

Status of the Machine Tool Program After Pearl Harbor

The weeks immediately following Pearl Harbor and official United States entrance into World War II brought a variety of criticisms of the progress of the defense effort including machine tool production, distribution, and utilization. The ANMB Machine Tool Committee completed a report on December 13, 1941—the substance of this report probably predated Pearl Harbor—which announced that machine tool production was at an annual rate of $1,000,000,000 and had overtaken current demand, that more tools were being delivered than ordered, and the current problem was one of balance in output. Following this encouraging introduction, the report listed a variety of weak points which the authors felt needed attention.

[31] RG 80, Office of Procurement and Material, Machine Tool Section, 1942U to 1941W. Letter from Burt to Forrestal, September 23, 1941.

[32] RG 179, WPB, Policy Documentation File (PD File) 481.001; Shaw Livermore, "The Machine Tool Problem," February 11, 1942, p. 20; RG 80, JJ 40/L8–3, Letter from Robert P. Patterson, and James V. Forrestal for Vice President Henry A. Wallace (actually sent to Donald M. Nelson), January 1, 1942; RG 179, WPB, Draft of PARB Special Study No. 35, pp. 207–208.

1. Deliveries of all but two types of tools were improving but not rapidly enough.

2. The critical tools were produced by a small group of the larger machine tool companies, and an "all out" effort was required of these companies which had not been made previously.

3. The main reasons why the machine tool companies had not exerted a full effort was their fear of the future effect of a short-lived effort; and, in some cases, a weak cash position.

4. Machine tool deliveries to the British had been continued without planned control.

5. Large reservoirs of used tools existed in many plants which were not being used for defense production, and there had been no energetic and comprehensive effort to make use of such tools.

6. Delay in establishment of an effective distribution system for machine tools until the final quarter of 1941 had resulted in more or less haphazard tooling of defense industries.

7. Defense contractors insisted on special or particular makes of tools based on peacetime predilections rather than current defense production needs.

8. Overloading of high priorities had adversely affected distribution of critical machine tools.

9. Technical branches and bureaus of the Army and Navy had been slow in translating armament programs into machine tool requirements; and the civilian agencies supervising machine tool production had not always accurately gauged the critical spots in the machine tool industry.

The report questioned whether industry provided the best source of personnel to exercise administrative control in a national emergency. The accomplishments of the OPM Machine Tool Section were said to have been due "more to devotion to duty and hard work than to acumen."

The report recommended that

1. Every effort be made to bring builders of critical tools to 100 per cent shift effectiveness . . . the Secretaries of War and Navy should call these tool builders to Washington to impress upon them the urgency of greater production.

2. Pool orders be placed for critical machine tools where this had not been done.

3. Competent engineers be assigned to analyze production problems of critical machine tool builders where such help appeared needed.

4. . . . all personnel authenticating preference rating certificates for critical tools first determine that all such tools in the purchaser's plant were being worked 24 hours a day including Sundays.

5. The ANMB should issue critical tool builders lists and instructions requiring every contractor seeking improved delivery or a higher preference rating to certify that he had attempted to purchase an equivalent tool from another company.

6. A new priorities directive be issued distributing the classes of munitions throughout the preference rating groups in approximately equal proportions. That . . . when any group was raised to a higher priority classification, some other group would be correspondingly reduced in priority . . . standing.

7. Direct widespread publicity be utilized to ascertain available unused machine tools.

8. The "Scheduling Unit" of OPM be greatly augmented to review defense contractors' machine tool requirements; revise delivery dates, recommend alternate makes or used tools, report surplus and excess tooling and advise on production techniques. . . . "This takes operation out of Washington and puts it in the field where it belongs."[33]

On December 25, 1941, Robert P. Patterson, Under Secretary of War, agreed that the tool situation was still unsatisfactory and concurred in the recommendations of the ANMB Machine Tool Committee. These included that top officials of the firms building critical tools be called to Washington for a conference at which either Secretaries Stimson and Knox or Under Secretaries Patterson and Forrestal would strongly impress on the tool builders the need to accelerate deliveries of critical tools. Ferdinand Eberstadt, Chairman of the ANMB who apparently had not approved the recommendation in the ANMB report, reminded Patterson that OPM was

[33] RG 80, ANMB, *Report on Machine Tools,* December 13, 1941.

holding meetings with small groups of machine tool builders in which representatives of the ANMB participated, that these meetings should produce good results, and that it might be a mistake to call the machine tool builders to Washington again.

Eberstadt also reported to Forrestal on a "Survey of Critical Machine Tool Builders" received from OPM. Eberstadt said that this survey and other reports on the machine tool industry confirmed that the conclusions he had given Forrestal a year earlier still held good. These were:

1. The industry is not working up to anything like its full capacity and had not been;

2. The amount of subcontracting is very limited compared to the possibilities in the field. . . .

3. There are a great many tools which are either not being used or not being used to anything like full capacity. . . . [34]

Eberstadt criticized what he considered to be the "tolerant attitude" in the OPM Survey Report and said the standards of performance used were much too limited. He suggested that "our first problem lies in winning the OPM over to the point of view that good performance is the ratio of 10:7 and that nothing less is satisfactory" (for each ten workers on the first shift there should be seven on the second shift). He concluded by predicting that if this could be accomplished, machine tool output would increase by at least 25 per cent.

The "Survey" referred to by Eberstadt showed that almost all of the companies surveyed (140 tool builders) were working two shifts and about 25 per cent, three shifts. The average work week of two-thirds of the companies averaged between fifty-five and sixty-five hours. It was indicated that the number of machine operators on the second and third shifts averaged about half that of the first shift. [35]

Based on the theoretical maximum of 168 hours per week, 101 machine tool plants showed a utilization factor of 49.9 per cent in

[34] RG 80, Memorandums from Patterson to Eberstadt, December 25, 1941; Eberstadt to Patterson, December 30, 1941; and Eberstadt to Forrestal, December 24, 1941.

[35] RG 179, PD File 481.04, Memorandum C. M. Lynge to W. H. Harrison, January 5, 1942.

February. This was said to be higher than that of twenty-three artillery and small arms plants, thirty-eight ammunition and explosive plants, nine machine tool accessory plants, and seventeen machine shops and foundries studied by from 5 to 11 per cent. Another analysis in March 1942 showed that twelve machine tool plants representing about 25 per cent of the industry's capacity, were operating at over 80 per cent of the theoretical maximum but also indicated that other large plants were operating at considerably lower levels.[36]

Late in January 1942, Eberstadt recommended that no further general facilities expansions be approved for the machine tool industry because such expansion took tools away from direct war production. He urged that "a large measure of the burden of solving this problem should be placed on the backs of the machine tool companies" and that they should

1. Make more extensive use of their existing facilities by working full shifts around the clock;

2. Make more extensive use of subcontracting; and

3. Search out and purchase tools using their knowledge of past deliveries.

He noted that the Bullard Company was tripling its 1941 production without adding a single new or used tool.[37]

Eberstadt said he believed that the machine tools branch of WPB and its predecessor OPM had "babied" the machine tool industry and that the industry "should be saddled with a heavy burden and compelled to show greater energy, ingenuity and resourcefulness than heretofore." He also recommended that machine tool builders no longer be given a high priority for tools except in cases of direct necessity, and that other orders be kept out of plants capable of producing machine tools.

Eberstadt emphasized the need to make the best possible use of existing machine tools and said that a recent inspection trip in the

[36] RG 179, PD File 221.6, Office of Progress Reports, "Average Percent Utilization of Plants," March 9, 1942; Memorandum from Stacy May to Donald M. Nelson, March 20, 1942 (PD File 481.042); WPB, Draft of PARB Special Study No. 35, pp. 195–196.

[37] RG 80, Memorandum from Eberstadt, Chairman ANMB for Under Secretaries of War and Navy, Patterson, and Forrestal, January 28, 1942.

Detroit area had indicated that only about 50 per cent of the available tool capacity was being used.

To accomplish this, the disposition of every prime and subcontractor to re-equip their shops with the newest and most complete tools of only the finest makes must be stopped. The obtaining of new tools must be circumscribed with every restriction and granted only in those cases where the use of present equipment is clearly not available.

He also said that he had recommended that WPB establish a series of tool clearing houses in territories having the greatest "tool population" to collect and distribute information on tool availability.

Machine tool builders and the Machine Tools Section of the OPM and WPB attempted to counter criticism that the machine tool plants were not making adequate use of multiple shifts by pointing out various difficulties. Some of these were claimed to be unique or more important in the machine tool industry than in plants mass producing war equipment and supplies. Thus it was alleged that much more supervisory and instructional time was required in machine tool plants and that supervisors could not be spread too thinly over a large number of untrained and inexperienced workers. It was also charged that the machine tool industry was losing many of its best foremen and machinists to armaments plants which could offer higher wages including substantial premiums for shift work and overtime. It was claimed that tool builders were at a disadvantage because their output was subject to price controls and the resistance of tool buyers to increased prices based on higher labor costs.[38]

Radical solutions suggested for these problems included

1. Direct government purchase of machine tools at negotiated prices on the assumption that production was being restricted by price controls.

2. Subsidies for output above assigned quotas to permit machine tool builders to compete for second and third shift workers by paying bonuses.

3. Freezing the labor force.

[38] Livermore, "The Machine Tool Problem."

4. Elimination or adjustment of price ceilings or permission to charge premium prices on particular tools where acceptable to the buyer.

The ratio of 10:7:5. was suggested as a standard for three shift operation in machine tool plants producing standard tools whereas a lower ratio of 10:5:3 was said to be about the maximum for custom machine tool shops producing special machine tools. One reason for lower ratios in the case of the special tool builders was that some major parts required more than one shift to complete and the skilled machinist, unlike the machine "operator" in mass production, would not tolerate a division of work with a worker on a succeeding shift. In such cases, the work remained in the machine until completed even though this took several days.

Many machine tool builders, however, preferred to operate on the basis of two long shifts rather than three and claimed that full utilization of equipment could be secured in this way. This theory was criticized on the ground that shifts long enough to use most of the theoretical 168 hours of a seven-day week were much too long for workers to accept and continue for any extended period of time even under wartime conditions. One advantage of the two-shift system over the three-shift system was that it allowed free time for maintenance and repair operations and some "set-up" work.

In March 1942, Eberstadt wrote William H. Harrison that WPB statistical studies showed that service requirements were not going to be met, and that full use was not being made of available machine tool capacity. He repeated previous warnings that there was a need to find additional sources of machine tools, increase subcontracting, concentrate production on a limited number of critical types of tools, and establish a clearing house for unused tools.[39]

Brainard, Chief of the WPB Tools Branch told a clinic of the Branch's Field Staff in April 1942:

> We have absolutely got to get our machine tool production up as early as possible this year, in order to meet the required maximum possible rate of production in the third or fourth quarters, and if we do that we will have done our part of the job. No one

[39] RG 179, Draft of PARB Special Study No. 35, p. 196; Memorandum from Ferdinand Eberstadt to W. H. Harrison, March 24, 1942.

in Washington is fearful of next year's capacity if we reach the peak this year.[40]

It was proposed to reassure machine tool builders against the threat of large quantities of surplus tools at the end of World War II, and at the same time provide tools in event of another emergency, that the government repurchase and store large numbers of such tools. Such a procedure would, it was hoped, encourage machine tool builders to expand production.[41]

During 1942, there was a drive to control new requirements and to encourage cancellation of orders where the tools were not essential to fulfillment of 1942 and 1943 production programs. Order cancellations in 1942 amounted to about $219,000,000 as compared to orders received of about $1,840,000,000.[42]

Conversion of Facilities versus Diversion of Individual Tools

Another method of meeting defense requirements for machine tools was to convert existing plants from the production of non-essential civilian-type products to direct defense items or to production of such essential indirect items as machine tools. For example, the automobile industry not only had a large number of machine tools in its production lines but also had tool rooms and "captive" tool building shops which provided many of the industry's special machine tools and accessories. The industry was unwilling, however, to reduce voluntarily or to stop automobile production. It took the position that most of its machine tools were not suitable for defense production either because they were specialized for automobile production, or because they were not designed to provide the degree of precision required. The leading automobile companies did contract, however, to build, equip, and operate large new government-owned plants for which large numbers of new machine tools were required. Automobile and truck production

---

[40] RG 179, PD File 481.04, Transcript of Proceedings of Clinic of the Field Staff, April 29–May 2, 1942.

[41] Livermore, "The Machine Tool Problem," pp. 3, 8–9.

[42] RG 179, Tools Division, "Shipments, Orders Received, Orders Cancelled and Balance of Unfilled Firm Orders," attached to "Report on the Machine Tool Industry," September 23, 1943 by a Sub-Committee of the WPB Machine Tool Industry Advisory Committee.

continued—and in fact increased in both 1940 and 1941. The automobile industry's position was apparently accepted by the army and navy and by the Office of Production Management until Pearl Harbor brought us directly into the war and made it clear that civilian production—"business as usual"—could not be continued.

The Senate Special Committee Investigating the National Defense Program (Truman Committee) was highly critical of the fact that automobile production had been allowed to continue rather than converting the industry's facilities to defense production. Robert P. Patterson, the Under Secretary of War, testified in June 1941 that the automobile producers and OPM told him that not over 10 per cent of their machine tools were suitable for the production of aircraft engines and that they did not have any of the critical tools. The committee concluded that this information "was quite inaccurate" and that "we could and should have made use of automobile plants and tools."[43]

The Truman Committee also issued an earlier report on November 17, 1941 which was critical of the alleged failure of the army, navy and OPM to make adequate use of small plants, and the tendency of procurement officials to take the easy way by giving virtually all contracts to large companies, even where they had to obtain new tools, while small plants were idle because of material shortages for their nondefense business. The report referred to a survey conducted by the National Association of Manufacturers and supposedly concurred in by the Chief of the Defense Contract Service showing that 50 per cent of the country's machine tool capacity was not being used. The information, however, was too general and incomplete to be of much use in locating needed tools.[44]

In general, there were relatively few cases where civilian plants (with substantially all their equipment) were converted from civilian production, and many other tools were added to equip the new production lines.[45]

Another alternative was to divert tools from plants where they were not being used, used for a small percentage of the time, or

---

[43] U.S. Senate, 77th Congress, 2nd Session, Special Committee Investigating the National Defense Program, Report No. 480, Part 5, pp. 31–36.
[44] *Ibid.*, Part 3, pp. 191–199.
[45] Livermore, "The Machine Tool Problem," p. 9.

used for nondefense work to plants needing such tools for defense or essential civilian production. The possible methods for accomplishing such diversion included

1. Sale of used tools by a non-defense plant to one working on armament contracts.

2. Leasing of new or used tools owned by the army and navy to defense contractors for a fee.

3. Voluntary or compulsory subcontracting of work to plants not fully engaged in defense production.

4. Private mobilization of tool facilities in a city or region by primary contractors, by contract-accepting associations, or by a special defense corporation operating under national supervision but with mixed private management.

5. Similar mobilization of tools on an industry basis by committee or trade associations.

6. Requisitioning of tools by a government agency, and lease or sale and physical transfer to another plant.

One factor which seems to have been forgotten in many discussions of conversion of facilities or diversion of individual tools was that, while in many cases it was possible to use tools of a much earlier vintage, such use often meant not only lower production than would have been possible with more modern tools, it also required more labor and more skill on the part of the operator. Since labor and particularly highly skilled labor was in short supply, in trying to solve the shortage of machine tools, labor problems were to some degree aggravated. Moreover, in practice it was difficult to transfer tools from one plant to another even where the tools were government-owned. Even after War Production Board Directive 13 was issued in February 1943 giving the WPB Tools Division authority to move government-owned machine tools, the authority was rarely used.

It was even difficult, though not impossible, to develop and maintain a reasonably accurate and up-to-date inventory of machine tools which would reflect what tools were being used for nonessential civilian production or which were being inadequately used. Since this type of information changed rapidly, it was of limited value unless it was kept up to date. The OPM attempted to solve part of the problem by requesting machine tool manufacturers to supply it with a complete list of critical machine tools manufactured and shipped subsequent to 1934. It was then necessary to try to determine the current location and use of these tools and to work out methods of diverting such tools to defense production where they were not already being so used. This was at best a slow and time-consuming operation and time was in very short supply.

Subcontracting of Tools and Components

Subcontracting of complete machines or of individual components and parts was frequently urged as a method of increasing tool production without further expansion of machine tool plants. There were, however, wide differences of opinion regarding the potential increases in output which could be achieved through subcontracting and as to whether the machine tool industry was pursuing this method aggressively enough. From the viewpoint of the tool builder, subcontracting had its limitations and serious problems. These were least serious, except for the danger of future competition, where a complete machine could be subcontracted to a single firm and greatest where individual parts were subcontracted and had to be shipped to the tool builder, inspected, stored, and assembled.

Many firms which had unused machine capacity were not capable of doing work to close tolerances. It was often impractical to contract with such firms for roughing operations and less difficult parts which were normally done by trainees or less skilled workers in the machine tool builder's plant. Additional machine tool work could be subcontracted to "civilian type" industries whose regular production had been curtailed. Such subcontracting was limited, however, by the fact that some production of other industrial and agricultural equipment was still needed.[46]

Some discussions of subcontracting also seemed to forget that the machine tool builder's problem did not end when a subcontract was let. A considerable amount of high-grade supervision and coordination was required to assure that work would not only be delivered when needed but would also meet quality standards and

46 *Ibid.*, p. 6.

specifications necessary to assure that finished equipment would perform satisfactorily and reliably and that components would be interchangeable with those produced by the machine tool builder or other subcontractors.

The machine tool industry made substantial progress in subcontracting and by the beginning of 1943 about 25 per cent of its productive hours was accounted for by subcontracts. By subcontracting or "farming out" many small machine shops were brought into machine tool production as well as machine shops in automobile plants and various machinery producing firms. The amount of subcontracting declined during the remainder of 1943 and the first half of 1944 when machine tool capacity was being reduced in favor of direct war production. Expanded requirements from the ammunition and mortar programs at the end of 1944 caused some extension of machine tool subcontracting and efforts to relieve tool builders of some of their subcontracts for other work in order to increase tool production.[47]

Pool Orders

Various efforts were made to speed up or short-cut the process of translating programs into action by providing tool builders with firm orders or other assurances that all tools produced could be sold, and financial assistance to cover facilities expansions and other costs. One of the devices adopted was for one of the Armed Services or the Defense Plant Corporation (DPC), upon recommendation of the Office of Production Management (later War Production Board), to place so-called "Pool Orders" with machine tool builders for the production of a specified number of machines of particular standard types. The tool builder could then obtain from DPC an advance of 30 per cent of the estimated contract delivery price of the machines. Such orders did not actually increase the ultimate total requirement for machine tools (except to a very minor degree where tools ordered and produced were later not needed) but assured the tool industry that sudden cancellations of orders would not result in large losses on inventories and partially

[47] RG 179, PD File 481.09, Memorandum from George H. Johnson to Charles E. Wilson, February 6, 1943; WPB, Draft of PARB Special Study No. 35, pp. 189–205.

completed work. However, tool builders tended to discount pool orders as a reflection of requirements in deciding whether to expand production.

On May 10, 1941, Under Secretary of War Patterson forwarded to Knudsen a list of tools required to carry out the aircraft programs covered by Schedule 8-E which included the 500-a-month Heavy Bomber Program. This list called for $399,241,706 worth of machine tools to be delivered prior to July 1, 1942 or the aircraft program would be delayed. One hundred thirty million dollars' worth of machine tools were already on order or being ordered. Patterson urged immediate steps to place the orders and increase the capacity of the machine tool industry to meet the requirements.

The Air Corps Scheduling Unit and the Aircraft Section of OPM both favored placing the entire $400,000,000 as pool orders but Mason Britton, Chief of the OPM Tools Section, felt that only the critical tools need be ordered through the Defense Plant Corporation (DPC) and that the contractors could later place orders for the remaining tools. His reasoning apparently was that if all were ordered at once, some would be delivered before they were needed, to the detriment of other programs.

Representatives of OPM, Air Corps, and the DPC met with Assistant Secretary of War for Air, Robert A. Lovett, on June 17, 1941, to discuss how the matter should be handled. This resulted in a compromise agreement proposed by John Snyder of DPC providing that in the case of the approximately $200,000,000 of tools to be ordered by prime contractors, DPC would issue letters of intent to the contractors authorizing them to place orders for specified tools with specified machine tool builders. For the remaining $200,000,000 of tools intended for subcontractors, the War Department and OPM were to specify the descriptions and quantity of tools to be purchased from each machine tool builder and the price. DPC would issue pool orders covering these tools. The War Department and OPM were to notify the tool builders of the overall requirements to be purchased from them to allow them to prepare to handle the orders.[48]

On December 14, 1941, Mason Britton, Chief, Tools Branch, OPM, sent a letter to all tool builders requesting them to require

[48] Sitterson, *Aircraft Production Policies*, p. 116.

all purchasers of machine tools to make an advance of 30 per cent on purchase orders in the same way as the army and navy had agreed to do in order to give the industry working capital for expanded operations.[49]

Ferdinand Eberstadt, Chairman, ANMB, estimated in January 1942 that total machine tool requirements for 1942 would be approximately $2.3 billion; said that this figure had been given to OPM; that OPM had been impressed with the importance of immediately placing pool orders with tool builders for approximately three times their 1941 production with some adjustments based on available knowledge; and that the orders must be issued without too much regard for the niceties of the situation.[50]

A new procedure for financing pool orders had been worked out with the WPB and the DPC whereby the 30 per cent advance remained available to the tool builder until the tool was shipped rather than having to be repaid when an order was received from a contractor. Reasonable provisions covering cancellation and liquidation had been accepted by DPC, and it was suggested that the same plan be adopted by the army and the navy. Eberstadt urged that the amount of pool orders which DPC would issue should be settled quickly and that the army and navy cover other orders.

As previously indicated, the device of using pool orders was begun as a means of accelerating expansion of machine tool production by providing tool builders with advance indication of what orders they could expect, financial assistance through advance payments when the pool order was placed, and insurance against losses in material and labor if contracts were cancelled before delivery. It was not possible to determine the exact effect of pool orders in increasing plant capacity or production from existing facilities. The Chief of the WPB Tools Division stated in 1945, however, that he considered pool orders to have been essential to the successful meeting of war programs and that

The pool order mechanism made possible the adequate supply

---

[49] RG 80, JJ 40/L8–3.

[50] *Ibid.*, Memorandum from Ferdinand Eberstadt, Chairman ANMB for Under-Secretaries of War and Navy, Patterson and Forrestal, January 28, 1942; the high peak of unfilled orders which was created became known as "Mount Eberstadt."

of machine tools for the war effort. It is one of the important and successful steps in the war which should not be overlooked in another war emergency.[51]

A total of $221,775,000 in pool orders was placed in 1941. Between January 1 and February 19, 1942 a total of $459,225,000 in additional pool orders was issued. Of a total of $1,863,000,000 in pool orders issued, only about $4,000,000 had not been used by September 1945.

Pool orders were issued at this rapid rate, although the Tools Branch of WPB did not feel it had all the information it needed on requirements. Placement of pool orders was slowed down in May 1942 by Brainard, Chief of the WPB Tools Branch who decided that such orders should not be placed extending beyond the first quarter of 1943 except where there was a need for specific machines with long production times. No pool orders were to be placed for noncritical machines beyond the end of 1942. In August 1942, however, Ferdinand Eberstadt, Chairman of the ANMB, expressed concern that pool orders were not being extended for the second quarter of 1943, and urged Brainard to place orders for all critical types of tools for the second quarter.

Brainard replied that they would start on September 1, 1942 to consider pool orders for critical tools for the second quarter of 1943 and for the third quarter, in the case of the long production time tools. Eberstadt was supported by Under Secretary of War Patterson in urging faster action but within two months the ANMB, chaired by August Richard (Eberstadt became Vice Chairman for Program Determination of the WPB), was suggesting that pool orders be reduced. The ANMB now predicted that the tooling up period would be completed by July 1943 and recommended that pool orders should be placed "only against probable firm orders." The WPB Tools Division took the position, however, that it must exercise its best judgment and maintain what it considered an adequate volume of orders.

A policy was worked out between the WPB Tools Division and the ANMB which provided that pool orders would be continued for

[51] RG 179, Draft of PARB Special Study No. 35, pp. 230–232, 238; "*History of the Tools Division,*" Chapter II; WPB, Tools Division, *1944 Annual Report,* pp. 1, 5, (PD File 053.508).

the specific types and sizes of tools which were clearly in demand, limited orders for tools in declining demand, and that other pool orders would be cancelled. Surplus plant capacity was to be released for direct war production. The armed services and some top WPB officials were not satisfied with the WPB Tool Division's position, however, and in December the WPB Production Executive Committee requested that orders for new tools be kept to a minimum.[52]

In May 1943, the WPB Tools Division announced that in the future pool orders would only be issued for machines covered by firm customer orders, and that, in view of the availability of "V Loans," the 30 per cent advance previously provided would no longer be needed. It was anticipated that this change in policy would force further conversion of machine tool capacity to direct war production but that the full effect would not be felt until early 1944. The amount of reduction was in doubt. George H. Johnson, WPB Tools Division, however, warned that future increases in tool production would require many months.[53]

Further pressure from the War Department and doubt on the part of WPB Executive Vice Chairman, Charles E. Wilson, and other top WPB officials regarding tool requirements resulted in a decision by the WPB Production Executive Committee on June 30, 1943 that further use of pool orders was not necessary despite the WPB Tools Division's attempts to justify their continued use.

By September 1, 1943, $159,813,000 of pool orders had been cancelled of the $1,863,641,000 issued, and $77,351,000 were still not covered by firm customer orders. DPC also had about $5,750,000 worth of tools in storage.

On September 23, 1943, a subcommittee of the WPB Machine Tool Industry Advisory Committee headed by Ralph E. Flanders presented a report which reviewed the situation of the machine tool industry and recommended that provision be established for

[52] RG 179, Memorandums from August Richard to Eberstadt, November 19, 1942 and from John S. Chafee to Eberstadt, November 21, 1942; Extract from *Production Executive Committee Minutes*, December 9, 1942 (PD File 481.0432).
[53] RG 179, Memorandum from Johnson to Richard, ANMB, May 20, 1943 (PD File 481.02); Draft of PARB Special Study No. 35, pp. 233–238.

so-called "continuity orders" (following British terminology) to be issued under the control of the WPB Tools Division which would control tool builder's order boards. The report also warned of the danger that tool output and capacity would drop below 1944 requirements estimated at $325,000,000 in new tools. John Chafee, Director of the Tools Division, presented this line of argument to C. E. Wilson but the latter was still not convinced of the need for pool orders. Chafee attempted to prove that the armed services and other claimant agencies had never been able to furnish reliable statements of machine tool requirements and that there was a danger of unforeseen emergencies which might be met by pool orders. He then proposed that tool builders be permitted to accept unrated orders for delivery after all rated orders, providing that labor requirements for war production were not affected. This proposal was very premature and was not approved.[54]

Pool orders were revived in December 1944 as a result of the expanded mortar and medium artillery ammunition program and other requirements following the "Battle of the Bulge" which made it apparent that the war in Europe was not going to end in 1944. An additional $34,000,000 in pool orders were placed in December 1944 and January 1945.

Tools or Guns—Conversion to Direct War Production

By the spring of 1942, and several months before peak tool production was reached, service representatives began anticipating the end of the "tooling-up" period when some machine tool plants would be available for other work and began to ask machine tool builders for information on their availability. This, in turn, suggested to the tool builders that the tool production job was about done and that they had better think about what was going to happen to them, their skilled labor, facilities, etc. This caused the ANMB and Tool Branch of WPB to become alarmed, and Brainard requested that there be no negotiations with machine tool builders for other production without prior clearance with the machine tools Branch of WPB and the ANMB. He also called a meeting with in-

[54] RG 179, PD File 481.001, "Report on the Machine Tool Industry," September 23, 1943.

dustry representatives on June 24, 1942 "to put the facts and necessities of this situation before them. . . . "[55]

Eberstadt pointed out that the machine tool industry still had the longest backlog in its history and that the machine tool order boards needed to be leveled off. Also he urged that instructions be issued against the placing of production orders for other than machine tools or components with machine tool builders without the prior approval of the ANMB Machine Tools Section.

In September 1942, a subcommittee of the WPB Machine Tool Industry Advisory Committee headed by Ralph E. Flanders of the Jones and Lamson Company was asked to study the situation with special regard to conversion of plants to war production based on the assumption that there were enough machine tools to fabricate all materials available. The subcommittee reported at the end of October and recommended that conversion be made on an individual company basis rather than industry-wide. It was believed that the existing backlog represented urgent needs for tools and that production of tools should be maintained to reduce the backlog and meet new requirements which were expected in substantial volume. The subcommittee proposed that "emergency producers" which had entered the machine tool field during the war should be converted first. Consideration should also be given to whether a plant could convert its existing facilities to war production or would require a substantial number of new tools.[56]

The subcommittee also recommended action to overcome contractor preference for particular makes of tools and to level off orders so that one producer was not overloaded while others had small backlogs. The report urged a review of military programs and advance planning of requirements in order that the tool industry would know what tools were essential to the war effort, and no more should be built. Other recommendations included increased output per manhour, full use of existing machines, real-

[55] RG 80, JJ 40/L8–3; Memorandum from Ferdinand Eberstadt for the Under-Secretaries of War and Navy and Assistant Secretary for Air, June 13, 1942, "Machine Tools"; Memorandum from Captain E. D. Almy for Forrestal, June 16, 1942; Memorandum of Navy Office of Procurement and Material to Bureaus of Ships and Ordnance, May 20, 1942, "Machine Tool Builders–Availability for Orders for War Equipment Items"; Memorandum from Eberstadt for Forrestal, June 18, 1942.
[56] RG 179, Draft of PARB Special Study No. 35, pp. 218–220.

location of machines not fully utilized, screening of tool orders to prevent contractors from overordering, substitution of used tools wherever possible, and insistence on realistic delivery dates.[57]

By the fall of 1942, there was considerable discussion of the possibilities of converting a substantial part of the machine tool industry's capacity to direct war production. The proponents of conversion based their case mainly on generalized statistical calculations purported to show that the machine tools already produced greatly exceeded in "machining capacity" the amount of metal available to be cut. It was assumed that a perfect balance between metal production and machining capacity could not be achieved but the question asked was "how much excess machining capacity is necessary?"[58]

The argument offered by opponents of conversion, that the machine tool industry was actually made up of a number of industries whose facilities were not interchangeable, was discounted on the ground that considerable numbers of firms did produce the same type of tools and many plants could be converted to different sizes and types of tools. Thus some plants making noncritical tools could be converted to those types still considered in critically short supply while other tool plants could be converted to direct production of war equipment requiring a capability for high precision work.[59]

An argument that changing designs in war equipment made it necessary to retain a large machine tool building industry was discounted on the ground that many design and production changes actually reduced rather than increased machining requirements. It was also contended that 50 per cent of existing tools were only being used an average of forty-five hours a week, and that much better use of existing tools could be achieved.

It was suggested that controls had not been effective in bringing used equipment into war production, filtering orders for new tools, or in concentrating production on the types of machine tools in short supply. Major emphasis should be placed on maintenance

[57] RG 179, Report from R. E. Flanders to Brainard, October 28, 1942 (PD File 481.04).

[58] RG 179, Memorandum from Norman J. Meiklejohn to Dr. Vergil Reed, "Machine Tools," November 9, 1942 and attached study (PD File 481.001).

[59] RG 179, Draft of PARB Special Study No. 35, p. 208.

and repair or rebuilding of used tools rather than on production of new tools. All idle machine tools meeting "certain standards of design and condition" should be purchased under government control and put in first-class working condition. These tools were then to be held in a reservoir from which war contractors could draw for new facility requirements, or to replace machines requiring repair or rebuilding.

A final decision to cut back machine tool production was not made until the spring of 1943 to be effective for the last quarter of 1943. During this period, production was to be reduced to 55 per cent of the first quarter, 1943 level. The smaller volume of tools was supposed to be sufficient to cover essential replacement and to equip new plants where used tools were not available or usable. Capacity not needed for machine tool production was to be converted to direct war production. One of the policy questions that arose was whether marginal machine tool builders, including those which had recently converted to machine tool production, should be released first although they might not be of much value in direct war production, or whether the larger and better equipped plants should be converted.

In March 1943, about thirty-five companies which had entered the machine tool field in 1942 were advised their facilities were no longer needed for tool production and that they could take on war contracts. Some of the larger established machine tool firms, which were faced with reduced demand, were also to divert part of their facilities to direct war production. Considerable pressure for conversion of the machine tool industry came from organized labor which was apparently motivated both by a desire to "get on with the war" as rapidly as possible and to avoid unemployment in the machine tool industry as demand for tools declined.[60]

Analysis of the 1944 tool program indicated that the industry would be operating at 40 per cent of capacity and that as a result approximately 60 per cent of its facilities would be available for war production. It was pointed out that this capacity was better suited to the more difficult types of precision production problems rather than to mass production of standard parts and components. This conclusion was based both on the type of equipment in the

[60] Ibid., pp. 222–225.

machine tool shops and the type of manpower usually found there. It was anticipated, however, that there would be some loss in capacity due to loss of balance in equipment and to reduction of shift work and overtime.

The United Electrical, Radio and Machine Workers of America (CIO) was highly critical of the progress being made in converting the machine tool industry and particularly of the WPB Machine Tools Division headed by John S. Chafee. The machine tool industry was also criticized for allegedly trying to avoid conversion in many instances.

Facilities Expansion

During the period of mobilization for World War II, machine tool plant capacity was expanded with new facilities costing a total of $160,645,000. Of this amount, $70,097,000 was provided by the Defense Plant Corporation (DPC) and $90,548,000 was privately financed. A part of the latter total, however, was financed by advances from DPC on pool orders. Of the total spent, $47,910,000 was for buildings and the remaining $105,590,000 for equipment.[61]

In 1947, a total of $13,836,000 in new plants and machinery was added to the industry of which $10,312,000 was for machinery and equipment. No comparable information was found for 1946, 1948, or 1949, but it seems likely that the average for the four years 1946–1949 was in approximately the same range as for 1947 amounting to about $56,000,000 or about one-third the amount for the wartime expansion years 1941-1944. If an allowance is made for the higher postwar prices, the difference in rate would probably be somewhat larger and below the rate for 1939 which was about $11,940,000. Because of the large wartime expansion, the relatively much smaller rate of new investment in the period following World War II, and the tendency to eliminate the older prewar equipment in the postwar period, it would seem logical to expect that the average age of facilities would first decline somewhat and then begin to increase at an accelerated rate beginning about 1949. This appears in fact to have been the case, based on the data in the "American Machinist Inventory" for 1953.

[61] RG 179, WPB *Tools Division History*, pp. 178–180; WPB, Draft of PARB Special Study No. 35, pp. 206–207.

Concentration

It has already been noted that the common picture of the machine tool industry as a collection of small companies requires some qualification despite the fact that the largest machine tool builder was small in comparison to the largest industrial firms, and that there were a large number of very small firms. For example, in 1947 there were 107 establishments with less than twenty employees each according to the *Census of Manufactures* for 1947. In the same year, there were four firms with over 2,500 employees each and a total of sixteen firms employed 50.6 per cent of the industry's total employees. The four largest firms employed 23.7 per cent. The latter figure can be compared with 13.8 per cent in 1935 and 21.7 per cent in 1945, thus indicating a continuing trend toward concentration. It seems likely that the indicated increase from 1935 to 1945 is somewhat higher than it should be because of the fact that the definition of the machine tool industry used in 1935 was broader and included a higher proportion of small firms, but the difference would probably not be very significant.[62]

In terms of value added by manufacture in 1947, the four largest firms reported 19.1 per cent of the industry's total as compared to 23.7 per cent of the employees, thus suggesting the possibility that the largest firms were relatively less productive than the average of all firms. The largest sixteen firms reported 43.2 per cent of the industry's value added by manufacture as compared to 50.6 per cent of its employees, thus also suggesting that these firms were less productive than the overall average.

Because of the wide variety of types, sizes, and quality of machine tools produced, no firm in the industry made more than a very small fraction of the total, and only a small number of firms (usually not over four) made any one specialized type. Even allowing for the fact that there is some interchangeability and competition among some of the standard types of machine tools and among tools of varying capacity, the number of machine tool builders directly competing at any given time and in a particular market

[62] *Census of Manufactures;* U.S. Senate, Special Committee to Study Problems of American Small Business, 79th Congress, 2d Session, *Economic Concentration and World War II* (Washington: Government Printing Office, 1946), p. 338.

usually did not exceed more than four or five domestic firms. Since many firms did not take any part in the export business, the number competing for foreign business at any time and location probably was not much different than in the domestic market.[63]

Following World War II (1946–1949), there were attempts to compensate for loss of machine tool business; first, by eliminating shift-work and reducing hours of work; and second, by trying to diversify production. The first meant the drastic reduction of employment, and loss of some highly skilled workers as well as the virtual elimination of women as production workers. The second approach required substantial capital for equipment and retraining of employees and appears to have had limited success. The alternatives, in many cases, were to liquidate or to consolidate. This resulted in the elimination of some pioneer tool builders. For example, William Sellers and Company of Philadelphia, a leader in building tools for railroad shops, sold out to the Consolidated Machine Tool Corporation of Rochester, N.Y., and Sellers' Philadelphia plant, which had employed about 600 men, was closed. Other firms which went out of business during this period included The Taylor and Fenn Company of Hartford, Connecticut (founded in 1834); The Universal Boring Machine Company, Hudson, Massachusetts; and, The Defiance Machine Company, Defiance, Ohio.[64]

Summary

In 1939, the United States was on the trailing edge of the worst depression in its history, and was, in most respects, poorly prepared for war either in terms of its existing armed forces or the industrial base from which to prepare for war. The depression had wasted many millions of work days of labor and had permitted much of the skilled labor supply to deteriorate through idleness and lack of replacement. Much of the country's capital equipment including machine tools was obsolete. That the American machine tool industry was not in worse condition was largely due to the fact that

---

[63] U.S. Senate, Special Committee to Study Problems of American Small Business, *Economic Concentration and World War II*, pp. 142–143.

[64] Frederick S. Blackall, Jr., President NMTBA, "A Letter to the Renegotiation Board on Behalf of the Builders of Machine Tools," February 12, 1952, pp. 6–7.

exports, including those to Russia and Japan, had been an important factor in keeping many firms in operation.

It seems clear in retrospect that too little effort was devoted to planning for war and developing an adequate industrial base for war production. Military planners had great difficulty in developing plans which were reasonably realistic in terms of the conditions of a major modern war and yet had any chance of being approved through the chain of command and then translated into Congressional authorizations and appropriations with which to procure needed weapons, carry on an active development program, and prepare for quantity production in the event of war.

Determination of machine tool requirements for the aircraft programs was perhaps even more difficult than for most other defense programs both because of the rapid growth in the aircraft programs and because it seemed almost impossible to stabilize designs long enough to determine what tools would be needed. In fact, it took longer in many instances to determine requirements and get contractors to place orders than to produce the tools.

Major plant expansions for the bomber program and the aircraft program as a whole clearly would require many machine tools. However, it was difficult to determine specifically what tools would be needed—how many tools could be diverted from other use, and how many new tools would be necessary. There was a widespread belief that aircraft could not be mass produced. In the case of pursuit types at any rate, each plane builder continued to produce a different design. This complicated the problem of determining machine tool requirements for aircraft production. There was also some competition with U.S. aircraft machine tool requirements from British and Russian orders.

It is apparent that aircraft industry requirements for machine tools were the dominant factor in the machine tool program during World War II. This was true both because of the quantity of tools involved—about one-third of the total number of tools added during the war—and the urgency of the requirements. Had there been no large scale expansion of aircraft production facilities, there would have been no substantial machine tool problem. The fact that the expansion of the aircraft industry was so large in relation to the prewar base and was concentrated within such a short period created the immediate problems of expansion and conversion of

facilities and machine tools. The fact that there was so little probability of the aircraft industry continuing at anything approaching
its wartime scale after the war presented a major threat to the machine tool industry at the end of the war.

The wartime aircraft expansion problem would have been somewhat reduced had the prewar proposal to build government-owned
aircraft plants been quickly approved and vigorously implemented.
The existing political situation and opposition of the aircraft industry prevented any action along this line. The aircraft industry,
like the machine tool industry, was very much concerned about the
threat of excess capacity.

World War II experience in expanding the aircraft industry indicated that, from the standpoint of the time required to get into full
production, there was little difference between building new plants
and converting existing plants from other industries. This was due
to the fact that many new machine tools were required in either
case; and that it was necessary in both cases to design and produce
a variety of special jigs, fixtures, dies, and cutting tools as well as
rearrange plant layouts.

Expansion of ordnance production facilities required many new
and used machine tools, but posed fewer and smaller problems.
Design changes were less rapid and radical than in the aircraft
program and the army and navy had had much more experience
with ordnance production. During the prewar period, there were
attempts to modernize government-owned production facilities and
some progress was made in 1938–1939 but it was a case of "too little
and too late." There were also efforts to prepare for ordnance
production in private plants, but here too the progress was very
small in comparison with future needs. Experience with using
educational orders to prepare contractors for ordnance production
indicated the potential value of this device if started soon enough
and on a substantial scale, but that it was of limited practical value
in preparing for World War II.

Ordnance planners during the thirties foresaw many of the machine tool shortages which would occur in the event of a rapid
mobilization. However, existing opposition to preparation for war
and the limited vision and energy of many military and civilian
leaders prevented effective action. It appears in retrospect that a
relatively small additional investment during the thirties together

with better judgment regarding the weapons which would be needed would have largely eliminated the machine tool shortages for ordnance production.

The problems of the shipbuilding program were in some respects similar to those of the aircraft programs. For one thing, a very large increase in output of U.S. shipyards was necessary, and, for another, traditional construction methods were not compatible with large volume production. Ships were not designed with much attention to high-speed production problems and the shipyards had little incentive to develop production short-cuts which would reduce the manpower or the time required for ship construction.

Machine tools were a critical factor in expanding ship construction prior to and during the first years of World War II. As in the case of ordnance, it appears that most of these tool shortages could have been avoided with a somewhat greater expenditure of money, energy, and imagination during the thirties.

There is some evidence that lack of balance and stability in program objectives aggravated machine tool shortages. Given the initial state of U.S. and Allied Armed Forces, the changing character of the war, and the nature of the U.S. political system, it is difficult to see how any other result was possible. It also seems certain that the concern of contractors for their future business situation caused them to order new tools where used tools would have been adequate, and to prefer the highest quality machines with many accessories rather than simpler and less expensive tools which could have met some of the immediate needs.

Machine tool builders were concerned about the problem of excess capacity in the industry and were reluctant to expand their own plants, go to multiple shift operation, see new firms enter the machine tool business, or spread available work by subcontracting to other firms until they were certain such measures were essential. They were also unwilling to undertake drastic standardization and simplification programs or concentrate production on particular machines in order to increase production with existing facilities. By the time the need for expansion could be demonstrated in the form of firm orders for specific tools, it was almost too late to expand production enough to meet wartime needs. Whether World War II could have been shortened had it been possible to deliver more machine tools sooner is an interesting point for speculation.

For any such speed-up to have been effective, it would probably have had to have been accompanied by corresponding increases in deliveries of scarce materials, accelerated construction, expanded production of many other industries, earlier forced conversion of civilian goods industries, and a considerable acceleration in troop recruitment and training. Whether all of this would have been possible seems very doubtful.

Major errors of the 1940–1941 period included the failure to concentrate tool production on the most important types rather than allow tool plants to continue production of their normal line of equipment. The two measures most needed in 1942 were to increase manpower on the second and third shifts, and increase subcontracting among tool builders or with closely allied machinery builders. Further expansion of tool plants was disapproved because of the time required for plant expansion, the demand for scarce tools required for expansion, and the problems involved in obtaining workers for second and third shifts would also apply to new facilities. The charge that machine tool builders had resisted expansion because of their fear of excess capacity at the end of the emergency seemed pointless in view of the currently compelling reasons against such expansion.

The large increase in the rate of machine tool production between 1939 and December 1942 resulted from a number of factors including the addition of some new firms and subcontracting of work to establishments in other metalworking industries. The major part of the increase, however, resulted from the expansion of facilities of the established machine tool builders, longer hours of work, increases in employment, multiple shift operations, and increased productivity through longer production runs on standardized machines and components.

Peak employment was reached at the end of 1942 and employment began to decline as a result of competition from other industries and military manpower requirements. Average hours worked had also begun to decline slowly and production was on a downward slope. Employment of wage earners in December 1942 reached 120,000 as compared to 37,000 in 1939. It declined to 54,400 in 1947 and to an estimated 38,600 in 1949. Since the average number of hours worked in 1949 was less than in 1939, the amount of productive time was probably about the same. The number of units shipped in 1949 was substantially lower than in 1939, but in 1947 was almost 20 per cent higher.

After the major machine tool production problems of World War II were solved, machine tool builders were reluctant to convert to production of military equipment—though the established firms in the industry were probably very willing to have some of their subcontractors and new tool producers convert to other lines. Their attitude in this case was based on a number of factors including their belief that new machine tool requirements were likely to develop, the difficulty of finding other products which they could produce efficiently and profitably, the danger of losing their position in the machine tool industry if they shifted their attention and facilities to other lines, and their desire to be able to prepare to supply new tools for the resumption of civilian production. Organized labor favored greater conversion both to speed up production of war equipment, and as a way of avoiding unemployment in the machine tool industry as production of tools was reduced.

In general, it is felt that the machine tool shortages of World War II were attributable to the inability of the army, navy, and emergency agencies to estimate accurately the requirements and to develop adequate programs to satisfy the requirements; to the inability of the President and Executive Departments to determine and convince Congress of the need for adequate funds to modernize existing government-owned manufacturing facilities; to failure to support greater research and development efforts extending through preproduction engineering, improvement of production methods, etc.; and to prepare private firms for rapid conversion to military production. Also both end-product manufacturers and machine tool builders were unwilling or slow to change or expand their operations until either forced to do so, or convinced that they could do so profitably and safely. Unfortunately, in the uncertainty of the prewar situation, it was difficult to overcome the various forms of inertia tending to perpetuate the economic status quo.

9

Problems Relating to Control of
Machine Tool Distribution, Prices,
and Profits in World War II

This chapter describes the principal problems met during World War II in efforts by the federal government to control the distribution of machine tools in order to accelerate the "tooling-up" of defense industries as rapidly as possible without permitting machine tool builders to raise prices unnecessarily or to make excessive profits from war-related production. It also attempts to present the machine tool builders' problems in complying with governmental directives; and building up capital reserves during the war within the limits imposed by price controls, wartime taxes, and the renegotiation process.

Export Restrictions

During the thirties, many machine tool builders tried to build up their export business. In the years preceding the outbreak of World War II much of the export business obtained was for tools desired by Japan and the U.S.S.R. for munitions production. In 1939 and 1940, however, Secretary of the Treasury Morgenthau and others became convinced there was good reason to limit such exports. There was little, if any, legal authority, for taking over tools intended for export except by negotiation. The Navy Department, at any rate, hesitated to act except where it had a requirement for the particular tools and where their use would not require extensive changes.

By May 1940, however, President Roosevelt was convinced that more drastic action was needed and directed the Secretary of the Navy, Charles Edison, and the Attorney General, Robert H. Jackson, to take immediate action to stop export of a large lathe being built by the General Machinery Company for the U.S.S.R., and to prevent William Sellers and Company from selling boring machines to Japan. The Navy Department then placed an embargo on machine tool exports to Russia and Japan based ostensibly on prior need of the navy. This measure cut off exports of machine tools to Japan and Russia and was accompanied by a relaxation of restrictions on exports to Great Britain and the Dominions. On July 2, 1940, Congress authorized the President to curtail or prohibit exportation of critical materials including machine tools under the Export Control Act.[1]

The Army and Navy Munitions Board (ANMB) Machine Tool Committee used information from export applications to locate tools and work out methods of diverting these to U.S. defense requirements.[2]

Tools were piling up in New York and Seattle, and in machine tool plants. It appeared they would continue to do so until the commandeering laws then having "hard sledding" in Congress were passed. The commandeering law recommended by the Navy allowed commandeering of any tool which was being or had been manufactured for export and relieved the tool builder of any contractual obligation and penalites. Commandeering authority was provided by the Selective Service and Training Act of September 16, 1940.

Machine Tool Coordinating Committee

A Machine Tool Coordinating Committee was established under

---

[1] RG (Record Group) 80, Navy Department, Office of Procurement and Material, Machine Tool Section Files, Letter Robert H. Jackson to Charles Edison, May 10, 1940; Ralph Elberton Smith, *The Army and Economic Mobilization* (Washington: Government Printing Office, 1959), p. 599; U.S. Civilian Production Administration, *Industrial Mobilization for War,* Vol. 1 (Washington: Government Printing Office, 1947), pp. 71–72.

[2] RG 80, Office of the Secretary, General Correspondence, JJ 40/L8–3, Memorandum from Capt. E. D. Almy, USN to H. S. Vance, June 13, 1940, "Export Policy"; ANMB, "Report on Machine Tools," December 13, 1941; Memorandum from Capt. E. D. Almy, USN for Assistant Secretary of the Navy, July 24, 1940; CPA, *Industrial Mobilization for War,* p. 66.

the Advisory Commission to the Council of National Defense (NDAC) with William S. Knudsen as Chairman and Harold S. Vance as Vice Chairman. This committee met with representatives of the army and navy to determine the functions of the army, navy, and civilian agencies. It was decided that the army and navy would establish priorities for military projects by joint action and that the Coordinating Committee would consider and attempt to resolve any conflicts

1. On the Army and Navy Program as a whole.
2. Affecting machine tool exports.
3. On requirements of munitions contractors.
4. On nondefense requirements.

The Machine Tools Coordinating Committee was superseded by the Machine Tool and Heavy Ordnance Section of the NDAC with Vance as Director and Mason Britton as Assistant Director.[3]

Controlling Distribution of Machine Tools

A "voluntary" preference rating system for defense orders under the direction of the ANMB was adopted in June 1940 and given Congressional authority in an act of June 28, 1940. The ANMB Priorities Committee and NDAC representatives under Donald M. Nelson undertook the job of working out a preference rating system for military items. It was soon recognized, however, that merely giving preference to military type end products would not be enough.[4]

In September 1940, Assistant Secretary of War Robert P. Patterson warned that proper scheduling of delivery of end products and major components was the key to the orderly progress of the War Department's program.

Proper scheduling will keep out of the market those who are not in immediate need of materials, tools, equipment, etc. Priority is designed to give orders so deferred the preferential treatment needed when their turn comes under the scheduling system.[5]

[3] RG 80, ANMB, *Report on Machine Tools*, December 13, 1941.
[4] CPA, *Industrial Mobilization for War*, pp. 64–65.
[5] Smith, *The Army and Economic Mobilization*, pp. 512–513, quoted from a letter from Patterson to COFAC, September 19, 1940, "Priorities and Scheduling."

By the end of September 1940, such a high percentage of machine tool orders were in the top priority category (A-1) that machine tool builders were becoming completely confused. It was then proposed to divide the A-1 priority into at least four subdivisions.

ANMB sent a letter to tool builders on November 5, 1940, which attempted to define the relative standing of orders within the A-1 priority rating. When the use to which tools were to be put could be determined, tool builders were asked to rank their orders as follows:

1. Gauges
2. Machine tools
3. Small arms and ammunition
4. Aircraft engines
5. Airframes
6. Fire control, optical and aircraft instruments
7. Heavy forgings, rolled and forged armor plate
8. Guns and gun mounts
9. All other defense items

This system was merely an interim device and on November 27, 1940 ANMB issued a directive which subdivided the A-1 rating into categories from A-1-a to A-1-j and specified the content of each rating band. This recognized the essentiality of tools and gauges to production of military items and placed them in the top A-1-a rating category.[6]

The Office of Production Management (OPM) was established in January 1941 and Mason Britton was designated as head of the OPM's Tools Section. On February 13, 1941, the Under Secretaries of War and Navy proposed procedures to be followed in handling machine tool problems and the functions of the agencies concerned. On February 17, William S. Knudsen, OPM Director-General, suggested to the Under Secretary of War that the Machine Tool Committee of the ANMB and its personnel be incorporated in the OPM Tools Section and that the Priorities Committee of the ANMB make no diversions of machine tools from one defense contractor to another without the approval of OPM. Patterson agreed to establish a liaison section of army and navy personnel to work with OPM. This group apparently functioned as a part of the OPM Tools Sec-

[6] David Novick, Melvin Anshen, and W. C. Truppner, *Wartime Production Controls* (New York: Columbia University Press, 1949), p. 44; Smith, *The Army and Economic Mobilization*, p. 521.

tion while retaining a separate identity with the ANMB. It was also agreed that all contracts with the machine tool industry relative to diversions of tools should be made by OPM.[7]

Mandatory Priorities

The "voluntary" preference rating system was succeeded by a preference rating system under which the OPM assigned priority ratings to defense programs on the recommendation of the army and navy. These ratings were then assigned to individual contracts by the contracting officers as the contracts were let. Scheduling of production and delivery of orders bearing the same priority rating was usually determined by the date on which orders for machine tools were placed and did not necessarily reflect the actual needs of the contractors for delivery by specific dates.

In the spring of 1941, aircraft contractors complained to the air corps of their inability to get delivery of machine tools. The air corps presented the case to Under Secretary of War Patterson who, in turn, referred it to Knudsen, alleging that if major contractors such as Continental, Ford, Allison and Wright-Cincinnati were not able to get needed machine tools, there would be such a shortage of aircraft engines that new planes could not be completed or existing planes kept in operation. Knudsen requested Mason Britton, Chief, OPM Tools Section to prepare a reply. Britton's reply declared that OPM had secured hundreds of tools for Continental, that Ford had only made one request for assistance a week earlier, and, that Allison's lists had been handled very quickly.[8]

Other actions were also taken by OPM and ANMB to expedite the delivery of machine tools ordered by aircraft contractors. The navy, however, had become alarmed at the effect the heavy bomber program was likely to have on other aircraft programs and other defense programs of the Army, Navy and Maritime Commission.

[7] RG 80, EEI(3)A3–1; Letters from William S. Knudsen, Director-General, OPM, to Under Secretaries of War and Navy Robert P. Patterson and James V. Forrestal, February 17, 1941, and from Forrestal to Knudsen, February 20, 1941.

[8] Smith, *The Army and Economic Mobilization*, pp. 564–566; J. Carlyle Sitterson, *Aircraft Production Policies Under the National Defense Advisory Commission and Office of Production Management, May 1940 to December 1941* (Washington: CPA, 1946), pp. 109–124.

Admiral Stark protested to the Secretary of the Navy and recommended that Secretary Knox confer with Secretary of War Stimson before the matter reached the President. Nevertheless, within a few days, the President assured Assistant Secretary of War for Air, Lovett, that the 500 bomber-a-month program would retain its A-1-a priority for tools and that nothing would be allowed to interfere with attainment of the program.

The conflict between the bomber program and other defense programs for machine tools was brought to William S. Knudsen's attention and was referred by him to Mason Britton who provided information intended to reassure the Secretary of the Navy. It was stated that the bomber program would require a maximum of $400,- 000,000 per year in machine tools rather than the $800,000,000 referred to by the navy and that with orderly scheduling there would be little interference with deliveries of navy tools which, for the most part, were of larger size and made in different plants. The navy was not convinced, however, and attempted to point out specific instances of interference and special treatment of the bomber program out of the priority order indicated in the ANMB Priority Lists.

A procedure was adopted on the suggestion of the air corps under which individual defense contractors reported to OPM their critical machine tool needs. The Tools Section of OPM then examined machine tool builders' order boards, consulted with the tool builders by phone or other means, and arranged for diversion of tools from one contractor to another. This procedure was very timeconsuming. On May 5, 1941 the ANMB Machine Tool Committee reported to Mason Britton, OPM, that of the first forty critical tool lists submitted only four had been acted upon, that there was a backlog of 15,000 critical tools, and that the number was continuously growing.

General Preference Order E-1 was issued by the OPM on March 26, 1941, directing machine tool producers to fill army, navy, and British orders first and not to make any nondefense deliveries except after release by the Priorities Division of OPM.

Lists of prime contractors considered by the contracting service to be critical were prepared by the army and navy and issued by the ANMB. One weakness of this procedure was that there were separate lists for each service and there was no basis, other than requested delivery dates, on which to resolve conflicts between contractors' delivery requirements.

Master Preference List Established

By the spring of 1941, both OPM and the navy were convinced that a single Master Preference List was badly needed but were opposed by the army which contended that

1. Joint lists would be too long.

2. Lists were not static and would need to be changed each time a tool was diverted from one contractor to another.

3. Their tools would be so far down the list that there would, in effect, be two lists with Navy orders at the top and Army orders at the bottom.

The navy replied that the army objections were largely groundless because

1. The joint list would need to include a comparatively small number of prime contractors.

2. The Master Preference List would result in "automatic scheduling" and would be very flexible.

3. It was not certain that all Army contractors would be at the bottom, but if this proved to be the case, it would merely reflect approved priorities and the Army's objections became an attempt to circumvent priorities.[9]

The conflicting views were ultimately resolved through the ANMB Tools Committee and the Combined Master Preference List was issued by OPM as Supplementary Order No. 1 on July 7, 1941 to be effective for light tools on August 15, 1941, and for heavy tools on September 15, 1941.[10]

[9] RG 80, JJ 40/L8–3, Memorandum from Capt. E. D. Almy, USN, for the Secretary of the Navy, May 15, 1941.
[10] RG 80, Office of Procurement and Material, Machine Tool Section, 1942U to 1941W, Memorandum from Ferdinand Eberstadt to Under Secretary of the Navy James V. Forrestal, June 28, 1941; Letter from John D. Biggers, OPM, to Forrestal, July 16, 1941, with comments on the Eberstadt memorandum; Smith, *The Army and Economic Mobilization*, pp. 564–566.

The ANMB Machine Tools Committee succeeded in having included with the Master Preference List, a control plan which required that all defense contractors go back to the contracting bureau or branch for authentication of the urgency of their requirements. Neither the army air corps or the Navy Bureau of Aeronautics was satisfied with the result. A major complaint was that the Master Preference List did not specify when tools would actually be delivered. Since the urgency standings were "open ended" those at the top could order more tools than were needed. Under Secretary of War Patterson asked OPM to survey the tools industry and determine when aircraft manufacturers would receive their tools.

Mason Britton's reaction was to point out that the Master Preference List had been prepared by ANMB and that if the War Department believed that any projects should be given higher ratings they should be handled through the ANMB. He also attributed much of the OPM Machine Tool Section's troubles to their lack of sufficient knowledge of what production programs were to be.[11]

There was an attempt by the Air Corps Scheduling Unit and OPM Aircraft Section to give the latter control of distribution of all machine tools for the aircraft program rather than the OPM Machine Tools Section and the ANMB which were trying to control the flow of machine tools to all projects. Part of the problem was that neither the OPM Tools Section nor ANMB had full information on the total machine tool requirements of all the defense programs and were trying to operate on the basis of ratings which were supposed to reflect the relative urgency of the programs. The slowness of aircraft contractors in placing machine tool orders also continued to be a problem.[12]

The NMTBA's Defense Committee endorsed issuance of the Master Preference List as a forward step and promised to do everything in its power to "establish the list throughout the industry as the accepted guide for the production and delivery of machine tools." A survey of the production plans of the first ten contracts on the Master Preference List disclosed that in many cases requested delivery dates, if met, would result in the delivery of tools weeks or months before they could be used. General Preference Order No. E-1 did not give the machine tool builder any discretion in arrang-

11 Sitterson, *Aircraft Production,* p. 119.
12 *Ibid.,* p. 122.

ing his order of delivery from the preference rating and required date stated. The NMTBA Defense Committee concluded

We find the following faults in setting the delivery dates required:

1. An acceptance by top management of dates for starting production which the production officials know to be impossible.

2. A demand for machine deliveries weeks or months in advance of the completion of the buildings in which they are to be installed.

3. Delivery dates set in advance of the completion of the jigs and fixtures which are essential to operation.

4. A demand for full equipment when only a pilot line can be used in the initial stages of production.

The procuring services were urged to give particular attention to the delivery dates requested and to periodically review and adjust requested delivery dates to reflect the current situation.[13]

Clayton R. Burt wrote to Forrestal on September 5, 1941 to report that an NMTBA-OPM team had completed its survey of the first fifty contracts listed in the Master Numerical Preference List, and that instructions had been issued to machine tool builders to deliver the machines produced where they were most needed and could be promptly put into service. Burt's letter suggested

. . . the orderly planning of government projects will help our industry meet the needs of the defense program without delay or confusion, and will advance the starting dates for actual production on defense projects.

Forrestal expressed satisfaction that the survey had been completed and agreement that orderly planning was essential. He added

I also still feel, however, that in spite of the substantial progress that the industry has made in training additional personnel and in expanding shift work that even further progress will have to be made along these lines.[14]

[13] RG 80, Office of Procurement and Material, Machine Tools Section, 1942U to 1941W, File "M," Letter from Clayton R. Burt to Under Secretary of Navy Forrestal, July 23, 1941, and enclosure; Smith, *The Army and Economic Mobilization*, p. 564.

[14] RG 80, JJ 40/L8–3, Letters from Burt to Forrestal, September 5, 1941 and Forrestal to Burt, September 10, 1941.

The complaints of machine tool builders and the Tools Branch of OPM that many contractors requested delivery of machine tools weeks or months before they could use them were paralleled by similar complaints from builders of electric motors and electrical controls against the tool builders. They claimed that it was general practice for tool builders to demand delivery as much as three months before they could be installed and then, when the electrical equipment was ready for delivery, the electrical manufacturers were told the tool builders would not accept the equipment until a much later date. This resulted in serious storage problems and deprived the electrical equipment firms of money for the equipment needed for working capital. Mason Britton, OPM Tools Branch Chief, agreed to issue instructions to the tool builders to schedule their requirements for motors and other equipment so that the required dates specified would be when they were ready to install the equipment.[15]

There were various problems with regard to the administration of priorities including the trend toward inflation due to the fact that new progrems tended to demand and get higher priorities than existing programs and a high percentage of defense orders was concentrated in the top priority brackets. It was hoped that the Master Preference List would go a long way toward solving these problems so far as critical machine tool distribution was concerned, and that closer supervision of machine tool deliveries and use would help.

When tool builders became confused by the trend toward overloading in the higher priority categories and by contradictory directives and advice from the government, they fell back on the practice of scheduling all defense orders on the basis of the date of receipt of orders.[16]

As the effects of the Master Preference List began to be felt in readjusted delivery dates, contractors who had been pushed back started to complain that OPM was making improper "diversions" of tools from one contractor to another. Most of these complaints

[15] RG 80, Office of Procurement and Material, Machine Tools Section, 1942U to 1941W, Memorandum from F. J. Cleary for Capt. E. D. Almy, USN, July 1, 1941; Memorandum from Lt. Cdr. R. E. W. Harrison to Capt. Almy, July 14, 1941.
[16] RG 80, ANMB, *Report on Machine Tools,* December 13, 1941.

appear to have been the result of a misunderstanding of what had taken place in implementing the Master Preference List.[17]

The Navy Bureau of Ordnance attributed its problems in obtaining tools to a combination of factors including

1. Higher priorities assigned to the 4-engine bomber and tank programs.

2. Their inability to obtain higher priorities from the ANMB.

3. The fact that most of the personnel in the machine tool section of OPM were from the machine tool industry.

4. Politics in OPM and the machine tool industry.

The Bureau of Ships and Bureau of Aeronautics faced a similar situation but reported better cooperation from the ANMB and OPM than did the Bureau of Ordnance.[18]

Status of Order Boards

During the summer of 1941, the Tools Branch of OPM attempted to establish a system by which it could collect and maintain current information on the status of all machine tool builders' "Order Boards" (basic information on each order from the time it was received until the machine tools were delivered or the order cancelled). Compilation and maintenance of all this information was difficult and time consuming and by July 1942, it seemed evident that WPB was not getting complete information. Nevertheless, the information available confirmed the fact that there were wide variations in distribution of orders both among firms producing the same type of tools and between producers of the "critical" tools and other types.[19]

This continuing imbalance in the order boards was frequently pointed out as a problem needing more attention, and the WPB

[17] RG 80, JJ 40/L8–3, Memorandum from Capt. E. D. Almy for Under Secretary of the Navy James V. Forrestal, November 20, 1941, "Unauthorized Machine Tools—Diversions."

[18] RG 80, Office of Procurement and Material, Machine Tool Section, 1942U to 1941W, Memorandum from F. D. Overfelt to James V. Forrestal, October 17, 1941, "Machine Tools."

[19] RG 179, WPB, Policy Analysis and Records Branch (PARB), Draft of Special Study No. 35, pp. 225–226.

Tools Branch was criticized on the ground that it was not taking sufficiently aggressive action. Two types of problems were identified. One involved customer preferences which caused many contractors to insist on ordering only the tools of particular manufacturers even though other firms could supply equivalent machines at an earlier date. There were attempts to overcome this tendency by education and persuasion but these efforts had limited effect. The other problem was the fact that there were large differences between the backlogs of some builders of the "critical" tools and those of firms building other types of tools. It was suggested that some of the firms producing noncritical tools should be converted to the production of the critical types as another way of securing better balance in production and reducing backlogs. The WPB Tools Division, and machine tool industry leaders, agreed that better balance in the distribution of orders and production was needed. They felt they were doing as much as possible to promote this objective, but that the critical types of tools were produced mainly by a few large companies, and that the possibility of converting the facilities of many other firms to production of these tools was very limited.

Part of the difficulty was attributed to lack of information in the hands of contractors as to the best source available for each type of tool, although OPM and WPB attempted to maintain and pass on this type of information when it was requested. The WPB and ANMB also periodically issued a booklet showing open dates for orders on each type of machine tool.

Revision of Preference Order

General Preference Order E-1-a was issued on January 6, 1942, making minor changes in the earlier order and reflecting changes in the Master Preference List. This order was replaced for machine tools on April 30, 1942, by General Preference Order E-1-b. Order E-1-b divided machine tool purchases into three groups:
1. Service purchasers;
2. Foreign purchasers; and
3. Other purchasers.
It allocated 75 per cent of each machine tool producer's output to service purchasers and the remaining 25 per cent to the other

groups. The 75 per cent was further divided by service and the Master Preference List was to determine sequence of delivery within each service group. Sequence of delivery for foreign orders and domestic civilian orders was to be determined by preference ratings and time of receipt of orders. One problem was the cumbersome procedure required to adjust the Master Preference List with the result that it was obsolete by the time revisions were published.[20]

Order E-1-b was amended on August 13, 1942 to revise the procedure for scheduling any unused excess in a given group's quota. The order was further amended on September 9, 1942 to modify the classification of service groups.

Aircraft Program "Green Light"

In August 1942, the air corps reported that 28,123 machine tools on order for delivery in 1942 did not have satisfactory promised delivery dates. The air corps also claimed that the percentage of machine tools allocated to it was not consistent with its requirements. The WPB Machine Tools Branch believed that the air corps requirements could be met but only at the expense of other defense programs.[21]

In September 1942, at the President's request, WPB reviewed the possibility of achieving the President's objective of 125,000 planes in 1943. The WPB Joint Aircraft Planning Committee predicted that aircraft production in 1942 would fall 10,000 planes short of the President's goal of 50,000 planes. Machine tools were identified as one of the limiting factors for 1943 and the committee concluded that the limitations could be overcome only by aggressive action including diversion of machine tools from other programs to the aircraft program. Such action, in the committee's view, would require a directive from the Commander-in-Chief giving the aircraft program a "green light" to take whatever was necessary from other programs. It was recognized that such action would hurt other programs but it was felt that less drastic action would not be sufficient to achieve the President's objective.

Discussions between the President, Donald M. Nelson, General

[20] Smith, *The Army and Economic Mobilization*, pp. 564–565; RG 179, WPB, *History of the Tools Division*, pp. 96–97.
[21] RG 179, Draft of PARB Special Study No. 35, pp. 386–387.

Marshall, and Admiral King followed, and on October 29, 1942, the President sent a letter to Nelson confirming his position regarding the 1943 aircraft program. On November 5, Amendment 3 to General Preference Order E-1-b was issued by WPB turning on the "green light" so far as machine tools for the aircraft and related programs were concerned. Under Amendment 3, defense orders were divided into two types namely Type 1 for the aircraft program and Type 2 for all other service programs.[22]

This action resulted in protests from the services whose programs were adversely affected and from the Joint Chiefs of Staff. These were followed by suggested changes which were strongly opposed by Brainard, Chief of the WPB Tools Branch, on the ground that Amendment 3 had already been issued and further changes would confuse the tool builders who were in the process of rearranging their order boards as directed. Admiral William D. Leahy wrote Nelson on November 12 on behalf of the Joint Chiefs of Staff, apparently without knowing that Amendment 3 had been issued a week earlier, and requested that any new priority directive be held up pending receipt of a policy statement from the Joint Chiefs. A second letter was sent to Nelson on the following day advising him that the Joint Chiefs were preparing a directive to the ANMB to guide it in establishing priorities for production. On November 14, Admiral Leahy sent Nelson a chart which was being forwarded to the ANMB showing the priorities in production desired by the Joint Chiefs and repeating that Nelson would be sent a copy of an implementing directive being prepared for the ANMB.

Nelson replied to all three letters on November 16 informing Leahy that he had relayed the President's instructions, that nothing should be allowed to interfere with the 1943 aircraft program, to Charles E. Wilson and Ferdinand Eberstadt; that the subject had been carefully considered by the WPB Production Executive Committee (PEC) on which the army and navy were represented; and, that the PEC had decided upon the change in Order E-1-b issued on November 5. Nelson conceded that the action would retard other programs but said "it was believed by us to be in accordance with the wishes of the President and to have been accepted by both the army and navy." Only later did he learn of the services' objections. Nelson concluded

[22] *Ibid*, p. 289.

In view of the very direct and concise instructions which I have received from the President, you will appreciate my reluctance in ordering any change in the present situation without his concurrence.[23]

Leahy wrote Nelson again on November 16, 1942 enclosing a priorities statement prepared by the Joint Chiefs for the ANMB showing the relative priority standings of the various programs. Nelson replied to this letter with a letter drafted by Eberstadt referring to the instructions received from the President regarding priorities for the aircraft, escort vessel, and merchant shipping programs which were not consistent with the priorities indicated in the Joint Chiefs' list. Nelson's letter added: "While I value the advice of the Army and Navy Munitions Board, I cannot and will not surrender to them the exercise of the priority power which the President has conferred upon me."

The services continued to press for modification of Amendment 3 to General Priorities Order E-1-b and eventually an agreement was worked out under which the WPB Tools Division attempted to avoid serious interference with the important defense programs other than aircraft by arranging for the diversion of essential tools. The navy was still unhappy that tools had been diverted from the escort vessel program to the aircraft program. The disagreement was settled more or less satisfactorily by the middle of December 1942.[24]

The ANMB issued instructions that military orders be rerated from A-1-a up to AA-5. This brought up the question as to the effect of such ratings on machine tools and whether the AA-5 orders took precedence regardless of the urgency ratings in the Master Preference List. Order E-1-b was amended in late December 1942 to provide that individual preference ratings would have no effect on defense orders for machine tools which would be governed by the urgency standings established in the Master Preference List.[25]

By the end of January 1943, the machine tool situation for the aircraft program had substantially improved and the air force

[23] RG 179, Letter from Nelson to Leahy, November 16, 1942 with copies to the President, Patterson, and Forrestal (PD File 481.033).

[24] RG 179, Production Executive Committee, *Minutes,* December 16, 1942 (PD File 481.025).

[25] RG 179, Draft of PARB Special Study No. 35, pp. 296–298.

indicated that some tools might be spared for more pressing army or navy requirements. Schedules were frozen for a period of 60 days in order to stabilize deliveries and minimize interruptions in production. George H. Johnson, who had replaced Brainard as Director of the Tools Division, recommended early in February that the "green light" for the aircraft program be turned off in April 1943. This proposal was accepted by the services and a new version of Order E-1-b drafted.

An amendment of January 26, 1943, placed a sixty-day freeze on all orders. On March 8, 1943 the distribution formula for service orders was revised to provide that instead of a specified percentage, each service group was entitled to the percentage which its net backlog of unfilled orders represented of the total net backlog. Dealer purchases for stock were prohibited.[26]

Order Board Reporting

The WPB Order Board reporting procedure was revised in October 1942, effective November 1. The new system provided essential information while eliminating double reporting and some of the paperwork previously required. A separate card was submitted for each tool and assigned a separate number to be used in submitting changes to the information originally submitted including diversions, revision of urgency standing, and changes in promised delivery dates. The basic data reported included dollar value of the machine, type of electrical equipment, required delivery date, priority rating, model including whether standard or special, customer's name, and the product or program for which the tool was to be used.[27]

The Order Board reporting system was apparently accepted by the machine tool industry without objection and the forms were said to be of value for internal management operations. The Tools Division decided to discontinue the system, however, in the spring of 1944 because of the expense involved. With the development of an expanded ammunition program in December 1944, tool builders

---

[26] RG 179, *History of the Tools Division*, p. 97.
[27] RG 179, Draft of PARB Special Study No. 35, p. 277.

were again requested to submit their order boards and to report any changes each week by telegraph.[28]

The WPB Tools Division was criticized by the Machine Tool Section of ANMB for "hand scheduling" the Order Boards contrary to the requirements of General Preference Order E-1-b causing confusion and delaying high priority programs. The ANMB proposed that the Order Boards be circulated among the services to determine whether they concurred. Also when Order E-1-b was amended in March 1943 to end the "green light" for the aircraft program, the WPB Tools Division notified some tool builders to ignore the amended procedures and continue to give Air Force orders preference. After ANMB's protest, the Tools Division agreed to instruct the tool builders to reschedule their orders under the amended Order.[29]

Order E-1-b was amended on July 5, 1943 to provide that within the Foreign and Other Purchasers' 25 per cent, sequence of deliveries for orders rated A-1-a or higher was to be determined on the basis of required delivery dates rather than rating. By the fall of 1943, there were proposals to greatly simplify or revoke Order E-1-b and it was said that it was

... very much out of date and is a laughing stock of the War Production Board. A majority of tool manufacturers regard it as meaningless. Mr. Chafee advised that the Order presently is and has been out of date for many months.[30]

Unfilled Orders versus Shipments

Fluctuations in the level of unfilled orders are more significant of changes in machine tool demand and the relationship between demand and capacity, than production, shipments, or employment. In January 1942, unfilled orders amounted to 82,800 units valued at $488,359,000 compared to shipments in 1941 of 185,000 units with a value of $775,000,000. In 1942, net new orders for 372,500 units valued at $1,624,950,000 were received compared to shipments of

[28] *Ibid.*, pp. 228–229.
[29] *Ibid.*, pp. 202–203.
[30] *Ibid.*, p. 300; *Minutes of the Meeting of Tools Division, WPB with Army, Navy and ARCO Representatives*, April 12, 1944 (PD File 053.505).

307,186 units valued at $1,321,748,000. The peak in unfilled orders was reached in July 1942, when 216,700 units were on order valued at $1,117,391,000. Peak shipments were achieved in December 1942 with 29,530 units valued at $131,960,000. By December 1942, unfilled orders had declined to 156,400 units valued at $866,578,000 (See Appendix Table 23).

During 1943, the order backlogs were gradually reduced, although shipments also declined as employment and hours on machine tool production were reduced, and some facilities were converted to direct war production. In January 1943, there were still 143,600 units on order valued at $796,101,000. These figures were drastically reduced in 1943 until in December 42,500 units valued at $210,606,000 were on order. At the then current rate of shipments of $60,873,000 per month, this represented less than four months work although it should also be remembered that the actual unfilled orders varied very substantially between different types of machine tools and between the different companies.

During 1944, and the first quarter of 1945, the level of unfilled orders increased rather significantly from 38,400 units valued at $181,538,000 in January 1944 to 65,800 units valued at $310,052,000 in March 1945. The increase was due basically to the reduction in shipments which reached a low point in July 1944 of 8,367 units valued at $32,753,000 as a result of the combinations of conversions to direct war production and the reduction in employment and hours of work previously mentioned. Unfilled orders declined moderately by June 1945 before the war in the Pacific ended and postwar cutbacks began. Net new orders for 1945 were about one-third lower than for 1944, declined still further in 1946, and more drastically in 1947, were somewhat higher in dollar value in 1948 though slightly lower in number of units, and declined drastically again in 1949 to 30,800 units valued at $233,100,000. Shipments in 1949 exceeded new orders (See Appendix Tables 23, 24, 25).

It has been pointed out that, despite the rapid increase in orders, the volume of unfilled orders at their peak in July 1942 did not exceed twelve months' output at current rates.[31] It should also be

---

[31] U.S. Senate, 82nd Congress, 2d Session, Joint Committee on Defense Production, *Defense Production Act, Progress Report No. 13, Machine Tools,* January 23, 1952 (Washington: Government Printing Office, 1952), p. 6.

pointed out, however, that this overall average ratio between un-filled orders and output concealed very wide variations among types of machine tools and among machine tool builders. Even among the large companies, backlogs in April 1942 varied from three months (in effect not really a backlog) to thirty-two months. Among me-dium-sized companies, the range was from one month to about one hundred months or over eight years at the then current rate. The range among small firms was from one month to fifty-four months. Probably more important than the wide range was the fact that some of the machines with very large backlogs were those most urgently needed. Efforts to redistribute orders and to "level-off" machine tool builders' order boards were discussed in Chap-ter 8.

Exports during the World War II period rose from $91,236,000 in 1939 to a peak of $237,433,000 in 1943 before again beginning to decline. From 1939 through 1942, the largest share of exports of machine tools was to the United Kingdom. Japan was in second place in 1939 followed by the U.S.S.R. in 1940, and 1941, Canada was second followed by the U.S.S.R. By 1942, the U.S.S.R. was in second place followed by Canada. In 1943, 1944, and 1945, the U.S.S.R. moved into first place followed by the U.K. and Canada (See Appendix Table 24). Exports as a percentage of total machine tool shipments were at their peak in 1939 and declined in relative importance during World War II, although the total amount ex-ported in 1943 was about three times that in 1939.

A breakdown of tool shipments by broad type indicates that, in World War II as in World War I, there was at least a partial sus-pension of the trend toward the specialized types of machines and increased production of the more standardized general purpose tools. Total machine tool shipments by type for January 1, 1942 to July 1945 were:

Lathes	$1,128,388,000
Grinding Machines	566,471,000
Milling Machines	545,340,000
Boring Machines	314,312,000
Drilling Machines	267,880,000
Gear-Cutting and Finishing Machines	146,877,000

Planers	69,089,000
Broaching Machines	21,902,000
Miscellaneous	206,057,000[32]

Price Levels

Machine tool prices increased gradually by about 4 per cent a year during the period from 1937 to September 1939. As the impact of war orders began to be felt, prices rose more rapidly. The average increase in new tool prices from October 1939 through December 1941 was about 18 per cent. Used tool prices were bid up rapidly when new tools were not available and in some cases substantially exceeded the current price of new tools.[33]

Used Tool Prices Controlled

Price Schedule No. 1 was issued by the Price Stabilization Division (OPACS) of the Advisory Commission to the Council of National Defense (NDAC) on February 17, 1941. This schedule attempted to prevent excess profits on sales of second-hand machine tools for defense use. The schedule provided a method of calculating maximum prices for secondhand machine tools based on percentages of the price when new related to the age of the machine as determined by the serial number of the machine. The schedule also provided for inventory reports by all dealers covering acquisition, sales, and prices of tools handled.

Price Schedule No. 1 was subsequently amended to

1. Provide a copy of the inventory report to the Machine Tools Section of the NDAC Production Division (later to OPM and WPB); and

2. Require additional information on sales and provide that the offering price must cover the basic machine exclusive of extras which were to be listed separately with prices figured by the same percentage as the basic tool.

[32] RG 179, WPB, Draft of PARB Special Study No. 35, pp. 190–191. WPB, "Facts for Industry," 34–3–5, October 31, 1945.

[33] RG 188, Office of Price Administration, Industrial Division, Director's File, "History of Price Control in the Machine Tool Industry."

Revised Price Schedule No. 1 was issued on September 24, 1941 adding a definition of a "Rebuilt and guaranteed" machine tool which could be sold at a higher price than a tool sold in "as is" condition. Amendment 1 to Revised Price Schedule No. 1 issued on November 3, 1942 added a provision for licensing dealers in second-hand machine tools or parts. After further amendments, Revised Price Schedule No. 1 was replaced by Maximum Price Regulation No. 1 of July 20, 1943.

Pricing Policy for New Tools

Machine tool builders and dealers followed various practices in quoting prices. The principal objective during the period from 1939 through 1941, when both demand and direct costs for labor and materials were rising, was to protect themselves against the effects of cost increases. The tool builder was not willing, in most cases, to quote a firm price on a tool which would not be delivered for many months. Some firms used a device by which they qualified price quotations with provisions for increases based on the list price current thirty days prior to shipment; or, that the price was subject to an increase of 10 or 20 per cent thirty days prior to shipment. One company, Brown and Sharpe, followed a procedure of quoting firm but high prices and then, after delivery, recomputed its costs and made refunds where they were considered justified.[34]

The Navy Department agreed, as an alternative to such provisions, to the adoption of various "Escalator Clauses" intended to provide adjustments in prices to cover increased labor and material costs. Some machine tool builders resisted this approach and attempted to insist upon their existing practice. The Navy Department became concerned over the effects of this disagreement on tools badly needed by navy contractors and in February presented the problem to the OPM. Mason Britton, Chief of the OPM's Tools Branch, arranged for a meeting with NMTBA representatives on March 4, 1941 to arrive at an alternative proposal.[35]

[34] RG 80, JJ 40/L8–3, Memorandum from Admiral W. H. P. Blandy, USN, Chief, Bureau of Ordnance to Secretary of the Navy, March 4, 1941, "Escalator Clause for Machine Tools."

[35] RG 80, Office of Procurement and Material, Machine Tool Section, 1942U to 1941W, Memorandum from Capt. E. D. Almy to Mason Britton, February 27, 1941, "Price Adjustment Clause."

The meeting with industry representatives apparently resulted in an agreement that the industry would accept the escalator clause although Frederick B. Geier, Cincinnati Milling Machine Company, representing the tool industry proposed that the percentages used for labor and material should be 40 per cent and 30 per cent respectively rather than the reverse figures. The escalator clause procedure was used in navy contracts until the Office of Price Administration (OPA) imposed maximum price controls.[36]

On May 6, 1941, OPA informally requested the machine tool industry to voluntarily hold to prices quoted on that date. A similar request was also made by OPA in August 1941. Price increases and adjustments continued, however.

On October 21, 1941, Leon Henderson, OPA Administrator, wrote Under Secretary of the Navy, James V. Forrestal, objecting to the use of escalator clauses in machine tool contracts on the ground that they were highly inflationary and a major cause of continuing and dangerous price increases. He stated that (1) Over 95 per cent of the machine tool industry's output was going into defense. (2) The escalator clauses allowed prices to be based on wage rates and material costs at the time of delivery rather than actual costs of production. (3) Unit costs did not usually increase as rapidly as wage rates or material prices. (4) Escalator clauses discriminated in favor of producers with long production periods or large inventories. (5) The machine tool industry was using escalator clauses "ranging from those based on national indexes of wage rates and material prices to clauses that amount to open pricing." (6) The clauses nullified the OPA ceiling letter of May 6, 1941. (7) The machine tool industry was making unusually large profits; could absorb a large part of its increased costs, and "it is reasonable to expect this contribution to the defense effort."

Henderson said he was not suggesting that no adjustments should be made in machine tool prices, but that they should be made by OPA rather than automatically by an escalator clause. Price adjustments should also be made on an individual basis "in order that we may profit by the experiences of the last war and obviate the

---

[36] RG 80, JJ 40/L8–3, Memorandum from W. B. Woodson, Advocate General to Chief of Bureau of Ordnance, April 9, 1941, Report on Conference of OPM with NMTBA, March 4, 1941 in Mason Britton's office.

extravagance of the bulk-line cost principle." The output of high-
cost producers could be secured while avoiding "heavy windfall
profits to low-cost producers." Adjustments in price might be specified in contracts providing they did not exceed the OPA fixed
price at time of delivery.

Henderson assured Forrestal that OPA's primary purpose was
to maintain and increase production and secondarily to prevent inflation.[37]

R. E. W. Harrison recalled that the Navy Department had
originally opposed use of escalator clauses on the ground that they
would encourage applications for wage increases and higher prices.
It had agreed to accept the clauses as a matter of expediency and
the clauses used were devised to be equitable both to the tool
builder and the Navy Department. Harrison objected to many of
the points raised by Henderson either on the ground that they
were misstatements of fact, incorrect assumptions, or unjustified
conclusions. Thus Harrison insisted that the escalator clauses used
by the navy allowed for gradual variance in labor and material
costs over the period in which machinery was built. Harrison said
the Navy Department had no information on manufacturers' profits
but he assumed that current scales of taxation were designed to
effect the Administration's policy of not permitting the national
emergency to be exploited by manufacturers of defense products.[38]

Harrison insisted that Henderson's proposal that all price adjustments be left to OPA would complicate the Navy's contractual
relationships, be prejudicial to the national interests, and that
"complete discrimination must rest with the Department if it is to
fulfill its role in this military emergency." He added that, while
he thought that OPA's statement of purpose was commendable, he
did not see how this purpose could be achieved due to the fact
that OPM limited manufacturers to a thirty-day supply of materials with the probability that material costs would be higher
on succeeding orders. Also no effort was being made to stabilize
wages. Under Secretaries of War and Navy, Patterson and Forrestal,

[37] RG 80, Office of Procurement and Material, Machine Tool Section,
JJ 40/L4.
[38] RG 80, Ibid., 1942U to 1941W. Memorandum R. E. W. Harrison to Capt.
E. D. Almy, USN, October 23, 1941.

agreed, however, that the questions raised by Henderson required careful study and designated representatives to work with OPA on the problem.

Apparently OPA was convinced that the attempt to secure voluntary control of tool prices was not working satisfactorily and met with industry representatives to consider a formal price schedule. The machine tool representatives indicated their concern over the effects of a mandatory price schedule and offered to try again to secure industry compliance with a voluntary program. The results of this voluntary effort did not satisfy OPA and further discussions with industry and government representatives followed leading to issuance of Price Schedule 67—New Machine Tools—on January 20, 1942. This price schedule froze list prices for machine tools at the levels in effect on October 1, 1941. It provided that if a tool builder had no list prices in effect on October 1, 1941, his maximum prices would be the last prices at which the tools were sold between January 1, 1941 and October 1, 1941. If he had neither a price list nor a sale between the specified dates, he was to use the price of the most nearly comparable tool adjusted to reflect increases or decreases in cost resulting from significant mechanical differences and submit this price to OPA for approval. In addition, manufacturers were required to file with OPA all list prices, discounts, and extra charges in effect on October 1, 1941 and all increases put into effect since May 6, 1941 (the date when OPA had requested voluntary restraint) plus a balance sheet and profit and loss statement for the period ending December 31, 1941. It was provided that any manufacturer could ask OPA for an adjustment to the schedule claiming undue hardship.[39]

OPA also adjusted ceiling prices where machine tool builders subcontracted complete tools to other firms whose costs were higher than those of the prime contractor's own plant. This was necessary since, in some cases, the subcontractor's cost without any profit exceeded the ceiling price established for the prime contractor and other producers of the same tool. The prime contractor was required to submit to OPA complete specifications, the

---

[39] RG 188, OPA, Price Department, National Office, Progress Reports, Industrial Materials Price Division—Machinery, "Weekly Progress Report." October 20–25, 1941; OPA, Industrial Division, Director's File, "History of Price Control in the Machine Tool Industry."

quantity to be produced, and a proposed price based on October 1, 1941 levels and price determining methods. The subcontractor was then required to submit cost data to OPA based both on current and October 1, 1941 levels. OPA then decided whether a higher price was justified. One amendment to Price Schedule 67 authorized manufacturers to enter into contracts at prices above established levels while waiting formal action from OPA on requests for price adjustments and was intended to eliminate claims that OPA was delaying production of critically needed machine tools.[40]

In the spring of 1942, an OPA study of the machine tool situation by Charles M. Piper, E. M. Hiatt, and J. J. White resulted in several controversial conclusions. One of these was that net income before taxes had been growing rapidly since 1935 primarily as a result of the growth in business, higher prices, and reduced overhead in relation to volume. Price ceilings could, they suggested, be reduced by 10 per cent except for special cases of newly developed machine tools. Twelve machine tool companies did five to ten million dollars worth of business in 1940–1941 as compared to only two firms in 1935. It was assumed that as the smaller companies grew larger, their overhead in relation to sales must have declined.[41]

Dealers' commissions, which were estimated at about 12.8 per cent of tool sales, were considered excessive in view of the fact that the great majority of tool sales were to the government or its contractors and presumably required very little selling effort or service. Suggestions were made as to how machine tool builders could be induced or required to reduce commissions by lowering ceiling prices. The suggestion that dealer commissions were not justified and should be reduced or eliminated was apparently made verbally to the President of the NMTBA by Piper and reported to other machine tool industry leaders who protested to the WPB and ANMB. Both of the latter supported the machine tool industry's position that their dealer organizations were performing

[40] OPA, *Second Report of the Office of Price Administration* (Washington: Government Printing Office, 1942), p. 151.
[41] RG 188, Office of Industry Advisory Committees, Industry Council, Subject File, 1941–1943, Memorandum from Charles M. Piper *et al.*, to Louis H. Harris, May 19, 1942, "Machine Tool Analysis."

a useful function and were entitled to a higher profit during periods of peak demand on the grounds that they made very little in the depressed periods.[42]

No general price reduction for machine tools was attempted by OPA, and no evidence was found that the other conclusions and suggestions made by Piper, Hiatt, and White were endorsed by their superiors in OPA. It is possible that such views may have influenced consideration of some applications for price adjustments, but it appears that where dealer commissions were paid they were allowed in computing adjustments. However, in at least one case, a tool builder allegedly attempted to increase his own profits by withholding dealer commissions and in this case the commission was disallowed.

Renegotiation of Tool Contracts

In the spring of 1942, machine tool builders complained that they were being called upon by various supply services and bureaus of the army and navy to renegotiate machine tool contracts. The tool builders protested to the ANMB on the ground that their products were covered by price ceilings; that the money recovered would come largely out of excess profits taxes; and that they were required not merely to engage in a single renegotiation with the army and navy but with the various branches of each. They urged that an effort be made to exclude items subject to price controls from the renegotiation law, and if this was not possible that renegotiation be handled centrally for all contracts. Ferdinand Eberstadt wrote the Under Secretaries of War and Navy on June 26, 1942 calling this situation to their attention, emphasizing that the management of the machine tool companies was "spread very thin" and that most of them were comparatively small companies with limited staffs of accountants and lawyers. He concluded that

I feel that their grounds for complaint are just, and that this may be only the beginning of a general wave of protest on the

---

[42] RG 188, Price Department, National Office, Machinery Branch, Legal Section, Misc. Commodity File, "Machine Tools"; Memorandum from Leslie A. Jacobson, to Harold Leventhal, June 3, 1942, "Eberstadt's Telephone Conversation with Ginsburg on Machine Tool Prices."

part of industry against the burdens which the administration of this act will necessarily impose upon people whose time is now very fully occupied.

A note from "JVF" (Forrestal) to Frank Folsom, June 27, 1942 said "I got a load of this on my visit to Springfield last week."[43]

The subject of renegotiation of machine tool contracts was also aired before the House Committee on Naval Affairs in 1943. The hearings included testimony by Herbert J. Taylor, Vice Chairman, War Department Price Adjustment Board on machine tool industry profits. Taylor testified that after a thorough study, the board had concluded that the machine tool industry was realizing excessive profits. Profits for the year 1936 through 1939 were used as a basis for comparison and statistics for nineteen firms representing about 40 per cent of the machine tool industry were cited showing an expansion of volume of sales of about eight times the annual average for the 1936–1939 base period. The total sales for the nineteen firms in 1942 was about $534,000,000 as compared to an average of $67,700,000 for 1936–1939. Profits before taxes were about sixteen times the average level for the base period, and the rate of profits before taxes to sales had increased from 15.6 per cent during the base period to 31.9 per cent in 1942. While taxes had drastically reduced the profits shown, net earnings after taxes were $45,000,000 in 1942 or about 5½ times the $8,200,000 average earnings in the base period. Profits after taxes amounted to 44 per cent of net worth during 1942. He also cited figures indicating that the machine tool companies' ratio of earnings after taxes to net worth were about four times the average of a large segment of American Industry in 1942. The industry had not reduced prices as costs declined with increased volume of business.[44]

The Price Adjustment Board had considered the machine tool industry's outstanding production record, its contribution in creating efficient production machinery, and the fact that it would face reductions in sales. Taylor suggested that the industry's greater

[43] RG 80, JJ 40/L8–3.
[44] U.S. House of Repreesntatives, 78th Congress, 1st Session, "Hearings Before the Committee on Naval Affairs: Investigation of the Progress of the War Effort," Vol. 2, June 25, 1943, p. 888f; Wayne G. Broehl, Jr., *Precision Valley*, (Englewood Cliffs, N. J.: Prentice-Hall, Inc., 1959), pp. 236–243.

danger from saturation of its market by surplus unused tools was balanced by the fact that it didn't have serious problems with conversion of plants to civilian production.

Ralph E. Flanders answered most of the points made in Taylor's statement. He objected to the 1936–1939 base period on the ground that many firms did not show postdepression earnings until 1937 and showed "red ink" again in 1938. He also contended that profits after taxes rather than before should be considered in deciding whether profits were excessive. He claimed that of eight war-related industries, the machine tool industry had paid out the smallest percentage of dividends with the exception of the air-craft industry. The remaining "surplus" was "overexpended" in additions to fixed assets and additions to inventory and was not available for distribution.[45]

Flanders also objected to use of "net worth" as a basis for com-paring profits and suggested that return on total assets would be a fairer basis of comparison. On this basis, profits for the 19 firms used by Taylor amounted to 13.9 per cent of total assets in 1942. Flanders then challenged most of the assumptions Taylor had made regarding the future outlook for the machine tool industry emphasizing the threat presented by the large number of used tools which would be available and restrictions on tool replacement. He agreed that, to some degree, the longer hours of wartime operation tended to wear out tools more rapidly than normal operations, but claimed that modern tools were much more durable than in the past and cited various factors contributing to this. He also offered figures to show that several large companies including General Motors and East-man Kodak had been permitted to retain a larger percentage of profits after taxes than many smaller firms including machine tool builders.[46]

Maximum Price Regulation 67

Maximum Price Regulation 67, issued on June 23, 1944, froze all prices in effect on October 1, 1941 rather than just list prices, in order to cover firms which did not use list prices. A new pro-vision permitted tool builders to add a resale discount to their prices

[45] *Ibid.*, pp. 244–245.
[46] *Ibid.*, pp. 248–249.

on machines, parts, and attachments which they planned to distribute through dealers for the first time. Prices for new models (not mere modifications of existing machines) were to be determined by the manufacturer's pricing formula as of October 1, 1941. If he had no formula, he was to submit a proposed formula to OPA based on costs in his locality on October 1, 1941. The regulation provided for only a manufacturer's price to the user and left dealers' discounts and commissions up to the manufacturer and dealers. It made the hardship adjustment clause more definite by requiring OPA to adjust prices whenever it could be shown that production was being impeded. OPA was to consider (1) total unit costs less selling and administrative expenses allocable to the internal management of the business, (2) total unit costs, and (3) whether the manufacturer's profit position was greater or less than his overall profit during the normal base period.[47]

The principal amendment to Maximum Price Regulation 67 was issued on April 19, 1946 and granted the machine tool industry a 20 per cent increase over existing maximum prices based on a survey revealing that such an increase was necessary to permit the industry to earn its 1936–1939 level of profit.

Effectiveness and Effects of Price Control

From OPA's viewpoint, the effectiveness of machine tool price controls was evidenced by the fact that machine tools remained at 118 in the Bureau of Labor Statistics' (BLS) Price Index from October 1941 through April 1946 when the industry-wide price adjustment was approved. It was recognized, however, that the BLS Index covered only a selection of established firms and did not necessarily reflect the industry as a whole. During the war, the machine tool industry included many new firms whose prices were established by a formula which usually resulted in higher prices than for the older firms making similar machines. The BLS Index also did not reflect individual price adjustments granted to high cost producers. A total of 107 adjustments were granted and 72 denied in the period from January 20, 1942 to October 1, 1946.

An OPA survey, made in the spring of 1946, disclosed that where-

[47] RG 188, Industrial Division, Director's File, "History of Price Control in the Machine Tool Industry."

as the machine tool industry showed a ratio of net profit before taxes to net worth of 77.1 per cent in 1941, its profits had declined to the point where, by the end of 1945, it was operating at a small loss. This trend was continued during the first quarter of 1946 because of further increases in material and labor costs and reduced volume of production. This was the basis for granting the industry-wide price adjustment of 20 per cent intended to restore profit margins to their 1936–1939 levels. Apparently the industry's actual price increases following the OPA action averaged only about 15 per cent.

OPA challenged claims that price controls restricted or hampered production, pointed to the fact that peak production was achieved when price controls were tightest, and quoted testimony of the Machinery and Allied Products Institute (MAPI) before a House committee to support this view.

> During the war, price control over machinery was integrated with other important controls—such as those over materials, components, wages and manpower—and conditions of wartime production were exceptional as to volume and nature of output. Under this combination of factors, production at 1941–1942 ceiling prices was possible and price control had very little practical effect on manufacturers' operations.[48]

The machine tool industry accepted price controls as a necessary evil and apparently tried to live up to both the letter and spirit of the law despite its effect on profits. This does not mean, of course, that it was convinced that price regulations as administered were in all respects either necessary or equitable. Within a month after V-J Day the industry presented a formal petition to OPA requesting elimination of price controls on machine tools. This proposal was based on the claim that capital equipment constituted a small part of the cost of finished products and did not represent a significant factor in the cost of living, that price control was interfering with reconversion to peacetime operations, that machine tool production and demand had declined since the peak in 1942, and that available idle capacity would provide sufficient competitive force to prevent excessive price increases.

OPA rejected this petition on the ground that the machine tool

48 *Ibid.*, p. 10.

industry had not met the requirements of the Office of Economic Stabilization's Directive 68 requiring that industries show that prices would not rise above existing levels if decontrolled and that its product was not an important element in the cost of living or doing business, and had failed to present facts to support its case.

Efforts in favor of decontrol continued through the fall and winter of 1945–1946 and culminated in a presentation by MAPI to the House Committee on Banking and Currency on March 12, 1946. It was charged that price controls were hampering production and discouraging technological progress, that increased production of civilian goods was limited by machinery shortages, and that high output was the real answer to threats of inflation. It was also alleged that OPA's adjustment criteria were unrealistic, that capital equipment prices would not rise excessively, that competition was assured by expanded capacity, and that an additional brake on prices would be supplied by the large stock of government-owned surplus machine tools. It was recommended that capital equipment be immediately exempted from price controls.

OPA presented a long opposing statement on March 22, 1946, in which it contended that decontrol could actually reduce production of consumer goods by diverting scarce metal to capital equipment production, and that selective decontrol was the best procedure. It challenged MAPI's contention that production had been restricted and contended that price control did not hamper development of new equipment. OPA also attempted to counter the claim that competition would control prices of many types of machine tools where there was little standardization of products, cited Industry Advisory Committee predictions that price increases would run from 15 to 30 per cent or possibly higher, and claimed that demand was far in excess of productive capacity. It denied that surplus tools would be a significant factor in controlling prices except for certain tools. Moreover, the small businessman would be hurt far more by equipment price increases than large manufacturers. There would be competitive bidding for scarce parts, and competition for scarce labor would increase pressure for decontrol from the consumer durable goods industries.[49]

Partially submitting to pressure from industry and Congress, OPA

[49] *Ibid.*, pp. 11–13.

suspended a list of items including large machine tools weighing over 50,000 pounds from price controls on April 8, 1946. Pressure for decontrol continued, however, until July 26, 1946 when OPA suspended controls on tools weighing over 2,000 pounds. The controls retained on the small tools were supposed to protect small businesses and veterans trying to start small businesses.

Machine tool builders were required to report price increases following decontrol and during August and September, OPA attempted to analyze the results of decontrol. This seemed to indicate that most tool price increases had not exceeded the 20 per cent granted in April 1946 although there were wide variations. Moreover, it did not appear likely that there would be rapid increases in machine tool prices, but rather gradual adjustments dictated by increasing costs.

Profit and Sales 1939–1949

Profits data were not found for the machine tool industry as a whole during World War II, but figures for the three tool companies at Springfield, Vermont studied by Wayne G. Broehl, Jr., are of interest and are probably reasonably typical of established and well-managed machine tool firms. Jones and Lamson Machine Company showed profits of $844,000 in 1939 and paid $147,000 in dividends. Its profits increased in 1940 and 1941 and totaled $1,599,000 in 1941. They declined slightly in 1942 but rose again in 1943 to $1,597,000. They fell drastically in 1944 to $481,000 and in 1945 were $284,000. A net loss of $415,000 was incurred in 1946 followed by moderate profits of $202,000 and $233,000 in 1947 and 1948. In 1949, the last full year prior to the Korean War, Jones and Lamson was operating at near the break-even point with profits of $54,000. The highest dividends of $386,000 were paid in 1940 followed by $315,000 in 1941 and $257,000 annually in 1942–1945.[50]

If these profit figures are compared as percentages of sales for the eleven-year period, there is a downward trend from 17.8 per cent in 1939 to a low of minus 6.4 per cent (loss) in 1946 and about .9 per cent in 1949. The percentages for 1941–1943, the peak "tooling-up" period, were 10, 6.2, and 5.9 per cent respectively. It would

[50] Broehl, Jr., *Precision Valley*, pp. 175, 206, 212.

also be desirable to compare profits to total capital investment and net worth during this period, but the necessary data were not found.

In the case of the Fellows Gear Shaper Company, there was more variation in the pattern of profits. Peak profits of $1,427,000 were secured in 1940 and were about 2½ times their 1939 level but were followed by a substantial decline in 1941 to $1,081,000 and to $912,-000 in 1942. There was an increase in both profits and volume of sales in 1943–$986,000 profit on sales of $20,469,000–followed by a drastic reduction in volume of sales in 1944 and a somewhat less severe drop in profits to $860,000 on sales of $13,984,000. In 1945, profits improved to $937,000 despite a small further drop in sales. The end of World War II brought a drastic drop in sales and in 1946 profits almost disappeared amounting to $34,000 on sales of $5,153,000. The company suffered a substantial loss of $475,000 in 1947 despite the fact that sales improved somewhat to $6,474,-000. In 1948, Fellows showed a profit of $133,000 on sales of $6,-193,000 and in 1949 did a little better with profits of $189,000 despite lower sales of $5,597,000. The firm paid dividends of $450,000 in 1939, $540,000 in 1940, and $360,000 in 1941, and drastically reduced dividends in 1942–1945 of $126,000, $108,000, $108,000, and $140,000 respectively.

In terms of profits as a percentage of sales, Fellows, like Jones and Lamson, earned its highest percentage in 1939 when profits represented 18.2 per cent of sales. The percentage dropped to 16.1 in 1940 and much more drastically to 10.7 in 1941 and 5.9 in 1942. They amounted to 4.9 per cent in 1943 on peak sales of $20,469,000. The percentage of profits improved somewhat in 1944 and 1945 to 6.1 and 7.0 per cent respectively but volume of sales dropped by almost a third to $13,984,000 and $13,421,000 respectively. The bottom was reached in 1947 when losses amounted to 7.3 per cent of sales followed by profits of 2.1 and 3.4 per cent in 1948 and 1949 on sales of $6,193,000 and $4,497,000.

The Bryant Chucking Grinder Company secured its highest profits in 1941 and 1942 when it had profits of $740,000 and $814,-000 on sales of $6,905,000 and $15,226,000. Its profits declined to $657,000 in 1943 despite the fact that sales remained at almost their 1942 level, and to $438,000 in 1944 on drastically reduced sales of $8,493,000. Both profits and sales declined in 1945 and 1946 to

$237,000 profits on sales of $4,906,000 in 1945 and $93,000 profits on sales of $1,372,000 in 1946. Profits declined still further in 1947 to $26,000 despite some increase in sales. The company experienced substantial losses of $250,000 and $221,000 in 1948 and 1949 on about the same level of sales. Bryant paid annual dividends of $200,000 from 1939 through 1944 and $150,000 in 1945.

Like other firms, Bryant's profits as a percentage of sales were highest in 1939 when they represented 20 per cent of sales. The percentage declined rapidly as volume of sales increased until in 1943 they were 4.3 per cent of sales of $15,207,000. The percentage improved somewhat in 1944 to 5.2 per cent but the volume of sales drastically declined to $8,493,000. Both percentage of profits and sales fell still further in 1945 to 4.9 per cent on sales of $4,906,000. In 1946, they were 6.8 per cent of sales of $1,372,000 while the percentage fell to 1.5 per cent of sales of $1,772,000 in 1947. Bryant suffered losses of 14.5 and 11.8 per cent of sales of $1,721,000 and $1,864,000 in 1948 and 1949—the highest percentage losses of the three firms.

Profits after taxes as a percentage of net worth for seventeen other firms are given in the Appendix Table 19. These firms show rather wide variations in profit ratios both between firms and from year to year. Peak profits for all of the firms for which information is available were earned in 1940 or 1941 and ranged from 14.1 per cent for one firm in 1941 to 65.1 per cent for another firm in 1940. Since these were large well-established corporations, it is likely that their profits ratio was somewhat higher than the average for all firms. In most cases, profit ratios were somewhat lower in 1942 than in 1940–1941. Most firms showed a declining profit ratio each year until 1947–1948 when six firms showed losses in at least one year. Three firms showed losses in 1949, but all showed profits in 1950, ranging from a low of 2.5 per cent to a high of 21 per cent. The declining profit ratios from 1942 were due to a combination of Excess Profits Taxes, renegotiation of government contracts, and increasing labor and material costs.

Wages and Hours 1939–1949

In 1939, the average weekly hours worked by production workers in the machine tool industry was 42.5. This average increased until it was 53.5 hours per week in 1942; declined to 50.7 and 50.6 hours in 1943 and 1944; to 47.9 hours in 1945; and much more drastically in 1946 to 42.8 hours. The average work week declined slowly in 1947 and 1948 to 42.1 hours and then more abruptly to 39.2 hours in 1949.

Average hourly earnings of production workers in 1939 was $.761 per hour. It increased to $.985 in 1942; to $1.193 in 1945; to $1.368 in 1947; and to $1.511 in 1949. Average weekly earnings of production workers in 1939 was $32.34. The average increased to $52.70 in 1942, to $58.19 in 1944 (the wartime peak), declined to $54.40 in 1946 before rising again to $61.68 in 1948, and then declined to $59.23 in 1949.[51]

Reconversion Planning

The general question of eventual reconversion to civilian production was probably never entirely out of the minds of machine tool builders during World War II. The industry could not, however, revert to civilian status as soon as the main "tooling-up" job was completed since there was still a big war production job of uncertain dimensions and duration to be done. The immediate question in 1943–1944 was the machine tool industry's role in direct war production. By the fall of 1943, however, WPB started to review its controls with a view to determining what reconversion policies should be and what changes should be made in the various orders in advance preparation for reconversion either immediately or when the right time came.

Donald M. Nelson wrote Bernard M. Baruch on December 29, 1943 that inventories of surplus machine tools were needed by WPB at the earliest possible date for use in preliminary planning for reconversion. In view of the great increase in tool shipments in the period 1940–1943, this was an obvious question and one of greatest interest to the machine tool industry.[52]

The opposition of the armed services to any relaxation of controls

---

[51] U.S. Department of Commerce, Bureau of the Census, U.S. *Census of Manufactures*, 1939, 1947, and 1954; U.S. Department of Labor, Bureau of Labor Statistics, "Employment and Earning Statistics—United States."

[52] J. Carlyle Sitterson, *Development of the Reconversion Policies of the War Production Board, April 1943–January 1944*, February 26, 1945 (WPB, PARB, Special Study 15), p. 59f.

or increase in civilian production before the invasion of Europe was completed, and the outcome of the war beyond doubt, prevented very much in the way of tangible action to prepare for reconversion. Much of the opposition to increased civilian production or construction, even where a strong case could be made for such, was based on the argument that manpower needed for direct war production would be drawn back to the civilian industries.

In April 1944, the Machine Tool Labor Advisory Committee recommended establishment of a WPB Management-Labor Committee to develop plans for fuller utilization of the machine tool industry's capacity and manpower in both war and peacetime production.[53]

Walter Reuther, UAW-CIO, speaking before a meeting of the WPB Automotive Labor Advisory Committee in April 1944, urged that advance tooling be permitted to facilitate transition to civilian production when war production made this possible and to absorb unemployment resulting from machine tool cutbacks. It should be recalled that machine tool shipments in April 1944 were less than one-third their peak of December 1942.[54]

When the Automobile Industry Advisory Committee met in July 1944 to discuss problems of reconversion and the Automotive Division's so-called "Blue Plan" for automobile production following V-E Day, it took up the problem of disposal of government-owned machine tools. The interrelationship between disposal of used tools and requirements for new tools was pointed out as was the fact that if the government could not say precisely what machines would be released after V-E Day, private companies could not count on any tools then in use in establishing their production plans.

Automobile Industry Advisory Committee members were told that where preference ratings were necessary to secure a machine tool with a long production time, individual applications for priorities would be considered. Some Committee members warned that failure to procure a small number of new machines could stop all production in the automotive industry, and that essential tools should be procured immediately.

In September 1944, when the end of the war in Europe seemed to be in sight, automobile industry representatives were critical of

[53] RG 179, Draft of PARB Special Study No. 35, p. 225.
[54] Sitterson, *Reconversion Policies*, pp. 59, 61–62.

government failure to take action to prepare for resumption of automobile production including particularly clearing plants of war materials and retooling for peacetime production. It was recommended that a special priority be assigned for tools to be used in car production and that other measures be taken. The request for a special priority was disapproved on the ground that it would be discriminatory since it could not be granted to all industries.

In the meantime, the machine tool industry was warning that unless it was given some consideration in regard to manpower, production of tools needed for peacetime conversion would be seriously affected. This contention was based partly on the claim that the industry had been able to do very little engineering work in preparation for civilian production.

In June 1944, Donald M. Nelson attempted to convince the members of the WPB of the need for preliminary action to prepare for reconversion including advanced retooling. Nelson's position was again opposed by service representatives. On June 18, Nelson announced his reconversion plans which, while placing first the necessity of getting military production up to schedule and keeping it there, also emphasized the need for preparing for civilian production although no immediate increase in civilian production could be undertaken. He also announced three additional steps including that, beginning July 1, 1944 manufacturers would be allowed to purchase machinery including tools and dies for civilian production. These were to come first of all from existing surpluses but, if necessary, orders approved by WPB could be placed for production without interfering with war production.[55]

The announced actions were again strongly opposed by the War and Navy Departments, Maritime Commission, and War Manpower Commission. Their only support within the WPB came from the two labor Vice Chairmen, Joseph D. Keenan and Clinton S. Golden, and from the Smaller War Plants Vice Chairman, Maury Maverick. They did, however, have strong political supporters including Senator Harry S. Truman, Chairman of the Senate Special Committee Investigating the National Defense Program, and Senator James E. Murray, Chairman of the Senate Small Business Committee. Further opposition came on July 7 in the form of a letter from

[55] *Ibid.*, pp. 90–91.

Admiral William D. Leahy for the Joint Chiefs of Staff addressed to Nelson and released to the press on the following day. The letter referred to the existing lag in war production and stated that issuance of the reconversion orders was "not consistent with the all-out prosecution of the war."[56]

Charles E. Wilson, WPB Executive Vice Chairman, and Sidney Weinberg also visited Nelson who was convalescing from pneumonia and tried to get him to agree to rescind his instructions to issue the orders. Nelson refused and wrote both Admiral Leahy and the President restating the reasons for the orders. Included in this explanation was the fact that he was convinced the orders would not interfere with war production, and that he had been advised by John Lord O'Brian, WPB General Counsel, that he (Nelson as Chairman of the WPB) had no legal authority to continue controls over materials in abundant supply. Following a demand from War Mobilization Director Byrnes that the matter be settled, Nelson agreed to staggered issuance of the orders and it was decided that the machine tools order would be issued on July 29 permitting manufacturers to place unrated orders for machine tools and equipment.[57]

Priorities Regulation 24 covering machine tools together with other machinery and equipment needed for civilian production was issued on July 29, 1944 after further discussion and opposition from the services and WMC. It provided for screening of orders for new equipment by WPB field offices to determine if the equipment was already available in idle or excess stock, approval of the placement of unrated orders by WPB field offices, and provision for applications for preference ratings for equipment to produce items which could not be produced under existing WPB restrictions. An amendment of August 28 authorized producers to begin production on unrated orders. Other amendments followed, and General Preference Order E-1-b was amended to eliminate the necessity for a preference rating on orders to be filled from the 25 per cent of machine tool orders reserved for nonmilitary orders. Since the war in Europe did not end in 1944 and there were in fact new or expanded military requirements both for the European War and the War in

[56] *Ibid.*, p. 98.
[57] *Ibid.*, pp. 99–100.

the Pacific, these measures had limited effect on retooling for peacetime production.[58]

Several provisions of the E-1-b Order were relaxed on June 22, 1944 including the prohibition on dealer stock orders and dealers were permitted limited inventories. On September 28, 1944 a General Revision of the Master Preference List was issued. The rating floor was eliminated on October 13, 1944 and on October 19, 1944, a tight policy on assignment of new ratings was established to reduce the volume of priority ratings and permit tool builders to schedule deliveries based on date of receipt of orders and requested delivery dates.

On January 26, 1945, an amendment was issued requiring tool producers to schedule all rated orders ahead of unrated ones if necessary to meet required delivery dates. The order was revoked on August 20, 1945, as part of a sweeping action by WPB revoking 210 individual orders which had limited production of a variety of items ranging from radios and domestic refrigerators to machine tools and construction machinery. Many other restrictions had already been removed in the period between V-E and V-J Days. This cleared most of the legal obstructions to resumption of full-scale civilian production. All the civilian goods producers needed were the machines, scarce materials, manpower, and a little time to rearrange their production lines. There was strong but largely ineffective opposition from labor, consumer representatives, and some other groups to the hasty removal of controls for fear of the effect decontrol might have on the supply of low-cost goods and low-cost housing construction, small businesses, unemployment, etc.[59]

The problem of the machine tool industry was somewhat different. Most tool builders had relatively little to do to clear out war work and return to civilian production other than to find enough customers to keep their shops going at anything approaching the then current level, even though this was far below the wartime peaks of 1942 and 1943. The industry was worried about the effect disposition of surplus tools would have on demand for new tools, and additional effort was put on preparing new models for production which hopefully would make many of the used tools obso-

[58] *Ibid.*, pp. 107–110.
[59] CPA, *Industrial Mobilization for War*, pp. 934–938, 950–956.

lete. Apparently, even though they supposedly had been fully occupied with war production, many firms had managed to find the time and technical manpower to work on improved designs. Most of the models appearing at the end of the war, however, did not involve radical departures from prewar or wartime machines.

The machine tool industry's postwar problems were increased by a decline in export business including the cutting off of sales to the U.S.S.R. and her satellites in 1947 and increased foreign competition for both domestic and foreign business. Exports of cutting tools dropped from $110,000,000 in 1946 to $105,300,000 in 1947 and much more drastically to $62,800,000 in 1948 and $72,600,000 in 1949. These figures, however, even allowing for higher tool costs, were still larger than prewar figures except for 1938 and 1939.

Disposal of Used Tools

In World War II as in World War I, the machine tool industry worried about the threat to postwar demand of a large volume of used government-owned machine tools which would no longer be needed at the end of the war. This concern was to prove well founded. In 1945, the *American Machinist's* "Inventory of Metal-Working Equipment" indicated that one-third the total number of machine tools in the country were government-owned. By 1949, this figure had dropped to 13 per cent though it appears some government-owned tools were not included in the total. Other machine tools had been disposed of and exerted a strong negative effect on the demand for new machine tools.

The policies and procedures used in the disposal of government-owned machine tools and their effects on defense readiness, the machine tool industry, and also on the long range competitive position of U.S. metalworking industry generally would seem to offer ample scope for another dissertation. Whether other policies were politically feasible is at best a highly speculative question for which the author has no adequate answer.

Machinery was set up for disposing of surplus machine tools before World War II ended but several elements needed to handle the problem appeared to be missing. These included realistic long range industrial readiness and mobilization plans on which the government agencies could decide what tools should be retained if any. Lacking these it was a slow and uncertain process to determine what tools were really surplus. There were also restrictions intended to prevent buyers of surplus tools from reselling them at a profit.

Late in 1945 government policy shifted to greatly accelerate the sale of government-owned tools. One of the objectives of the disposal program was to increase civilian production as rapidly as possible and by so doing reduce inflationary pressures which otherwise would have made it necessary to retain price control and perhaps other controls for a longer period. At any rate, over 200,000 machine tools were sold very rapidly at what appeared to be bargain prices. By the end of 1947 the liquidation process was largely completed so far as the government was concerned but its effects would be felt at least until the end of the Korean War and possibly far beyond.[60]

In 1950, the NMTBA announced that

There is no useful remaining reserve of machine tools left from World War II. The best of those machines have long since been absorbed by metalworking shops. Contractors have found it very difficult to find the machines they need in the National Security Reserve and they are often in bad order or have been cannibalized. . . .

On the eve of the Korean War machine tool orders were again growing more rapidly than production.[61]

Industry Input versus Output, 1939 and 1947

Relationships between the cost of labor and materials used by the machine tool industry and the value added by manufacture appeared to remain unchanged in 1947 as compared to 1939. In view of the fact that volume of output was greater in 1947 than in 1939, some change in the relationship between direct costs and

[60] Robert Stanley Himes, "A Study of the Machine Tool Industry With Emphasis on the Problem of Stability," Ph.D. Dissertation, The American University, 1962, pp. 202–204.

[61] National Machine Tool Builders Association, "Statement of the Machine Tool Industry to the National Production Authority," November 8, 1950; U.S. Senate, 82nd Congress, 2nd Session, Joint Committee on Defense Production, "Defense Production Act, Progress Report No. 13, Machine Tools," p. 11; U.S. Senate, 82nd Congress, 2nd Session, Select Committee on Small Business, *Machine Tool Shortages*, p. 42.

value added by manufacture would have seemed reasonable.

For 1947, machine tool builders reported purchases of $30,474,-000 of iron castings, $997,000 of steel castings, $9,848,000 of steel mill shapes and forms, $778,000 of copper castings, $549,000 of aluminum castings, and $145,000 of brass and wire mill shapes and forms. The total value of materials, fuel, electricity, and contract work reported amounted to $150,655,000 as compared to total shipments of $493,853,000. Included in the cost of materials, etc., were components such as electric motors and controls purchased, but no separate figures were reported for these although this information would be of interest.

The materials costs for particular materials shown above reflect only firms purchasing more than specified minimum amounts and do not cover small firm purchases which cumulatively would probably be a substantial amount.

Total payrolls reported in 1947 were $233,997,000 of which $165,-003,000 represented wages of production workers. Thus about 70 per cent of the payroll went to wage earners and 30 per cent to salaried employees.[62]

Value added by manufacture in 1947 was reported at $343,198,-000 or about 70 per cent of the value of total shipments of $493,-853,000. In 1939, value added by manufacture amounted to $155,-941,000 or almost exactly the same percentage of shipments of $221,267,000 as in 1947.

In 1939, machine tools represented 78 per cent of the industry's total output. A similar figure for 1947 was 77 per cent. In 1939, the machine tool industry produced about 94 per cent of the total output of machine tools and in 1947 about 86 per cent. This apparent downward trend in the machine tool industry's share in total machine tool output was apparently a temporary result of the war since the percentage again increased to 93 per cent in 1954.

Summary

Exports were an important factor in the recovery of the machine tool industry from the depression of the early thirties. However, following the outbreak of war in Europe, the United States began to modernize and build up its own armed forces and defense in-

[62] U.S. Bureau of Census, *Census of Manufactures.*

dustries. The President and top government officials became concerned both about competition between export sales and domestic requirements, and the direct value of machine tools to potential enemies. By the spring of 1940, it was decided that exports of machine tools to Japan and the U.S.S.R. must be stopped and assistance to Britain increased. Machine tool shipments to Japan and the U.S.S.R. were embargoed on the grounds of the Navy Department's need for tools. This step was followed by the Export Control Act of 1940 giving the President authority to stop or curtail exports of critical materials and machine tools, and an executive order establishing the control mechanism. It was also felt necessary to secure legislation authorizing the government to commandeer machine tools intended for export and divert them to other use without waiting for extended legal action against the machine tool builders for failure to live up to contracts. This was provided in the Selective Service and Training Act of September 16, 1940.

Action was also needed to direct machine tools into the expanding defense programs. The "voluntary" priority system adopted to give defense orders preference over nondefense orders, quickly proved inadequate. It was recognized that merely giving preference to orders for military end products was not enough. It was also necessary to control delivery of essential materials, components, and capital equipment to ensure that production would not be delayed or deliveries made long before needed. Machine tool builders were confused by the fact that almost all their orders were grouped in the top priority category with the result that they had no real guidance as to which machines should be delivered first. In November 1940, an ANMB Directive was issued subdividing the top A-1 preference rating category into rating bands from A-1-a to A-1-j. Machine tools and gauges were placed in the A-1-a category because they were essential to expand the production of military items. The preference ratings also became mandatory rather than voluntary. Unfortunately, the preference ratings were open-ended since they did not place a limit on the volume of orders which could be rated for a particular program, and did not establish when deliveries were required.

By the spring of 1941, aggressive efforts began to speed up deliveries of machine tools to aircraft contractors. The heavy bomber program was given top priority, but the Office of Production Management (OPM) tried to reassure the navy that other urgent programs would not be seriously hurt. The OPM Tools Section attempted to improve deliveries of individual machine tools which defense contractors and the services considered critical by informal, but very time-consuming, personal contacts with machine tool builders and by diverting individual tools from one contractor to another. This procedure led to complaints that critical tool lists were not being acted upon quickly enough, that OPM was playing "politics," and that it was too closely identified with the machine tool industry.

The army and navy issued separate numerical preference lists of prime contractors considered critical by the contracting services, but there was no basis other than requested delivery dates on which the lists could be reconciled. A Combined Master Preference List was issued by OPM on July 7, 1941. The major complaints against the list included that it was obsolete before being issued and that it didn't determine when tools would be delivered. The urgency standings assigned were open-ended with no restrictions on how many tools could be ordered under a given urgency rating. The NMTBA complained that many delivery dates requested were unreasonable in that they were well in advance of the time when the machine tools could actually be installed or used. Similar complaints were also made against the machine tool builders for requesting delivery of electric motors long before they were really needed.

When machine tool builders became confused by the concentration of orders with the same preference rating and urgency standing, they resorted to the practice of scheduling defense orders on the basis of the date of receipt of orders thus largely defeating the intent of the preference system.

The OPM set up a system to obtain and maintain current information on the status of all machine tool builders' "Order Boards." While this information was not always accurate or up to date, it confirmed that there were wide variations in the distribution of orders among firms producing the same type of machine tools as well as between producers of different types. This type of imbalance was frequently criticized as one of the causes of slow delivery, but efforts to level off the Order Boards had limited effect.

Under General Preference Order E-1-b of April 30, 1942, a

system of allocation began to evolve under which machine tool orders were put into three categories: (1) service purchases, (2) foreign purchases, and (3) other purchases. Seventy-five per cent of each producers' output was reserved for service orders, and the remaining 25 per cent was divided between the other groups. Limits were subsequently set on the number of machine tools which could be ordered under each Urgency Rating, thus eliminating the "open-end" problem.

In November 1942, the WPB gave the aircraft program a "green light" over other defense programs. This resulted in protests from the services and the Chairman of the Joint Chiefs of Staff. Donald M. Nelson of the WPB took the position that the President had confirmed his decision that the aircraft program should be given first priority for whatever was necessary to meet its approved production objectives even though this would hurt other important defense programs. An understanding was reached by mid-December 1942 which was intended to minimize the effect of aircraft priorities on other high-priority programs such as the escort vessel program. Machine tool deliveries for the aircraft program were sufficiently improved by early in 1943 so that the "green light" was officially turned off in April 1943. By the fall of 1943, the machine tool situation had improved to a point where there were proposals to simplify or revoke Order E-1-b which had become obsolete.

During the period from 1939 to 1941, machine tool builders tried to protect themselves against increased costs by inserting in contracts provisions for adjusting prices prior to shipment. As an alternative, the Navy Department proposed use of "Escalator Clauses" to provide adjustments for increased costs of labor and material. These were accepted by the machine tool builders after some objections. Machine tool prices were rising rather rapidly in the period from 1939 to 1941 with used tool prices increasing more rapidly than those for new tools, and Price Schedule No. 1 was issued on February 17, 1941 to control prices of secondhand tools in relation to the price of the tools when new.

In May 1941, the OPA requested that the machine tool industry voluntarily hold its prices at their level on May 6, 1941. This request was repeated in August 1941, but price increases continued. OPA concluded that other action was necessary. Leon Henderson, OPA Administrator, protested to Under-Secretary of the Navy Forrestal the use of escalator clauses on the ground that they nullified the efforts at voluntary price control, that increased volume had resulted in high profits to machine tool builders, and that machine tool builders could and should absorb a large part of cost increases. Negotiations between OPA, the services, and the machine tool industry resulted in an industry offer to try again to get voluntary price control, but the results did not satisfy OPA. Further discussions led to issuance of Price Schedule 67 for new machine tools on January 20, 1942, freezing machine tool prices at their level on October 1, 1941. Adjustments were made where a firm contracted for production of a machine by a subcontractor with higher costs, and an amendment authorized tool builders to enter into contracts at prices above established levels while awaiting formal action on requests for price adjustments.

The machine tool industry accepted price control and tried to comply with OPA regulations. Machine tool prices reflected in the Bureau of Labor Statistics (BLS) Price Index remained stable, and prices in general remained relatively stable from October 1941 until April 1946, although price increases were approved for particular firms and tools which were not reflected in the BLS index. In April 1946, an industry-wide price adjustment was approved. The industry was anxious to get rid of price controls and contended that they were interfering with reconversion following V-J Day even thought it also insisted that competition and excess capacity would prevent excessive price increases. The first request for decontrol was rejected, but NMTBA and MAPI continued their efforts until July 1946 when controls on all tools weighing over 2,000 pounds were suspended.

Machine tool builders' profits like those of other defense industries were also subject both to wartime Excess Profits Taxes and to renegotiation under the Renegotiation Act after contracts were completed. In the spring of 1942, machine tool builders objected to the fact that not only were they subject to price controls and the excess profits taxes, but were being required to renegotiate contracts with various branches of the army and navy. They urged that price controlled items be excluded from renegotiation, or at least that renegotiation be handled centrally for all contracts. The latter suggestion was sympathetically received and later renegotiations were handled in this way.

The subject of renegotiation was reviewed by the House Committee on Naval Affairs in 1943. The Vice Chairman of the War Department's Price Adjustment Board explained why the board had concluded that the machine tool industry's profits were excessive in 1942. Ralph E. Flanders objected to the 1936–1939 base period used by the Price Adjustment Board on the ground that many firms did not make profits until 1937 and had losses in 1938. He also suggested that total assets rather than net worth should be used as a basis for comparing profits. Moreover, he suggested that large companies such as General Motors and Eastman Kodak had been permitted to retain higher percentages of profits than many smaller firms including machine tool builders.

Other available information on profits of machine tool builders in relation to invested capital during the period from 1939 through 1949 seems to indicate that average profits after taxes were certainly adequate even though they might not provide sufficient reserves to cover an extended and severe postwar recession. This does not prove, of course, that individual firms did not fall much below the averages for the larger firms for which profits information was available.

The issue of reconversion planning and perhaps also of advance production of machine tools and other equipment which would be needed for reconversion to civilian production was raised in 1943 long before the shooting stopped. The major tooling-up operation was largely completed by the end of 1943 and machine tool orders and production were declining. Part of the machine tool capacity was converted to direct war production, but there was still time for machine tool builders to begin thinking about and trying to prepare for postwar production. The armed services and many groups within the war agencies were strongly opposed to anything which might divert effort or attention from the war.

The automobile industry which had been very reluctant to stop civilian production until forced to do so was also very anxious to get started on the job of preparing for reconversion. It was interested in both the disposition of surplus used machine tools which might be used in automobile production, and in getting new machine tools which would be needed to rebuild automobile production lines.

The aircraft industry was faced by the reverse situation since its postwar sales were almost sure to be far below wartime levels which peaked in 1944 and drastically declined in 1945. In any case, the aircraft industry did not appear likely to be a very important user of machine tools compared to its dominant wartime position.

In June 1944, Donald M. Nelson of WPB, despite internal opposition and that of the armed services, announced reconversion plans which emphasized the necessity of keeping military production up to schedule, but also provided for certain immediate steps to prepare for reconversion including authorizing manufacturers to purchase machine tools and dies for civilian production. The machine tools relaxation order was issued on July 29, 1944 in accordance with a staggered schedule adopted because of opposition to the measures. The fact that the war in Europe did not end in 1944 as hoped, and that there were new military requirements for both fronts restricted the effect of the new rules. Removal of controls on production and distribution for machine tools came about a year later along with the removal of controls on many other items. The machine tool builders then faced the long foreseen problem of trying to maintain machine tool demand, so far as possible, and of reducing hours and employment as orders declined. The reduction in domestic orders in 1946 was offset by increased exports, but both exports and total sales declined in 1947, and there was a drastic reduction in exports in 1948. The total number of units shipped declined each year from 1945 through 1949 before beginning to recover in 1950 as a result of the Korean War.

10

Summary

Machine Tool Development Trends and Problems

Machine tool development problems during the first half of the twentieth century were primarily those of evolving designs which could provide the greater speed, strength, and rigidity made necessary by the characteristics of high-speed tool steels, cemented carbides, and superior abrasives; which would take advantage of the electric motor and electrical controls to simplify power transmission, plant layouts, and control of cutting speed; and would satisfy the special needs imposed by new industries and materials. Progress was often stimulated by developments in other industries rather than new discoveries or inventions from within the machine tool industry. In general, the major changes may be said to have resulted from a combination of applications engineering and skilled workmanship to solve practical metalworking problems rather than from either major inventions or systematic research.

The machine tool industry or, at least, particular firms in the industry deserve full credit for having greatly improved machine tool capacity and performance on a wide variety of machining problems. This is true even though it is believed that greater technical progress could have been made had the industry devoted greater effort to research and development and had been given greater support in these efforts by machine tool users, and the federal government. It also appears, however, that as machine tool builders became more preoccupied with business problems, cost accounting, statistics, controlling price competition, profit ratios, reserves, etc., they devoted less attention to purely technical problems.

Technical improvements in machine tool design were often not sufficient to convince machine tool users that they should replace earlier models. In some cases, this was probably due to the financial situation or current investment policies of the particular firm or to the fact that it was operating at far below existing capacity and could see no real need to invest in new equipment until demand improved. It seems likely, however, that even though technical development had been more rapid, it would almost certainly have been largely concentrated in a comparatively few firms. It would have increased sales and profits of some companies, but would not necessarily have acted as a stabilizing factor for the industry as a whole. Thus increased success of some firms might well have resulted in higher mortality among others.

Improvements in machine tool design tended to reduce the skill required of the machine operator as well as the amount of physical effort and danger involved in machine operation. Increased capacity and cutting speeds put greater emphasis on the development of better jigs, fixtures, and other machine tool accessories which would simplify the job of setting up machines for new jobs and speed up insertion and removal of work from machine tools. Improvements in power transmission and speed changing mechanisms including better gears and forced lubrication made it possible to deliver greater power, to adjust cutting speeds more quickly and accurately, and made machine tools operate more quietly and dependably.

During wartime, the development of highly specialized machines was slowed down and greater emphasis was placed on maximum production of standard machine tools which could be adapted to a variety of work. Greater emphasis was put on the standardization and simplification of machine design and construction. These efforts contributed to the expansions in output achieved, but there does not appear to be any way to determine their effect quantitatively. Also though the disposal of government-owned tools no doubt reduced the total demand for machine tools, it is not certain how it affected machine tool development.

Geographic Distribution of the Machine Tool Industry

The regional distribution of the machine tool industry in 1947 or 1954 as compared to 1900 changed less drastically than in the preceding half century. The major changes were the decline in the

Middle Atlantic States from about 18.6 per cent of the industry in 1900 to 11.6 per cent in 1939 and 12.1 per cent in 1947. The East North Central States increased their share from 44.4 per cent in 1900 to 53.0 per cent in 1939 and 53.2 per cent in 1947. The New England States maintained their position better than the Middle Atlantic States with 35.0 per cent in 1900, 33.2 per cent in 1939, and 33.1 per cent in 1947.

The intraregional shifts were more drastic than those between regions. Thus in New England, Massachusetts declined in importance as a machine tool producer from 15.7 per cent in 1900 to 5.7 per cent in 1947. Vermont made the largest gains from 1.7 per cent in 1900 to 4.6 per cent in 1947. Connecticut and Rhode Island also increased their share but by much smaller percentages.

Within the East North Central States, the leading machine tool producing state, Ohio, lost the most in relative importance, from 37.4 per cent in 1900 to 23.1 per cent in 1947. Michigan made the largest gains in the nation from .5 per cent in 1900 to 12.3 per cent in 1947. Wisconsin and Illinois also made major gains from 2.0 per cent in 1900 to 7.5 per cent in 1947 in the case of Wisconsin and from 3.3 to 6.5 per cent for Illinois.

The increased importance of Michigan as a machine tool producer was largely due to the rapid development of the automobile and internal combustion engine. The developments in Wisconsin and Illinois were closely related to the mechanization of agriculture and the development of the construction machinery industry largely as a result of the rapid expansion of road paving stimulated by the automobile and the truck.

The major change in the Middle Atlantic States was the declining importance of Pennsylvania which had about 9.7 per cent of the machine tool industry in 1900 and only 3.4 per cent in 1947. This trend was closely related to the decline of the steam locomotive and the comparative stagnation of rail transportation and the railroad equipment industry.

The geographic distribution of machine tool production was compared with the geographic distribution of machine tool use in order to estimate how much influence the location of machine tool demand had on the expansion or contraction of machine tool production in particular regions. It seems certain that industrial expansion in a particular area did stimulate increased machine tool production in that area, but that the proximity to market factor became less important during the first half of the twentieth century than it had been during the nineteenth century. It also seems evident that where a machine tool builder developed a reputation for producing high quality machines for particular types of work, such as grinding hardened gears, the geographic location of the firm became of negligible importance. This appears to have been so in the case of the three machine tool builders in Springfield, Vermont.

The East North Central States were relatively more important as machine tool producers than as users, although this area was also the center of the most rapidly expanding metalworking industries. This region increased in importance as an exporter of machine tools both to other countries and to other regions of the United States such as the Southern States and Pacific Coast which rapidly expanded their metalworking industries during the latter part of the period. It also appears that this region's share of the machine tools used in metalworking industries declined from about 50 per cent in 1935 to less than 40 per cent in 1949, although the total number and value of the machine tools held increased rapidly during World War II.

New England maintained its relative position as a machine tool producing region, but declined in relative importance as a machine tool user and market. The latter was a result of increased industrialization in the South and West rather than an absolute decline in the region's metalworking industry.

The Middle Atlantic States declined significantly in importance as a center of the machine tool industry and became an importer rather than an exporter of machine tools. This region maintained its relative position in metalworking manufacturing as a whole better than in the machine tool industry.

Distribution of Machine Tools

The distribution of machine tools by using industries during peacetime differed rather drastically from that during World War II. This is most obvious in the dramatic wartime increase in machine tool holdings of the aircraft industry followed by a drastic contraction between 1945 and 1949. It is also reflected in the great increase in holdings of the motor vehicle industry during the war for production of aircraft, tanks, and other military equipment rather than conventional motor vehicles, and the correspondingly drastic reduction between 1945 and 1949 to almost pre-World War II levels as the industry reconverted to peacetime production.

If the numbers of machine tools held by the major machine tool using industries in 1949 are compared with those in 1945 and 1940, it is found that the "Fabricated Metal Products" industry still held the largest number of machine tools in 1949, but that the number was only a little higher than 1940 and far below the 1945 level. The "Shipbuilding, Ordnance and Miscellaneous" industry had moved up from third to second place with a large increase (about 100 per cent) during the war, followed by a still more surprising increase of almost 40 per cent between 1945 and 1949. The "Electrical Equipment" industry moved into third place by 1949 with large increases (over 100 per cent) during World War II and between 1945 and 1949 (over 50 per cent). The "Metalworking Equipment" industry was in fourth place in 1949 having made a relatively small increase (about 25 per cent) during World II and more than doubling its holdings between 1945 and 1949. The "Motor Vehicles" industry increased its holdings in 1949 only by a small percentage over 1940 despite a huge wartime increase for war production. The "Special Industry Machinery" industry increased its holdings of machine tools by over 100 per cent between 1945 and 1949. The "Precision Mechanisms" industry also increased its machine tool holdings by over 100 per cent in World War II and by about 40 per cent additional between 1945 and 1949.

It would be helpful to have additional information on these changes including the value of the additions and reductions in machine tool holdings, the number and value of used machines sold or scrapped, etc., but such information is not available except for some individual firms. Since machine tools vary widely in cost and the distribution of tools of different types varies rather widely from industry to industry, statistics on numbers of machines held may be misleading.

Organization and Concentration

Beginning with the establishment of the NMTBA in 1902 and including the formation of MAPI and the NRA Machine Tool and

Forging Machinery Code Authority in the thirties, and the war-time control organizations in World Wars I and II, there was a tendency toward increased self-regulation in the machine tool industry during the first half of the twentieth century. This tendency was largely due to the increased interest of machine tool builders in trying to find ways of controlling price competition and related business practices considered unfair, unwise, or otherwise objectionable, and in stabilizing business conditions. It was also, in part, a reaction to developments outside the machine tool industry including the merger movement, activities of the National Association of Manufacturers, and the U.S. Chamber of Commerce, the major wars, and the impact of depressions. This tendency was symbolized by the adoption of the Code of Ethics for the machine tool industry in the mid-twenties and the effort to give many of the same principles legal sanction under the NRA in 1933–1934. The attitude of the executive branch of the federal government was generally favorable to the efforts at "voluntary" cooperation and controls in peacetime and compulsory measures under predominantly business management direction in wartime and under the NRA. Enforcement of antitrust legislation, while apparently rather inconsistent with the above, was sporadic.

At the individual firm level, there was a tendency for the largest firms to become larger, and to increase their relative share of the total machine tool business though no single firm achieved an overall position of dominance. The degree of concentration was far greater, however, for particular types and sizes of machine tools with the result that there were in effect a rather large number of subindustry groupings which were often largely dominated by a single large firm or within which competition was very narrowly limited. There was also a tendency for the many small firms to either fail and be liquidated or to be merged with larger firms. There was a somewhat less marked tendency for new firms to be split off from existing firms than in the nineteenth century though this did continue to occur from time to time.

Between 1900 and 1919, the trend toward corporate organization proceeded rapidly as indicated by the fact that in 1919, 79.4 per cent of machine tool firms were corporately organized and that these firms employed 94.3 per cent of the industry's employees and produced 94.5 per cent of the industry's output. Most of these firms were closely held corporations. The basic motives for their formation were the desire for limited liability, permanence, tax benefits, etc., rather than the need to have a wide source of investment capital. Actually most expansions of facilities were financed from retained earnings rather than issuance of stock. There were a few major exceptions to this pattern.

By 1947, the four largest firms had increased their share of the wage earners employed in the machine tool industry to 23.7 per cent as compared to 21.7 per cent in 1939 and 13.8 per cent in 1935. By contrast, there were 107 firms in 1947 with less than twenty employees each, or a total less than that of any one of the four largest firms. The sixteen largest firms employed 50.6 per cent of the industry's total employees in 1947. It seems certain that while the machine tool industry was not sufficiently concentrated to give any firm clear control, there had been an increase in the amount of influence the largest firms could exercise.

The degree of product specialization did not increase very greatly during the period studied, but production of particular types and sizes of machine tools was confined in almost all cases to not over four or five firms. This situation did not appear to be significantly affected by the increase in firms during World War II or efforts to overcome production bottlenecks on some types of machine tools.

Capacity versus Production

The machine tool industry normally operated on a single-shift basis. Estimates of its capacity were usually made on this assumption by taking what appeared to be a period when all firms in the industry were generally operating a full shift, but not working a large amount of overtime and considering the value of production during this period as representing "capacity." This capacity could, of course, be substantially increased during wartime or other periods of peak demand by extending the work week and by multiple-shift operation and longer production runs on standard machines and components, without significant additions to plant and equipment.

Through most of the period studied, with the exception of the peak wartime expansions, and short periods of peak peacetime demand, the machine tool industry considered itself burdened with excess capacity. Machine tool builders attempted through the NMTBA and in other ways, to discourage new firms from entering the machine tool business, and to encourage firms already in the industry to diversify their output or convert to other lines in order to reduce the industry's capacity to a lower and presumably more profitable level.

Whether as a result of such educational efforts or the effects of the slump of 1920–1921, and the great depression of the thirties, the capacity of the machine tool industry was probably lower in 1939 than in 1919. Under the impact of war increased demand, plant capacity was expanded to about double its prewar level, and production was further expanded by all of the devices referred to above such as multiple-shift operation, extension of the work week, longer production runs, etc. Whether this expansion was as rapid as it could have been or whether it could have been made less of a limiting factor on wartime production and military operations had a more foresighted policy been followed in the prewar years can perhaps never be conclusively proven. By the time the industry reached its peak output in December of 1942, the machine tool shortages and backlogs were reduced sufficiently that it was considered safe to begin reducing machine tool output in favor of other types of production for direct military requirements.

Probably the most important limitation on machine tool expansion was the limited supply of trained machinists, engineers, and experienced supervisory personnel, and the competition of other expanding industries for the available manpower. Improvements in machine design, operation, and simplification of production methods tended to reduce the amount and degree of skill required in machine tool production and operation, but could not wholly solve the labor problems resulting from wartime demands for almost unlimited production of many products and frequent shifts in production schedules for different items.

Some machine tools were produced by other industries than the machine tool industry, and this percentage increased from 1939 to 1947, but then the trend reversed again and in 1953, the machine tool industry produced 93 per cent of the machine tools shipped as compared to 94 per cent in 1939 and 86 per cent in 1947. It appears that a variety of firms in other industries could produce machine tools, but probably could not, as a rule, do so at sufficiently low cost to compete with the established machine tool builders except in a period of peak demand and high prices. It also appears evident that over the period covered by the study, the machine tool industry became more dependent upon other industries for such components as electric motors and controls, hydraulic and mechanical power transmission and speed changing mechanisms, bearings, and lubrication equipment. Machine tool building did not become largely an assembly operation to the degree true of most automobile companies, but became less self-sufficient than it was in the nineteenth century.

Cause and Effects of Fluctuations in Demand

The major problem faced by the machine tool industry during the first half of the twentieth century was that of instability of demand. If this problem could have been solved, other business problems could have been handled with comparative ease. The industry's technical problems would likewise have been less difficult and progress greater because the industry would have had less difficulty in recruiting, training, and holding the production experts, tool designers, engineers, highly skilled machinists, and other technical people it needed to produce whatever number and variety of machine tools the domestic and export markets required, and to maintain a fairly stable development effort. Stable demand would also have made it possible to improve efficiency in tool plants and reduce costs by longer production runs. It might also have encouraged a greater degree of standardization in major components, and—to a lesser degree—in completed machines. The machine tool industry would have been able to offer lower prices to the tool buyer while maintaining an adequate level of profit.

It is equally apparent that demand was not stable for very long although, at least during the two major wars, there were periods when there was too much and too urgent demand rather than too little. Many individual firms could find few markets for their products even in periods of general prosperity when other firms in the industry were highly successful. It seems evident that the machine tool industry was not the only industry which suffered from wide fluctuations in demand for its products. It is more difficult to determine, however, whether the machine tool industry did suffer both more severely and for longer periods than any other or most other industries as spokesmen for the machine tool industry have frequently claimed. Part of the difficulty of proving or disproving this point conclusively is that to do so, it would be necessary to have comparable data on orders as well as production or shipments for the whole period under study and for all the individual industries to be compared. Such data was not available and it is difficult to see how it could be secured at this date. Existing *Census of Manufactures* series for the machine tool industry are not complete before 1919 and are in various respects not fully comparable for the census years since 1919. The situation appears to be no more satisfactory in the case of many other industries, and the major indices of industrial activity, manufacturing output, etc., probably conceal many significant variations in demand and production for individual industries just as industry averages often conceal wide variations in the performance of particular firms. Comparison of one industry with such broad averages is almost certain to be misleading. It is still more unfair to compare—as the NMTBA has sometimes done—machine tool demand or orders with a general index of manufacturing production.

The volume of new orders received is a better indicator of trends in machine tool demand than is either current shipments or production which usually lag behind orders during the up phase of the business cycle and run ahead of orders on the down side of the cycle. In addition, if the machine tool industry is to be considered a "bellwether" of the economic cycle, as some writers have suggested, it must certainly be on the basis of either new orders or predicted changes rather than on shipments or production.

Data on new orders are far from complete, or completely satisfactory, for the period prior to 1939, but are probably adequate to indicate something about the major changes which took place and the relation between new orders and shipments.

The major factors which directly affected machine tool demand and which largely account for the drastic fluctuations in demand appeared to be of two sorts. The first, which applied particularly to periods of peace, was the rapid expansion of a major machine tool using industry—in the first half of the twentieth century, the best peacetime example is the automobile industry. The other factor was felt most strongly in the initial and "tooling-up" phases of the two major wars when industry was expanded and reorganized to meet wartime needs. The aircraft industry was the best example of this type. Thus machine tool demand was greatly accelerated in periods of rapid industrial expansion whether the expansion was due to a general increase in economic activity, technological development involving primarily a single major industry, or mobilization for war.

Conversely, in periods of relatively stable though generally prosperous conditions, the machine tool industry was forced to reduce its operations to a fraction of its total capacity. Replacement orders resulting from the wearing out of machine tools, and what may be considered normal obsolescence, were usually far too small in volume to keep the industry fully occupied. It also appears that during the major periods of peacetime expansion, machine tools were replaced earlier than when business activity was stable or declining with the result that at the end of such expansion periods, the average age of machines and the number approaching the end of their useful life was relatively small in proportion to the total number of machine tools in use. World War II was apparently an exception to this pattern since during the war most used tools were retained while an almost equal number were added with the result that at the end of the war there was a very large number of older machines. By 1949, there were so many tools over twenty years old that if these alone had been replaced, the industry would have had ample demand without the Korean War.

There is convincing evidence that the machine tool industry did suffer from unstable and seemingly unpredictable demand whether or not it was any more subject to these "facts of life" than other industries including other capital equipment industries. There is greater basis for doubt, however, as to the effectiveness of measures taken, proposed by, or available to machine tool management to obtain greater stability. It was often emphasized that the machine tool industry chronically suffered from a "bad load factor," that is, that much of the time the industry operated at far less than capacity. Machine tool replacement policies and investment policies generally varied between industries and were dependent on tool age, wear, improvements in tool design and construction, and upon the financial condition and policies of individual firms; the availability of retained earnings or risk capital, etc. The tool user was likely to concentrate most of his purchases in the periods when major changes in product design, materials used, or volume of demand required additional machines. He was also influenced by the cost of new machines in relation to labor costs, by the availability of skilled machinists, tax incentives, and other factors. Adoption of forced lubrication and other improvements in design and construction tended to increase machine tool life. Longer hours of work and inadequate maintenance common during wartime tended to reduce machine life and to build up potential replacement requirements. Machine tool replacement was often almost indefinitely deferrable and was, therefore, an undependable element in machine tool demand.

The number of machine tools in metalworking industries was about the same or a little less in 1940 than in 1925, but the percentage over ten years old was much higher in 1940 when it was about 72 per cent as compared to 44 per cent in 1925. This represented a difference of about 280,000 in the number of tools over ten years old or a total of over 700,000 tools. It is reasonable to assume that most of the replacement business would come from this group and that if 10 per cent a year were replaced this would amount to about 70,000 units for replacement purposes alone. It is apparent, however, that machine tools were not being replaced at anything approaching this rate. It also seems certain that nearly all machine tools were kept in service through World War II, since the number of tools in use in 1945 was about equal to 1940 holdings plus wartime shipments allowing for exports.

In the postwar period 1945–1949, replacement of machine tools over ten years old was at a rate of about 5 per cent per year based on the estimated input of new tools and the rather small increase in total machine tools in use. In 1949, about 377,000 machine tools in use were over twenty years old, so if it is assumed that all of the replaced tools were from this group, it would still represent only about 10 per cent per year. While this seems definite evidence that the overall replacement rate was too low to maintain the machine tool inventory at the 1945 or 1949 average age and condition, it also suggests that the total number of machine tools held in 1949 was well above the number really needed for peacetime production.

In view of the Korean War to come, it was both unfortunate that a higher percentage of machine tools was not replaced in the period between 1945 and 1950, and fortunate that a large number of tools were still available for use. A higher rate of disposal of the older tools between 1945 and 1950 would not, in itself, have guaranteed larger purchases of new tools and might have represented largely a "house cleaning" operation. In this event it would have reduced the number and percentage of tools over ten or twenty years old, but would not have increased the actual number of newer tools available for use. Had all the government-owned machine tools been either held in government reserves for emergency use or scrapped, this would have increased the demand for new tools, have maintained a higher level of machine tool production capacity, and would have greatly reduced or eliminated the machine tool problems of the Korean War. It would probably also have slowed down the process of reconversion to civilian production, resulted in higher consumer goods prices, made extension of price controls and possibly other controls more essential, and deprived many companies of equipment bargains on government-owned machinery.

Undoubtedly other capital equipment industries and many other types of industry were also subject to rather violent and not always predictable fluctuations in demand and a "bad load factor." Industries such as transportation, communications, and power suffered rather extreme variations in load on a daily, weekly, monthly, and seasonal basis which required these industries to maintain capacity which would have not been needed had the load been more stable.

The fact that machine tool demand, like demand for other capital equipment, is "derived demand," in contrast to demand for consumer goods or other end products, was often emphasized as an explanation of machine tool demand's instability. This point seems of questionable validity, however. While basic needs for food, clothing, and some other consumer goods may be comparatively stable, income and other available purchasing power with which to purchase these or such products as automobiles and television sets was far from stable. Modern economic enterprises are so interdependent that significant fluctuations in one area will produce related fluctuations in other segments of the economy, and it is very difficult to isolate cause from effect. Increases in orders for capital

equipment, such as machine tools, stimulated employment, requirements for materials, and ultimately demand for consumer
goods. Conversely, an increase (or anticipated increase) in requirements for consumer goods or munitions stimulated demand for
machine tools.

The first method used by tool builders to adjust production in
line with fluctuations in demand was to increase or reduce the work
week. Thus in periods of peak demand, the average work week for
the machine tool industry was among the highest of any manufacturing industry. As demand dropped, the work week was correspondingly reduced. Another method of increasing production was
to subcontract particular parts and components or complete machines. This avoided or limited the need to expand production
facilities or recruit and train a large number of additional workers.
Production was also expanded by means of shift-work to the extent
possible with available supervisors and workers. The industry
was organized to operate on a one-shift basis. In most cases, tool
builders appeared to prefer a two- rather than three-shift system
where shift-work became essential. When demand began to fall
again the process was reversed and shift-work either eliminated
or drastically reduced. Lastly, new equipment was added to existing plants, and in some cases, new plants were built to meet
demand.

The machine tool industry's existing manpower requirements
were met by recruiting and training new workers and by upgrading
existing workers. Recruitment of new workers included experienced
machinists and other production workers and recent graduates of
vocational and technical schools who had some basic training in
tool operation, reading blueprints, planning work, etc., but needed
specialized training or experience in a particular plant, and untrained workers. As World War II progressed the latter category
included a sizeable percentage of women production workers and
particularly so in the larger plants.

Some tool builders saw export markets as a promising counterbalance to fluctuations in domestic demand. Export sales did, at
times, partially offset reductions in domestic demand as in 1927
when exports increased substantially, in 1930 when they remained
virtually stable, or in the later thirties when exports rose much more
rapidly than domestic sales and played a major part in the ma-

chine tool industry's recovery. Very often, the tool builders' interest in foreign markets seemed to vary inversely with the level of domestic demand. The fact that their efforts in foreign markets were not always sustained from year to year was one reason U.S. firms sometimes lost out to German or English firms which gave more consistent and better organized attention to export sales. It also appears that, while the Commerce Department's Bureau of Foreign and Domestic Commerce attempted to encourage foreign trade, its advice during the twenties and thirties was not of much practical value. It was based on the comfortable assumption that U.S. machine tools were clearly superior to those of foreign builders and that U.S. firms could insist on financial arrangements which involved no risk to the seller. However, some U.S. machine tool builders recognized that to secure and hold much foreign business required both hard work and some financial risk.

U.S. machine tool builders were usually much more concerned about the effect of foreign competition on export sales than as a threat to their domestic markets, and machine tool imports were a minor competitive factor during the first half of the twentieth century. U.S. tool builders in the late twenties and early thirties sought government assistance to counterbalance the credit guarantees given to German and British firms by their governments and enable U.S. firms to secure a higher percentage of Russian business, but they were unsuccessful. While cooperative action in export trade was frequently discussed, machine tool builders did not form a "Webb-Pomerene" Association to seek foreign business until after World War II.

As machine tool builders became increasingly conscious both of the effects of fluctuating business and the possibility of collective action through their trade organizations, they became more interested in the possibility of predicting when fluctuations would occur. It was believed that if changes in demand for machine tools regularly followed corresponding changes in another industry by a relatively fixed interval, this would provide a workable means of predicting changes in machine tool demand. Unfortunately, so far as is known, such a reliable indicator of future events was not found despite the rapid growth in the volume of business statistics available, and the variety of theories offered regarding the business cycle.

Public statements by NMTBA staff members and leading machine tool builders during the twenties express a degree of optimism concerning the value of business statistics and cost accounting as guides to management decisions which seems hardly believable, and which judging by the unwillingness of many tool builders to provide all of the data desired by the NMTBA, was not shared by all of its members. Certainly, there is little evidence that the efforts of the NMTBA, other business organizations, or the federal government to improve statistical reporting and economic analysis helped to predict the timing, severity, or duration of the great depression. This is believed to be true, although the volume of new machine tool orders received apparently did begin to decline by June or July of 1929. This shift in direction was generally dismissed as a temporary phenomenon rather than as a definite warning. It is highly unlikely, that, given the economic theories and political conditions of the twenties, effective action would have been taken even if the business statisticians, economists, psychologists, and other experts had accurately predicted and agreed upon the shape and timing of coming events.

Prices, Profits, and Competition

NMTBA efforts to raise and stablize price levels and limit price competition were more successful than its efforts to stabilize demand, ensure a higher level of profits, or even persuade all NMTBA members to cooperate in improving and standardizing cost accounting systems. There also appears to have been some price competition and price cutting during periods when demand was declining despite the insistence of most NMTBA leaders that lower prices would not significantly stimulate demand or avoid losses.

In part, machine tool price increases can be attributed to increased costs of labor, materials, purchased components, design changes, and other factors entering into machine tool production, but they also were influenced by management policies on pricing and the belief that the major source of increased profits was to be found in higher prices. There were efforts to discourage price reductions even where cost reductions made this possible, but some machine tool builders were convinced that price reductions were necessary in periods such as the "Slump" of 1920–1921. They appeared to recognize the cost accounting principle that overhead costs should be allocated to the product on the basis of normal volume rather than attempt to recover all overhead expenses on a drastically reduced volume of business or fail to include adequate overhead when business was at a peak level.

It is difficult to determine how much effect the industry's policy of price maintenance had on machine tool sales, but it seems certain that it had some negative effect, and at times provoked significant buyer resistance. While demand for capital equipment such as machine tools is no doubt less elastic than demand for many consumer goods, price was nevertheless a factor partially determining whether machines would be replaced and which machines would be selected when there was a choice.

An effort was made to establish official price controls—based on a form of "open pricing" for standard machines and prohibition of sales below cost for special machine tools—under the NRA, but the invalidation of the National Recovery Act stopped this experiment before it was determined whether it would be effective or what its effects would be. The only formal industry-wide price control during the period studied was that imposed by the government during World War II, and was intended to keep machine tool prices generally from going up beyond the 1941 levels in effect when controls were established. It was successful in stabilizing basic machine tool prices during World War II though increases were approved for particular machine tools and high-cost producers.

During the period preceding the United States' entrance into World War II, machine tool builders tried to protect themselves against cost increases by including in their contracts provisions for price increases prior to delivery. This practice was replaced by so-called "Escalator Clauses" to adjust prices based on increases in costs of labor and materials. These were later strongly criticized by OPA Administrator Leon Henderson on the ground that the clauses were highly inflationary and that machine tool builders were able to, and should be required to, absorb a large part of any cost increases. Navy Department staff members argued that many of Henderson's criticisms of the escalator clauses were invalid, but army and navy representatives were designated to work with OPA and the tool builders in establishing price controls on new machine tools.

Machine tool builders contended that the combination of price controls, excess profits taxes, and renegotiation procedures during World War II prevented them from accumulating adequate reserves and imposed unnecessary administrative burdens on firms subject to renegotiation. They denied that their wartime profits after taxes were excessive, objected to the 1936–1939 base used by the War Department's Price Adjustment Board as unfair, and claimed that certain large companies were permitted to retain higher percentages of profits than machine tool builders and other small companies.

Profits between World War II and the Korean War were greatly reduced or eliminated by the drastic reduction in volume of sales even though unit prices were increased following removal of price controls. New business reached a low point in July 1949 and then began to improve gradually until June 1950 when the outbreak of the Korean War caused new orders to rise rapidly to another wartime peak. New orders did not again reach their average 1945–1947 level until April 1950 shortly before the outbreak of the Korean War.

As a business man, the machine tool builder was interested in building and selling machine tools at a price which would yield what he considered a reasonable profit on his capital investment and initiative. He usually had an interest in improving the machines he built and in advancing the art of metalworking, but these interests were secondary to that of making a profit. These conclusions seem axiomatic, although the public statements of some machine tool industry executives might suggest that profit making was secondary or even incidental to their desire to serve tool users, advance the public welfare and national security, etc. Such altruism may, of course, have been the primary motivation in a few instances, but there appears to be little evidence that it was significantly more characteristic of machine tool builders than other types of businessmen during the period studied.

Machine tool builders usually preferred to discuss profits, if they were to be discussed at all, in relation to total investment of the industry as a whole or as a percentage of sales rather than as a percentage of net worth. However computed, profit ratios were subject to wide variations at different points in the business cycle and among firms.

Firms which were able to combine the technical knowledge and experience necessary to design and build high quality machine tools with adequate management and financial resources to operate at a reasonably efficient level were usually able to earn an adequate and at times excellent return except during periods when demand was severely depressed. They were able in periods of near capacity operation to develop substantial reserves and finance expansion or modernization programs from retained earnings. Such firms were able to survive even severe recessions of reasonably short duration without great difficulty, but a major depression made it very difficult for all firms to maintain their basic organization, highly skilled workers, and an adequate level of development effort. Many of the small, high-cost firms entering the industry during periods of peak demand as in World Wars I and II had little chance of surviving when demand declined. These account for a large percentage of the firms liquidated. There were also a few medium-sized and large firms which failed to develop new or improved designs, to maintain efficient production and sales organizations, or which remained closely tied to a declining industry. These too were either liquidated or consolidated.

Management and the Machinist

Machine tool builders took an active interest in the development and application of some of the management theories and techniques associated with the scientific management movement. Some of the techniques such as time-and-motion studies were considered better suited to the mass production industries where long production runs justified intensive studies, careful planning of work, and elaborate tooling. The tool builder, distributor, and salesman needed to be knowledgeable as to what could be done to improve efficiency, and the effect on machine tool requirements.

Some machine tool builders continued to depend upon straight hourly or daily pay systems or adopted simple premium-pay plans which were comparatively inexpensive to install and maintain. Group bonus schemes were also favored as methods of securing the cooperative efforts needed to turn out high quality machines at reasonable cost.

During World Wars I and II, machine tool builders expanded their work forces through upgrading, increasing the number of

helpers used, greater job specialization, and adding women for production and assembly operations as well as for clerical work.
No evidence was found that nonwhite persons were recruited for
skilled or semiskilled production jobs. Some progress was made
during World War I in improving working conditions and in providing medical care and other employee services. The machine
tool industry generally opposed efforts to enact mandatory unemployment or accident insurance as uneconomic and urged voluntary
cooperative measures as an alternative. It was assumed that the
worker would have to absorb much of the impact of reduced demand through shorter hours, lower pay, or unemployment. The
machine tool builder's position on these subjects was probably
very similar to that taken by most other manufacturers of the
period.

Machine tool builders were active in employer organizations opposing the spread of unions and the closed shop in the metalworking industries, but the NMTBA officially declared that it was not
concerned with labor questions.

Some machine tool builders attempted to improve and adapt
their apprentice training programs to meet changing needs and
conditions. Others, however, either hired no apprentices or merely
used them as a method of securing low-cost labor and provided
very little in the way of systematic training. Some tool firms were
active in establishing cooperative training programs with local
schools and encouraged their employees to get additional shop-
related education.

A few firms, such as the Brown and Sharpe Manufacturing Company, continued to operate apprenticeship programs much as they
had for almost three-quarters of a century. Other firms developed
special apprenticeship courses. Shop training by most firms, however, was likely to be rather highly specialized, and the broader
types of training for the metalworking trades were left to the industrial and vocational schools.

The old-fashioned general apprenticeship became almost a thing
of the past. The system was a victim both of progress as represented
by the specialization of labor, transfer of skills from the machinist
to the machine, etc., and of the growing unwillingness of employers
to invest the trouble and expense of training young men as general
machinists or other skilled craftsmen with the possibility that such

employees might then be attracted to other firms or industries. This trend began prior to 1900, greatly accelerated during World War I, and was largely completed during the twenties.

Public statements by the NMTBA, individual tool builders, and others frequently emphasized the importance of the skilled worker, and the difficulties faced by the machine tool industry in recruiting, training, and retaining workers in competition with other industries. There is little evidence, however, that this expressed interest was reflected in practical and effective measures to make recruitment easier, training more adequate, or wages fully competitive.

The term "pirating" was frequently used by tool builders in connection with recruiting of machine tool industry workers by other metalworking industries, but the term hardly seems appropriate since the only force used was that of persuasion, the promise of better pay in expanding industries, more rapid upgrading, and steadier employment. During peacetime when demand for machine tools was usually substantially below capacity, the machine tool industry took the position that it was unable to pay as high wages as some competing industries. When the industry was expanding for war, wage and price controls were imposed which also prevented the industry from paying fully competitive wages including premium pay. The industry also complained that its relatively long production lead-time and the fact that it was sometimes committed many months ahead to deliver tools at fixed prices made it difficult for the machine tool builder to raise wage rates enough to meet competition for labor.

Industrial Mobilization for War

During U.S. mobilization efforts for World War I, machine tool industry spokesmen and trade journals tried to emphasize the importance of machine tools and the machine tool industry in war production and the need to assign the industry high priorities for necessary materials and manpower. The industry was also well represented in the Machine Tools Section of the War Industries Board and successfully opposed efforts at standardization of machine tools which it considered unnecessary and undesirable because of their future effects on competition. The war ended before many of the production and administrative problems were solved.

The Defense Act of 1920 authorized the use of educational orders as a means of preparing in advance of mobilization for production of hard-to-produce military products, but Congress refused to appropriate any money for this purpose throughout the twenties and first half of the thirties. By the time money was appropriated, it was too late to be of any value, with very limited exceptions. There was also very little money available to modernize government-owned arsenals and other industrial facilities.

Military industrial mobilization planners in the period before World War II took it almost for granted that machine tools would be a serious bottleneck in the event of a major war, but were unable to develop realistic requirements for machine tools or incorporate them into a program which would have both a chance of securing approval and of being adequate to solve the problems involved. These included the rapidly changing designs of major items such as aircraft. There was also a belief originating in the aircraft industry that aircraft could not be standardized or mass produced. Aircraft engines were the major exception to this theory and engine production was largely concentrated in two firms.

After mobilization began for World War II, it was seldom possible to determine requirements for machine tools far enough in advance for them to be produced and delivered by the time they were needed. This problem was partially overcome in the case of standard machine tools by use of the pool order device in which a central agency placed large advance orders for machine tools likely to be needed, tool builders were given immediate financial assistance plus insurance against loss, and firm orders from contractors were subsequently deducted from the pool orders on hand. This device provided an incentive to machine tool builders to expand production and a method of short-cutting the time-consuming process of contracting and subcontracting.

The aircraft expansion program of World War II was the dominant factor in machine tool requirements both in terms of the very large number of machine tools required and the high priority assigned to their procurement. Had there been no large scale aircraft program, there would probably not have been a significant machine tool production problem. There were, of course, other important programs which required machine tools such as the tank program, escort vessel program, shipbuilding program, and some of the ordnance programs.

In the World War II industrial mobilization, time was the most critical factor and anything which could speed up the tooling operation and get plants into production weeks or months early might save lives on the fighting fronts. It was sometimes assumed that existing automobile plants or other consumer durable goods plants could be converted to production of aircraft, tanks, or other military items almost overnight, but wartime experience seemed to prove that new plants could be built and equipped about as quickly as existing plants could be converted, additional equipment and special tooling and accessories added, and production lines rearranged. It was also found, however, that the automobile industry prior to conversion had greatly underestimated the percentage of its tools which could be used in war production. Certainly conversion of existing plants did reduce the total number and cost of machine tools required.

During the prewar planning and mobilization phases of World War II, machine tool builders were worried about the threat of excess capacity and were reluctant to expand their own plants, convert to multiple-shift operation, have new firms enter the business, or spread available work by subcontracting. As in World War I, they were also opposed to drastic standardization and simplification programs which would have the effect of making machines more nearly alike and be likely to have a depressive effect on postwar business or place greater emphasis on price. It is possible that acceleration of machine tool production at the beginning of mobilization could have shortened the mobilization period and perhaps the war. However, to do so, earlier tool deliveries would have had to have been accompanied by a speeding up in other programs.

After the major tooling-up problem was solved in 1943, most machine tool builders were still reluctant to convert to military production though willing for subcontractors and firms which had recently started machine tool production to convert. Their attitude was based on their belief that there would be additional urgent machine tool requirements; the difficulty of finding items which they could produce efficiently and profitably; and a desire to get started on preparations for civilian production.

As in World War I, one of the first steps taken to control machine tool distribution in World War II was to impose restrictions on exports to unfriendly nations and to seek authority to commandeer machine tools intended for export for diversion to defense use. Domestic shipments were then subjected to control by so-called voluntary priorities controlled by the ANMB. This system quickly proved inadequate and was succeeded by mandatory priorities. Gauges and machine tool expansion requirements were given top priorities based on their being essential to expand production of military end products. The priorities systems, however, tended to break down for various reasons including a tendency for ratings to become inflated and concentrated to the point that they became almost meaningless. They were reinforced or superseded by other formal and informal controls intended to ensure that available machine tools would be delivered when actually needed and with due regard to the urgency of the various production programs. There was ample room for strong differences of opinion between the army, navy, and ANMB on one side, and the civilian industrial mobilization agencies on the other as to whether or not machine tool problems were being properly handled. These included charges by the armed service representatives that the Machine Tools Branch of OPM and WPB was too completely controlled and staffed by representatives from the machine tool industry, that it babied the industry, and that it "played politics."

A system was established for allocating tools to claimant agencies under WPB Order E-1-b of April 30, 1942 and in conformance with a Combined Numerical Urgency Rating List. This brought a reasonable degree of order out of the earlier scramble for machine tools. By this time, tool production was catching up to receipts of new orders though there were still large backlogs of orders for some of the critical types of machine tools. There were also good reasons to feel that available facilities were not being adequately used, and that contractors were insisting on particular makes and models when other machines which were more readily available would serve as well; that more could be done to level order boards, etc. The "green light" given the aircraft program interfered with other programs and caused frequent protests from other claimants. Unrealistic construction and production schedules also aggravated the tooling problem by causing machines to be requested for delivery well before they could be used.

Major reasons for the machine tool shortages of World War II included the inability of the armed services and emergency agencies to develop reasonably accurate estimates of requirements and to translate these into orderly programs to satisfy the requirements in a minimum amount of time. The President and Executive Departments failed to convince Congress of the need for adequate funds to modernize existing government-owned manufacturing facilities, to support greater research and development efforts plus preproduction engineering and pilot-plant operations to test and improve production methods, or to prepare private contractors for rapid conversion to military production. There was also strong opposition from the aircraft industry and other industries including the machine tool industry to proposals to build and equip standby government-owned plants to supplement private plants in the event of mobilization. This opposition was based on the assumption that existing plants were either adequate or could easily and relatively quickly be expanded to provide additional capacity if needed and fear of competition from government-owned plants. Major civilian goods producers were also unwilling to convert to military production until civilian production was stopped by the government.

Planning and other preliminary preparation for reconversion to civilian production at the end of World War II was delayed because of opposition to any measures which might divert manpower or resources from war production. This opposition was at least partially based on psychological factors and their possible effect upon morale rather than just the limited amount of materials, labor, and plant facilities required. Despite this opposition, WPB began to relax production and distribution controls for machine tools and other items needed for civilian production in the summer of 1944. However, new requirements for the war in the Pacific prevented much from being done until mid-1945.

As the war ended, controls were removed and machine tool orders fell drastically below the level of the first half of 1945. During the last quarter of 1945 and the first half of 1946, foreign orders compensated to some extent for reductions in domestic business, but in the summer of 1946, new orders started a further decline. The rapid disposal of government-owned machine tools at low prices was a major factor in this situation.

Postscript

It seems almost self-evident that machine tools and the machine tool industry were indispensable to the development of metal products manufacturing and almost equally, if less directly, essential to the evolution of all sectors of modern economic life. It is much less easy, however, to prove that the machine tool industry was, or conversely was not, as aggressive and effective in either research and development aimed at improving the capacity and performance of machine tools or in reducing the cost of producing tools, as it could or should have been. In general, it appears that machine tool builders were more interested in improving the performance of their tools and advertising their superiority than they were in reducing costs and prices of tools. It also appears that they tended at times to take for granted the technical superiority of U.S. machine tools and forgot both their inheritance and copying or borrowing from the pioneer English tool builders of the nineteenth century, and the contributions of German engineers.

There appeared to be some basis for concluding that even after 50 years of organizing effort led by the staff and officers of the NMTBA, and given the blessing of other business organizations and the federal government, machine tool builders did not form a single integrated industry but rather a loose federation of smaller groupings of producers of specialized types of metalworking machinery, many of which had little in common. However, during the first half of the twentieth century, the producers of metal cutting-machine tools had enough in common and acted cooperatively with sufficient frequency and unity to justify the conclusion that they should be treated as a separate industry.

It also seems that twentieth century machine tool builders as a group pictured themselves as the forgotten heroes of the mechanical age who were victims of a blind fate, astigmatic bureaucrats, and shortsighted tool users. They also assumed that many of their problems were unique when in fact they were common to many industries and any differences were rather small differences of degree and timing.

In the fifty years covered by this study, there were only rare instances where either machine tool builders or the federal government found effective solutions to major managerial problems.

This is particularly true of the problems of industrial mobilization for war and orderly reconversion. The Korean War is beyond the scope of the present study, but a review of one of the reports of the Joint Committee on Defense Production regarding the machine tool problems of the Korean War period tends to confirm this conclusion and the rather pessimistic view expressed in Georg W. F. Hegel's frequently quoted lines:

> What experience and history teach is this—that people and governments never have learned anything from history or acted on principles deduced from it.[1]

The doctoral dissertation on which this volume was based ended with the above quotation. This was included as a kind of private joke reflecting the author's rather meandering education and interests in the fields of philosophy and history. It was not intended to suggest, as one reader supposed, that there were easy solutions to the machine tool industry's problems which had been overlooked or ignored by machine tool builders, tool users, and governmental agencies. It did reflect some pessimism on the author's part regarding the ability of either groups of people, industries, or other institutions to learn very much from past experience or to apply whatever has been learned to practical affairs. It is also doubted that the historian should be expected either to discover such lessons of history or to subscribe to theories offered by businessmen, economists, political scientists, or others though I see no objection to him doing so if he wishes and is candid in expressing his views.

The machine tool industry during the mobilization period for the Korean War did appear to apply its interpretation of the lessons of World Wars I and II by declining to expand its production until given assurances that it could do so safely and profitably. Also at the end of the Korean War the federal government managed its holding of used machine tools and the disposal of surplus tools in a way which minimized their impact on machine tool demand thus appearing to have learned something from earlier experience. Whether business and government, which are now so closely interlinked that they can often scarcely be separated for purposes of study, have become wiser and more farsighted since World War II is a moot question beyond the scope of this volume.

[1] *Oxford Dictionary of Quotations*, 2nd Ed. (London: Oxford University Press, 1953), p. 240.

It would be desirable to be able to cover some more recent problems, developments, and trends in the almost twenty years since 1950. These would no doubt include an examination of the impact of electronic controls; some of the newer metalworking processes; and application of the modular concept to machine tool design, construction, and use. They would also include the changes which have taken place in the organization and location of the machine tool industry; the rapid growth of machine tool production in Japan, Germany, the U.S.S.R., Switzerland, and other countries; establishment by U.S. machine tool builders of subsidiaries in other countries, and the increase in the number of firms which have given or accepted licenses to produce particular machine tools.

It would be interesting to examine recent theories and policies regarding national defense as they relate to the machine tool industry and the industrial production base generally. There are many other topics which should probably also be included such as the effects of investment policies on technological innovation and the ability of U.S. metalworking industries to compete for markets; the balance of emphasis within private industry, educational institutions, and government; between basic scientific research and applications engineering; and development of improved production methods.

Adequate treatment of the period since 1950, however, would require another volume. Also some of the topics have already been covered at considerable length elsewhere. It is difficult to say whether the author will be able to extend the history at a later date though some material has been collected and some of the topics are of special interest.

Possibly, if there are historians in the twenty-first century and they are a fully integrated part of the highly automated scholarly world which now seems technically possible, they will be able to produce fully rounded and balanced histories of the machine tool industry and other industries which helped to make their world possible. If there are no historians, it is also likely there will be no economists or other specialists, no philosophers or kings to try to understand the basic meaning of our experience, and no readers or critics to judge the results of efforts to write histories. Possibly then history, if any, will again be left to the story tellers, and wars will again be fought with bows and arrows or clubs.

APPENDIX

TABLE 1
MACHINE TOOL PRODUCTION BY STATES AND TYPE
($000's Omitted)
1900

State	Total	Lathes	Milling Machines	Boring & Drilling Machines	Grinding Machines	Planers	Shapers and Slotters	Threading Machines	Other
Connecticut	$ 1,798	1,030	141	167	77	53	150	19	161
Illinois	556	173	—	145	92	—	—	—	146
Massachusetts	2,628	1,348	318	490	124	262	79	—	7
Michigan	89	—	—	—	12	—	59	—	18
New Jersey	566	177	168	132	7	—	—	—	82
New York	1,023	225	298	83	55	—	78	129	155
Ohio	6,411	3,037	439	1,120	17	691	421	364	322
Pennsylvania	1,702	383	111	397	143	249	178	97	144
Rhode Island	1,121	334	445	75	267	—	—	—	—
Vermont	284	284	—	—	—	—	—	—	—
Wisconsin	320	240	—	—	48	—	—	—	32
All Other	2,750	1,100	253	170	38	553	171	90	375
TOTAL	$19,248	8,331	2,173	2,779	880	1,808	1,136	699	1,442

Based on U.S. Bureau of the Census (Special Bulletin 67), *Metal Working Machinery*, Fred J. Miller.

TABLE 2
MACHINE TOOL PRODUCTION BY STATES AND TYPE
($000's Omitted)
1905

State	Total	Lathes	Milling Machines	Boring & Drilling Machines	Grinding Machines	Planers	Shapers and Slotters	Threading Machines	Other
Connecticut	$ 1,533	701	218	154	126	25	62	209	38
Illinois	586	84	—	335	6	—	—	—	161
Massachusetts	2,029	857	376	257	225	243	34	—	37
Michigan	158	—	—	—	83	—	66	—	9
New Jersey	335	25	116	111	13	—	—	—	70
New York	840	165	117	50	71	—	14	128	295
Ohio	5,753	2,821	529	906	115	467	332	247	336
Pennsylvania	1,722	312	110	317	267	253	198	109	156
Rhode Island	1,409	414	586	66	343	—	—	—	—
Vermont	322	322	—	—	—	—	—	—	—
Wisconsin	308	193	—	—	33	—	—	—	82
All Other	2,896	949	424	175	29	564	141	206	408
TOTAL	$17,891	6,843	2,476	2,371	1,311	1,552	847	899	1,592

Based on U.S. Bureau of the Census (Special Bulletin 67), *Metal Working Machinery*, Fred J. Miller.

TABLE 3
GEOGRAPHIC DISTRIBUTION OF THE MACHINE TOOL
INDUSTRY FOR SELECTED YEARS

Region/State	Percentages*				
	1900	1919	1939	1947	1954
New England	35.0	39.9	33.2	33.1	33.6
Connecticut	10.8	10.3	12.4	13.3	13.7
Massachusetts	15.7	12.2	7.2	5.7	7.0
Rhode Island	6.8	13.6	8.9	9.5	6.9
Vermont	1.7	3.8	4.7	4.6	6.0
Middle Atlantic States	18.6	13.0	11.6	12.1	9.8
New Jersey	3.3	3.1	2.3	2.0	1.0
New York	5.6	3.0	5.4	6.7	6.7
Pennsylvania	8.7	6.9	3.9	3.4	2.1
East North Central States	44.4	44.9	53.0	53.2	53.4
Illinois	3.3	6.1	7.4	6.5	8.9
Indiana	1.2	2.3	2.4	2.3	1.9
Michigan	.5	6.0	7.7	12.3	11.3
Ohio	37.4	26.1	29.5	23.1	24.2
Wisconsin	2.0	4.4	7.0	7.5	7.0

* Percentages for 1900 are based on production of selected types of machine tools from U.S. Census Bulletin 67, Fred J. Miller, *Metal Working Machinery*. The percentages for 1919, 1939, and 1954 are based on the number of wage earners employed in the machine tool industry as reported in the U.S. *Census of Manufactures*.

TABLE 4
WAGE EARNERS—AVERAGE EMPLOYMENT

State	1919	1921	1929	1933	1939*	1947
Connecticut	5,472	2,398	6,402	1,379	4,530	6,694
Massachusetts	6,471	1,042	3,361	920	3,569	2,882
Rhode Island	7,169	2,966	n.a.	n.a.	3,258	5,334
Vermont	2,024	623	2,610	412	1,720	2,200 (est)
New Jersey	1,678	572	662	73	492	1,028
New York	1,590	2,435	2,730	523	2,009	3,394
Pennsylvania	3,671	1,522	2,982	1,048	1,411	1,644
Illinois	3,273	1,528	3,653	1,355	2,595	3,287
Indiana	1,228	754	1,245	361	879	1,250 (est)
Michigan	3,196	747	1,554	923	2,650	6,920
Ohio	13,855	5,593	11,857	3,371	10,807	13,239
Wisconsin	2,352	688	2,330	471	2,206	4,500 (est)
Other	1,132	439	8,005	2,417	498	2,720
Total	53,111	21,307	47,391	13,253	36,624	54,892

SOURCE: U.S. Bureau of the Census, *Census of Manufactures*.

* Statistics for 1937 and prior years included such metalworking machinery as bending machines, die casting machines, forging machines, presses, punching machines, and portable metalworking tools which starting in 1939 were included in "Metalworking Machinery and Equipment, Not Elsewhere Classified."

n.a.—not available.

TABLE 5
MACHINE TOOL INDUSTRY PRODUCTION—BY STATE
($ Millions)

States	1919	1929*	1939	1947*	1949
Ohio	$62.6	$67.6 (56.3)	$65.5	$133.7	$81.8
Massachusetts	23.4	20.1 (14.8)	24.6	25.1	18.1
Rhode Island	22.3	n.a.	n.a.	32.4	n.a.
Connecticut	18.4	27.9 (18.3)	23.7	53.1	21.3
Pennsylvania	16.8	15.6 (11.7)	n.a.	12.4	10.0
Illinois	15.0	22.6 (16.3)	15.7	38.5	n.a.
Michigan	12.7	8.1 (6.8)	16.9	66.9	20.6
Vermont	9.6	14.0 (10.3)	11.6	n.a.	n.a.
Wisconsin	9.4	12.0 (10.1)	13.5	n.a.	18.6
New Jersey	6.8	3.9 (3.1)	2.1	11.8	3.1
New York	5.0	16.5 (12.6)	13.0	29.4	13.8
Indiana	4.3	7.6 (6.4)	5.9	n.a.	n.a.
Other	6.1	28.6 (19.4)	28.7	98.7	54.1
Total	$212.4	$244.5 (186.1)	$221.2	$502.0	$241.4

SOURCE: U.S. Bureau of the Census, *Census of Manufactures*, except 1949 figures are from "Facts For Industry." Information includes secondary products of machine tool industry since machine tool figures alone are not distributed by state for all years.

* Shipments.

Numbers in parenthesis are machine tool shipments alone as defined in 1939, excluding metal-forming machines.

TABLE 6
ESTIMATED SHIPMENTS OF MACHINE TOOLS
(Cutting Types Only)

Year	Units (000s)	Shipments ($ millions)	Unit Price	Exports ($ millions)
1901	n.a.	17.9	n.a.	4.1*
1902	n.a.	22.8	n.a.	3.0
1903	n.a.	23.7	n.a.	2.8
1904	n.a.	18.3	n.a.	3.7
1905	n.a.	28.7	n.a.	n.a.
1906	n.a.	36.4	n.a.	n.a.
1907	n.a.	41.3	n.a.	8.4†
1908	n.a.	16.8	n.a.	6.9
1909	n.a.	33.5	n.a.	2.8
1910	n.a.	44.3	n.a.	4.8
1911	n.a.	32.8	n.a.	7.6
1912	n.a.	44.4	n.a.	9.4
1913	n.a.	44.6	n.a.	12.3
1914	n.a.	35.3	n.a.	14.0
1915	n.a.	103.4	n.a.	28.0
1916	n.a.	141.4	n.a.	n.a.
1917	n.a.	168.5	n.a.	n.a.
1918	n.a.	220.6	n.a.	27.6
1919	99	161.0	1,626	28.1
1920	79	151.5	1,918	25.5
1921	21	36.0	1,714	9.0
1922	28.5	43.3	1,519	3.4
1923	36	79.3	2,203	4.6
1924	25	69.6	2,784	5.9
1925	31	86.7	2,797	10.9
1926	36.5	105.0	2,877	7.2
1927	28	87.0	3,107	12.6
1928	36	128.0	3,556	16.0

TABLE 6 (Continued)

Year	Units (000s)	Shipments ($ millions)	Unit Price	Exports ($ millions)
1929	50	185.0	3,700	18.9
1930	23.5	96.0	4,085	18.0
1931	12	51.0	4,200	17.6
1932	5.5	22.0	4,150	6.2
1933	6	25.0	4,000	4.4
1934	13.5	50.0	3,704	12.1
1935	23	85.0	3,696	17.4
1936	40	133.0	3,325	24.9
1937	55	195.0	3,545	38.5
1938	34	145.0	4,265	64.5
1939	51.5	200.0	3,883	79.8
1940	110	440.0	4,000	185.5
1941	185	775.0	4,189	166.5
1942	307	1,320.0	4,300	157.5
1943	266	1,180.0	4,436	237.1
1944	136	497.0	3,654	163.6
1945	103	423.7	4,114	78.5
1946	75	334.8	4,464	110.0
1947	60	306.0	5,100	105.3
1948	50	288.4	5,769	62.8
1949	34.5	249.1	7,222	72.6
1950	41.5	305.5	7,363	
1951	70.8	632.3	8,930	
1952	96.8	1,125.9	11,630	
1953	91.5	1,191.2	13,019	

SOURCE: NMTBA estimates.
* U.S. Census Bulletin 67, *Metal Working Machinery.*
† Data for Exports for 1907-1913 from *Iron Age* 94: No. 4, July 23, 1914, pp. 189–190.

TABLE 7
MACHINE TOOL PRODUCTION
($000's Omitted)

Class	1919	1929	1939	1947
Boring Machines	8,768	6,925	14,166	25,825
Broaching Machines	1,395	397	2,296	4,956
Cutting-Off Machines	n.a.	1,205	1,121	5,621
Drilling Machines	11,430	17,295	12,376	33,517
Gear-Cutting Machines	5,846	8,980	11,242	17,719
Grinding Machines*	15,803	22,690	32,227	56,364
Lathes†	47,100	49,554	50,108	92,908
Milling Machines	18,526	16,857	23,136	35,278
Planers	8,129	2,517	4,484	4,018
Threading Machines‡	2,381	4,448	3,535	10,190
Shapers & Slotters	4,231	3,586	1,893	7,259
Other	31,313	24,833	25,030	71,139
TOTAL	$155,022	$159,287	$181,616	$364,794

SOURCE: U.S. Census Bureau, *Census of Manufactures.*
n.a.—not available
* Includes Honing and Lapping Machines.
† Includes Screw Machines.
‡ Includes Pipe Cutting and Threading Machines.

TABLE 8
Machine Tool Industry by State (1900-1950)

State	Number of Establishments	Employees April 1934	Employees Dec. 1942	Shipments Rate Apr. 42	Rank
				$(000)	
California	9 *(4)		709	193	
Colorado	1		500	235	
Connecticut	55 (17)	1,220	12,398	10,674	2
Delaware	2 (1)				
Illinois	45 (12)	800	6,060	4,710	7
Indiana	13 (8)	200	3,273	3,799	11
Iowa	5 (2)		79	11	
Kentucky	3 (2)	35	333	426	
Maine	2 (2)				
Maryland	3 (2)				
Massachusetts	54 (23)	708	12,706	10,420	3
Michigan	48 (19)	578	5,916	6,078	9
Missouri	5		340	291	
New Hampshire	7		285	308	
New Jersey	12 (5)		1,292	763	12
New York	46 (14)		5,930	4,370	8
North Carolina	1				
Ohio	131 (50)	2,644	35,221	32,788	1
Pennsylvania	28 (4)		3,660	3,183	10
Rhode Island	12 (7)	1,470	7,716	4,296	5
South Dakota	1				
Tennessee	1		41	27	
Vermont	5 (1)	759	6,520	5,326	6
Virginia	1 (1)				
Wisconsin	26 (7)	167	9,569	9,857	4
Other	16		2,574	1,624	
Totals	532 (181)	8,581	115,122	99,229	
Net	351				

Sources: Tables 8-15 are based on data from National Recovery Administration Records; from War Production Board Reports; NMTBA Historical File; and Moody's *Industrial Manual*.

* Numbers in parenthesis are establishments converted, liquidated, or merged by 1950.

TABLE 9

TOTALS BY SIZE CLASS (1900-1950)

LARGE SIZE

(Over 500 Wage Earners Producing Machine Tools)

State	Number of Establishments	Employees April 1934	Employees Dec. 1942	Shipments Rate April 1942 ($000s)
California	1		709	193
Colorado	1		500	235
Connecticut	4	950	10,911	9,832
Delaware				
Illinois	6	780	4,272	3,232
Indiana	3	200	3,180	3,702
Iowa				
Kentucky				
Maine				
Maryland				
Massachusetts	7	600	10,273	8,228
Michigan	2	300	2,000	2,027
Missouri				
New Hampshire				
New Jersey	1		579	294
New York	5		3,968	2,639
North Carolina				
Ohio	15	2,077	27,888	26,782
Pennsylvania	3		2,894	2,691
Rhode Island	2	1,420	7,049	3,755
South Dakota				
Tennessee				
Vermont	4	759	6,520	5,326
Virginia				
Wisconsin	3		7,676	7,812
Other				
TOTALS	57	7,086	88,419	76,748

TABLE 10
Totals by Size Class
Medium Size
(Between 100 and 499 Wage Earners Producing Machine Tools)

State	Number of Establishments	Employees April 1934	Employees Dec. 1942	Shipments Rate April 1942 ($000s)
California				
Colorado				
Connecticut	6	150	1,305	677
Delaware				
Illinois	7		1,517	1,122
Indiana				
Iowa				
Kentucky	2	35	333	426
Maine				
Maryland				
Massachusetts	10	108	2,093	2,068
Michigan	18	184	3,658	4,030
Missouri	2		340	291
New Hampshire	1		285	308
New Jersey	2		637	426
New York	6		1,863	1,464
North Carolina				
Ohio	30	504	6,927	5,688
Pennsylvania	1		400	199
Rhode Island	2	35	579	446
South Dakota				
Tennessee				
Vermont				
Virginia				
Wisconsin	8	17	1,721	1,994
Other	10		2,201	1,379
TOTALS	105	1,033	23,859	$20,508

TABLE 11
Totals by Size Class
Other
(Less than 100 Wage Earners on Machine Tool Production)
(000s omitted)

State	Number of Establishments	Employees April 1934	Employees Dec. 1942	Shipments Rate April 1942 ($000s)
California	8			
Colorado				
Connecticut	45	120	182	$175
Delaware	2			
Illinois	32	20	271	256
Indiana	10		93	97
Iowa	5		79	11
Kentucky	1			
Maine	2			
Maryland	3			
Massachusetts	37		340	94
Michigan	28	94	258	21
Missouri	3			
New Hampshire	6			
New Jersey	9		76	43
New York	35		99	267
North Carolina	1			
Ohio	86	63	406	318
Pennsylvania	24		366	293
Rhode Island	8	15	88	75
South Dakota	1			
Tennessee	1		41	27
Vermont	1			
Virginia	1			
Wisconsin	15	150	172	51
Other	5		373	245
TOTALS	368	462	2,844	$1,973

TABLE 12
TWENTY-FIVE LARGEST MACHINE TOOL BUILDERS
(Ranked by Number of Wage Earners Working on Machine Tools in December 1942)

Rank

1	Cincinnati Milling Machine Company, Cincinnati, Ohio
2	Brown & Sharpe Company, Providence, Rhode Island
3	Bullard Company, Bridgeport, Connecticut
4	Warner & Swasey Company, Cleveland, Ohio
5	National Acme Company, Cleveland, Ohio
6	Kearney & Trecker Corporation, Milwaukee, Wisconsin
7	Van Norman Machine Tool Company, Springfield, Massachusetts
8	Gisholt Machine Company, Madison, Wisconsin
9	Monarch Machine Tool Company, Sidney, Ohio
10	Heald Machine Company, Worcester, Massachusetts
11	Norton Company, Worcester, Massachusetts
12	Gleason Works, Rochester, New York
13	New Britain Machine Company, New Britain, Connecticut
14	Pratt & Whitney Company, Hartford, Connecticut
15	Jones & Lamson Machine Company, Springfield, Vermont
16	Cone Automatic Machine Company, Windsor, Vermont
17	Fellows Gear Shaper Company, Springfield, Vermont
18	Hendey Machine Company, Torrington, Connecticut (liquidated and sold 1954 to Barber-Coleman)
19	Ex-Cell-O Corporation, Detroit, Michigan
20	General Machinery Corporation, Div. Niles Tool Works, Hamilton, Ohio
21	American Tool Works Company, Cincinnati, Ohio
22	Landis Tool Company, Waynesboro, Pennsylvania
23	Bryant Chucking Grinder Company, Springfield, Vermont
24	Lodge & Shipley Machine Tool Company, Cincinnati, Ohio
25	Landis Machine Company, Waynesboro, Pennsylvania

TABLE 13
Selected Data for Twenty-five Large Establishments

Establish-ments	Life Span	NMTBA	Employees April 34	Employees Dec. 42	Shipments Rate Apr. 42 ($000s)
Ohio 1	1880	1902	1,400	6,902	$8,590
R. I. 1	1868	1911	2,200	6,163	2,964
Conn. 1	1880	1905	500	5,538	3,725
Ohio 2	1880	1906		5,027	3,882
Ohio 3	1895	1906–22,27		4,166	2,880
Wisc. 1	1898	1906		4,105	3,795
Mass. 1	1888–1961	1912		2,779	1,211
Wisc. 2	1889	1907		2,690	2,429
Ohio 4	1909	1917		2,491	1,911
Mass. 2	1890–1955	1906		2,311	2,830
Mass. 3	1885	1903–05,06	600	2,291	2,142
N. Y. 1	1865	1910–57,59		2,128	1,029
Conn. 2	1895	1907–22,27		1,955	2,297
Conn. 3	1869		1,100	1,914	2,982
Vt. 2	1898	1907	309	1,755	1,049
Vt. 3	1916–63	1933	200	1,774	1,283
Vt. 2	1898	1907	309	1,755	1,049
Conn. 4	1870–1954	1902C–19, 25–54		1,504	828
Mich. 1	1919	1929	300	1,464	1,877
Ohio 5	1871	1930		1,416	1,270
Ohio 6	1898	1902	285	1,391	1,386
Penna. 1	1889	1910		1,258	1,725
Vt. 4	1903–58	1910	100	1,119	1,228
Ohio 7	1892	1902		1,069	646
Penna. 2	1903	1912		1,017	226
		TOTALS	6,994	66,099	$55,951

TABLE 14
FIRMS LEAVING MACHINE TOOL BUSINESS
(Percentages of Total Firms for which Data were Obtained
and by Size Class)

Year	Average	Large	Medium	Other	Year	Average	Large	Medium	Other
1900	—	—	—	—	1926	1.39	—	—	2.27
1901	—	—	—	—	1927	.69	—	—	1.13
1902	—	—	—	—	1928	1.73	—	—	2.86
1903	.81	—	—	1.96	1929	1.03	—	—	1.70
1904	—	—	—	—	1930	.33	—	—	.55
1905	.71	—	—	1.61	1931	1.70	—	—	2.82
1906	.61	—	—	1.22	1932	2.08	—	—	3.47
1907	.56	—	—	1.11	1933	2.31	—	—	4.12
1908	—	—	—	—	1934	.34	—	—	.58
1909	—	—	—	—	1935	.34	—	—	.57
1910	.48	—	—	.86	1936	—	—	—	—
1911	1.33	—	—	2.29	1937	1.04	—	—	1.74
1912	2.04	—	—	3.31	1938	.69	—	—	1.15
1913	1.22	—	—	1.90	1939	1.05	—	—	1.75
1914	2.45	—	—	4.06	1940	.69	—	—	1.17
1915	.79	—	—	1.31	1941	.69	—	—	1.15
1916	1.14	—	—	1.85	1942	1.68	—	—	2.84
1917	–0–	—	—	—	1943	.33	—	—	.57
1918	–0–	—	—	—	1944	1.01	—	—	1.68
1919	1.28	—	—	1.99	1945	1.03	—	1.56	1.12
1920	1.24	—	—	1.89	1946	1.03	—	1.58	1.11
1921	6.71	—	1.72	9.95	1947	2.36	1.85	1.61	2.82
1922	4.69	—	—	7.48	1948	1.73	—	1.63	2.27
1923	.67	—	—	1.08	1949	2.76	1.85	3.33	2.28
1924	2.76	—	—	4.47	1950	1.06	—	1.72	1.15
1925	1.39	—	—	2.27					
					Yearly Avg. 1900-1950	1.17	.11	.26	1.83

TABLE 15
Business Failures 1900-1950
(Percentages for All Businesses and Machine Tool Industry)

Year	All Types Per Cent Failed	Machine Tools Per Cent of Total	Year	All Types Per Cent Failed	Machine Tools Per Cent of Total
1900	.92	–0–	1925	1.00	1.39
1901	.90	–0–	1926	1.01	1.39
1902	.93	–0–	1927	1.06	.69
1903	.94	.81	1928	1.09	1.73
1904	.92	–0–	1929	1.04	1.03
1905	.85	.71	1930	1.22	.33
1906	.77	.61	1931	1.33	1.70
1907	.83	.56	1932	1.54	2.08
1908	1.08	–0–	1933	1.00	2.31
1909	.87	–0–	1934	.61	.34
1910	.84	.48	1935	.62	.34
1911	.88	1.33	1936	.48	–0–
1912	1.00	2.04	1937	.46	1.04
1913	.98	1.22	1938	.61	.69
1914	1.18	2.45	1939	.70	1.05
1915	1.33	.79	1940	.63	.69
1916	1.00	1.14	1941	.55	.69
1917	.80	–0–	1942	.45	1.68
1918	.59	–0–	1943	.16	.33
1919	.37	1.28	1944	.07	1.01
1920	.48	1.24	1945	.04	1.03
1921	1.02	6.71	1946	.05	1.03
1922	1.20	4.69	1947	.14	2.36
1923	.93	.67	1948	.20	1.73
1924	1.00	2.76	1949	.34	2.76
			1950	.34	1.06

TABLE 16
Total Capital in Major Branches of Manufactures
(In Millions of 1929 $s)

Series	1899	1904	1909	1914	1919	1929	1937	1948
82 Total Manu-facturing	17,452	23,295	31,563	36,737	46,094	63,292	55,319	77,982
83 Food and Kindred Products	3,598	4,656	5,517	6,515	7,593	9,591	9,180	10,488
92 Textiles and Textile Products	2,876	3,482	4,636	5,163	6,752	8,195	5,638	6,892
115 Petroleum Refining	195	254	327	552	1,380	6,092	6,503	11,188
117 Iron & Steel Products	1,599	2,886	4,305	5,166	6,735	6,666	6,719	9,645
124 Machinery, Excluding Transporta-tion Eqpt.	1,917	2,710	3,654	4,293	5,595	6,166	5,286	10,352
129 Transporta-tion Eqpt. (Other than RR)	349	333	567	991	2,480	3,476	3,672	5,642
130 Motor Vehicles	73	57	267	616	1,936	2,742	2,792	4,016
131 Locomotives and Railroad Equipment	276	274	299	375	523	616	680	618
132 Airplanes					19	118	201	743

Source: U. S. Bureau of Census, *Historical Statistics of the United States, 1960.*

TABLE 17
DISTRIBUTION AND AGE OF MACHINE TOOLS
(By Industry)
(Percentages by Age and Number of Units)

	Units (000's)	Per Cent at least 10 yrs. Old							Over 20 yrs.
		1925	1930	1935	1940	1945	1949	1953	1953
Agricultural Machinery	70.4	65%	58%	60%	69%	55%	50%	50%	23%
Construction, Mining, Oil Well	44.8		49	74	73	49	48	58	22
Metalworking Machinery	161.0		45	66	71	45	43	60	21
Special-Industry Machinery	121.5	56	47	76	74	57	54	62	30
General Industrial Equipment	102.2	52	46	75	78	54	44	55	21
Office and Store Machines	41.1	48		74	68	62	52	56	31
Domestic and Service Equipment	52.7			62	83	47	42	52	17
Electrical Equipment	190.1	45	51	65	70	47	37	51	18
Misc. Machine Parts, Jobbing	118.9				72*	59*	41	58	19
Motor Vehicles and Parts	171.2	27	27	55	63	37	56	57	23
Complete Aircraft	41.6							45	5
Aircraft Engines, Propellers & Parts	60.3		3	13	29	2	16	51	4
Railroad Equipment	18.7	56	74	71	83	42	48	66	28
Fabricated Metal Products	385.2	59	49	70	76†	47	45	52	18
Shipbuilding, Ordnance, Misc.	259.5		52			40	36	63	17
Precision Mechanisms	102.4				61	36	35	45	13
TOTAL	1,941.6	44%	52%	67%	72%	38%	43%	55%	19%

SOURCE: *American Machinist*, Mid-November 1953, "1954 Production Planbook."

* Includes job shops only.

† Does not include navy arsenals.

Note: Percentages from previous inventories have been adjusted in some cases to provide comparable data.

Blanks mean no comparable data are available.

TABLE 18
MACHINE TOOLS IN USE BY INDUSTRY

Industry	1940	Units in Place 1945	1949
Agricultural Machinery	18,156	31,632	48,498
Construction, Mining, Oil Well	17,721	41,089	34,983
Metalworking Machinery	71,271	91,430	147,327
Special Industry Machinery	46,052	93,194	136,412
General Industrial Equipment	99,441	11,945	26,939
Office and Store Machines	14,505	17,307	45,645
Domestic and Service Equipment	12,971	45,568	48,151
Electrical Equipment	43,315	105,096	161,914
Misc. Machine Parts, Jobbing	49,883	17,235	100,847
Motor Vehicles and Parts	130,518	243,686	138,595
Complete Aircraft			
Aircraft Engines, Propellers & Parts	8,780	276,466	54,711
Railroad Equipment	43,620	37,304	16,075
Fabricated Metal Products	358,988	449,021	375,717
Shipbuilding, Ordnance, Misc.	73,783	151,127	240,713
Precision Mechanisms	40,390	84,042	113,136
TOTAL	941,898	1,711,137	1,762,165

SOURCE: *American Machinist,* "Inventories of Metalworking Machinery," 1940, 1945, 1949.

TABLE 19

Profits After Taxes as a Percentage of Net Worth

(Companies Filing under Securities and Exchange Act. "L" Indicates Loss)

Company	1936	1937	1938	1939	1940	1941	1942	1943	1944	1945	1946	1947	1948	1949	1950
Brown & Sharpe Mfg. Co.	n.a.	n.a.	n.a.	n.a.	24	25	11	11	8	6	10	11	4	1L	6
The Bullard Company	32	37	1L	10	57	48	28	20	9	10	4	1L	6	7	11
Cincinnati Milling Machine Co.										10	10	6	7	7	7
Clearing Machine Corp.				22	76	14	15	18	13	8	48	51	17	8	13
The Cross Company										46	24L	2L	20	4L	13
Ex-Cell-O Corp.	17	26	16	28	56	58	41	30	21	19	11	17	19	24	20
Giddings & Lewis Machine Tool Co.						24	33	20	11	13	15	9	7	8	7
Gisholt Machine Co.						36	10	20	10	7	3	3	1	4	5
Kearney & Trecker Corp.							35	18	11	9	5	2L	5	3	3
Micromatic Hone Corp.	22	27	1	39	42	44	30	35	24	19	3L	4L	2	12	12
Monarch Machine Tool Co.	31	43	24	35	65	61	35	22	18	14	17	14	11	9	10
National Acme Co.	21	42	4	13	47	49	28	20	15	15	20	16	9	7	12
New Britain Machine Co.	24	22	11	12	40	49	28	23	21	9	9	2L	1	2	19
Seneca Falls Machine Co.							28	11	7	8	6L	2	1L	1	7
Sundstrand Machine Tool Co.	31	20	11L	26	64	58	53	19	15	12	17	34	10	15	21
Van Norman Machine Tool Co.		34	26	20	38	42	28	22	8	7	26	13	7	1	11
Warner & Swasey Co.							19	16	4	10	4	3	5	5L	14

TABLE 20
VOLUME OF OUTPUT FOR SELECTED PRODUCTS
($ Millions)

Year	Passenger Motor Vehicles	Tractors	Farm Equipment	Industrial Machinery
1900	6.0	—	100.6	347.6
1901	7.8	—	110.4	330.3
1902	9.3	—	152.9	371.3
1903	11.3	—	120.2	405.9
1904	21.4	—	125.2	327.1
1905	35.6	—	130.2	404.7
1906	62.7	—	160.5	504.6
1907	89.6	—	161.6	510.9
1908	132.2	—	137.7	331.2
1909	154.3	—	166.5	446.9
1910	203.8	—	170.6	512.4
1911	209.2	—	168.2	476.6
1912	311.3	8.1	187.3	517.1
1913	372.8	4.4	202.4	543.4
1914	399.6	16.7	187.8	460.2
1915	537.8	22.7	205.1	536.8
1916	973.7	25.8	237.1	906.0
1917	996.7	50.7	250.0	1,358.1
1918	762.7	136.6	301.8	1,578.8
1919	1,296.6	171.6	394.6	1,434.3
1920	1,628.3	197.4	270.6	1,635.8
1921	1,115.5	49.6	248.1	922.8
1922	1,546.1	43.4	160.7	1,085.2
1923	2,188.8	63.5	315.5	1,510.9
1924	1,922.5	52.1	265.9	1,303.8
1925	2,340.2	70.3	306.5	1,486.4

TABLE 20 (Continued)

Year	Passenger Motor Vehicles	Tractors	Farm Equipment	Industrial Machinery
1926	2,504.3	87.4	355.4	1,606.8
1927	1,967.8	91.3	340.4	1,476.0
1928	2,294.9	104.1	356.5	1,644.1
1929	2,567.0	121.8	386.5	2,017.2
1930	1,538.0	95.4	338.5	1,457.8
1931	1,074.1	19.6	163.4	938.2
1932	603.2	15.8	70.9	525.8
1933	725.3	12.6	78.8	577.1
1934	—	—	—	—
1935	1,688.3	133.3	345.3	1,126.0
1936	*2,016	—	—	—
1937	*2,244	223.7	668.5	1,883.7
1938	*1,237			
1939	*1,765			
1940	*2,371			
1941	*2,567			
1942	164			
1943	Less than 5			
1944	—			
1945	* 57			
1946	*1,980			
1947	*3,936			
1948	*4,870			
1949	*4,870			
1950	*8,468			

SOURCE: U.S. Department of Commerce, Bureau of the Census. *Historical Statistics of the United States—Colonial Times to 1957*, pp. 250–306 and p. 420.

* Moody's *Industrials, 1964* (From Automobile Manufacturers Association).

TABLE 21
RAILROAD EQUIPMENT LOCOMOTIVE
PRODUCTION/ORDERS

Year	Locomotives	Year	Locomotives
1900	3,153	1927	1,176
1901	3,384	1928	747
1902	4,070	1929	1,161
1903	5,152	1930	1,134
1904	3,441	1931	222
1905	5,491	1932	123
1906	6,952	1933	63
1907	7,362	1934	110
1908	2,342	1935	205
1909	2,887	1936	202
1910	4,755	1937	615
1911	3,530	1938	346
1912	4,915	1939	355
1913	5,332	1940	560
1914	2,235	1941	1,107
1915	2,085	1942	1,018
1916	4,075	1943	1,164
1917	5,446	1944	1,438
1918	6,475	1945	3,213
1919	3,272	1946	*1,681
1920	3,672	1947	2,884
1921	1,823	1948	3,162
1922	1,534	1949	1,920
1923	3,785	1950	4,750
1924	2,036	1951	4,436
1925	1,285	1952	2,056
1926	1,770	1953	2,263

From: *Historical Statistics of U.S.* and Moody's *Industrial Manual, 1964.*
* Orders 1946–1950.

TABLE 22
Net Profits as Per Cent of Sales (1913–1941)

Year	Jones & Lamson		Fellows Gear Shaper		Bryant Chucking Grinder	
	Net Profit (000s)	Per Cent of Sales	Net Profit (000s)	Per Cent of Sales	Net Profit (000s)	Per Cent of Sales
1913	$203.0	19.8	$ 55.3	16.0	$ .1	.2
1914	4.6 (L)	.7 (L)	39.5	13.4	12.0 (L)	57.1 (L)
1915	495.2	28.7	288.5	41.1	41.7	34.4
1916	951.0	43.3	616.6	46.0	100.8	29.7
1917	480.0	18.2	340.0	19.7	45.6	13.9
1918	445.7	14.1	166.2	9.3	36.5	5.7
1919	357.9	12.7	525.7	19.0	35.4	7.1
1920	221.3	8.0	171.5	6.7	19.2 (L)	5.6 (L)
1921	648.8 (L)	190.1 (L)	227.4 (L)	66.9 (L)	43.0 (L)	56.4 (L)
1922	41.6 (L)	4.1 (L)	72.9	8.3	19.8 (L)	8.4 (L)
1923	128.6	8.1	430.3	26.6	8.7 (L)	2.7 (L)
1924	94.8 (L)	8.5 (L)	236.1	17.7	5.1 (L)	2.5 (L)
1925	48.1	3.0	453.8	23.7	13.3	3.9
1926	317.0	16.2	287.6	16.9	3.0	1.0
1927	9.0	.1	472.7	21.8	19.9	5.2
1928	546.4	18.4	834.5	29.3	40.3	8.3
1929	578.7	17.4	1,073.1	30.4	102.4	13.0
1930	254.5 (L)	15.9 (L)	350.1	16.1	61.5	9.4
1931	247.6 (L)	25.1 (L)	26.7	1.9	21.0 (L)	6.1 (L)
1932	337.2 (L)	45.4 (L)	108.1 (L)	14.4 (L)	36.2 (L)	71.2 (L)
1933	218.5 (L)	44.4 (L)	102.1	9.7	6.6 (L)	5.6 (L)
1934	141.7 (L)	15.9 (L)	134.6	11.7	38.2	8.5
1935	.3	13.4	.3	17.5	.04	8.3
1936	.2	7.9	.5	22.5	.03	4.9
1937	.7	15.2	.6	20.4	.09	8.9
1938	.2	8.5	.1	6.3	.4	22.1
1939	.8	17.3	.6	19.0	.4	20.4
1940	1.2	12.6	1.4	16.4	.6	14.9
1941	1.6	9.8	1.1	10.5	.7	10.7

Source: Extracted from several tables in W. G. Broehl, Jr., *Precision Valley*.

TABLE 23
MACHINE TOOLS—UNFILLED ORDERS AND SHIPMENTS
(1939–1949)

Period	Unfilled Orders Units (Thousands)	Unfilled Orders Value ($Millions)		Total Shipments Units (Thousands)	Total Shipments Value ($Millions)
1939					$ 199.9
1940					442.6
1941					771.5
1942			Total	307.2	$1,321.7
January	82.8	$ 488.4		19.8	83.5
February	99.8	582.2		20.2	84.4
March	147.5	843.5		23.2	98.4
April	183.2	995.6		24.2	103.4
May	199.6	1,059.8		24.6	107.3
June	209.8	1,096.4		25.4	111.1
July	216.7	1,117.4		27.3	113.6
August	210.3	1,096.0		28.1	117.3
September	194.3	1,050.7		28.4	119.9
October	181.7	986.7		29.4	130.0
November	171.7	941.8		27.1	120.9
December	156.4	866.6		29.5	132.0
1943			Total	265.8	$1,180.2
January	143.6	$ 796.1		25.9	117.4
February	137.3	745.8		25.4	114.6
March	127.0	704.9		29.1	125.4
April	115.1	643.6		26.9	118.0
May	101.7	578.4		25.5	113.9
June	89.8	509.3		24.3	108.7
July	78.9	441.2		21.2	97.5
August	69.4	386.8		19.8	87.8
September	60.1	333.1		19.3	85.8
October	53.9	286.6		17.9	78.3
November	48.1	244.2		16.2	71.8
December	42.5	210.6		14.3	60.9

TABLE 23 (Continued)

Period	Unfilled Orders Units (Thousands)	Value ($Millions)		Total Shipments Units (Thousands)	Value ($Millions)
1944			Total	136.2	$ 497.5
January	38.4	$ 181.5		14.2	56.4
February	37.3	164.5		12.9	50.1
March	37.7	153.6		14.0	51.9
April	39.1	167.2		11.7	41.4
May	42.6	185.7		12.3	41.8
June	44.7	194.5		12.2	41.5
July	42.5	191.3		8.4	32.8
August	43.5	196.8		10.1	35.2
September	42.6	194.1		10.3	35.9
October	45.6	213.7		10.6	37.5
November	50.5	235.4		9.9	36.3
December	54.5	260.9		9.8	36.8
1945			Total	103.0	$ 423.7
January	59.1	$ 281.3		10.1	37.4
February	63.9	302.6		9.8	36.0
March	65.8	310.1		11.4	40.0
April	64.5	289.1		11.0	40.2
May	64.8	274.8		10.8	39.8
June	63.6	256.9		11.5	41.0
July-December				38.5	189.3
1946			Total	75.0	334.8
1947			Total	60.0	306.0
1948			Total	50.0	288.5
1949			Total	34.5	249.2

Source: WPB, *Product Reports-Machine Tools-Non-Portable* August 29, 1945. Data for 1939—November 1941 based on NMTBA Reports; for December 1941—June 1945 from WPB-417 Form; from July 1945 they are from NMTBA.

TABLE 24
MACHINE TOOL EXPORTS
($ Millions)

Period	Total	U. K.	Canada	Australia	U.S.S.R.	Other
1939	$ 91.2	$ 24.9	$ 3.5	$ .7	$ 15.4	$46.8
1940	208.9	122.7	14.4	4.5	14.1	53.9
1941	185.0	114.7	48.0	6.7	4.2	11.3
1942	159.4	72.5	30.3	12.3	35.9	8.4
1943	237.4	69.1	15.8	17.4	119.6	15.5
1944	163.6	19.4	4.0	1.2	122.2	16.8
1945						
Jan.	5.1	.8	.3	.0	2.8	1.1
Feb.	6.0	.6	.5	.0	4.0	.8
Mar.	9.7	.8	.6	.0	6.9	1.3
April	10.8	.5	.5	.0	8.6	1.1
May	11.1	.4	.4	*	9.3	1.1
June	6.2	.3	.3	*	4.7	.9
1940-Je-45		$402.0	$115.2	$42.2	$332.3	
1942-Je-45		$164.6	$ 52.8	$31.0	$314.0	

SOURCE: WPB, "Facts for Industry," 34–3–5, October 31, 1945.
* Included in "Other."

TABLE 25
YEARLY MACHINE TOOL NEW ORDERS
Metal-Cutting Types Only

	Gross New Orders		Net New Orders	
Year	Units (Thousands)	Dollars ($Millions)	Units (Thousands)	Dollars ($Millions)
1939	n.a.	354.8	n.a.	n.a.
1940	n.a.	621.7	n.a.	n.a.
1941	n.a.	998.1	n.a.	n.a.
1942*	422.9	1,844.9	372.5	1,625.0
1943*	187.0	663.1	148.4	526.3
1944*	158.2	585.5	149.2	550.1
1945	128.4	486.0	93.3	353.3
1946	86.9	342.6	78.9	311.1
1947	50.4	263.8	45.9	240.1
1948	47.3	274.1	45.0	261.0
1949	32.4	245.4	30.8	233.1
1950	73.6	729.2	71.9	712.5
1951	140.2	1,688.4	126.9	1,528.0
1952	82.0	1,057.4	62.2	802.6
1953	68.4	861.8	59.4	748.1
1954	43.2	560.4	39.7	514.5
1955	62.6	967.8	60.0	927.1
1956	68.6	988.3	65.5	924.0
1957	42.9	581.8	39.4	519.8
1958	24.9	298.6	23.8	281.4
1959	38.6	526.2	37.7	509.0
1960	33.9	537.4	32.6	503.1
1961	30.8	584.2	29.7	556.3
1962	34.5	567.8	33.1	537.6
1963	35.7	742.8	34.6	713.9

* War Production Board estimates 1941 through July, 1945. All other years estimated from reports to NMTBA.

n.a.　not available.

TABLE 26
GEOGRAPHICAL DISTRIBUTION, 1949

Area	No. Tools	Per Cent Over 10 Years	Per Cent Over 20 Years	Estimated Population (000s)	Machines Per 1000 Population
Boston	149,536	47	27	4,207	35.5
Bridgeport	107,983	48	33	1,385	77.8
New England	61,986	56	39	3,564	17.4
New York	140,785	39	15	12,684	11.1
Buffalo	48,787	43	19	1,680	29.0
Philadelphia	73,941	43	22	4,747	15.6
Pittsburgh	28,058	54	27	2,500	11.2
Middle Atlantic	130,111	43	26	8,066	16.2
Baltimore	7,423	39	13	1,306	5.7
Southern	135,028	35	7	29,388	4.6
Cleveland	92,300	39	22	2,511	36.8
Cincinnati	32,863	46	27	1,275	25.8
Detroit	122,443	51	26	3,038	40.4
Milwaukee	37,315	43	22	950	39.3
Chicago	120,437	40	15	4,950	24.3
Indianapolis	11,580	34	4	500	23.1
Midwestern	273,829	43	23	16,164	16.9
Minneapolis	11,883	33	13	1,006	11.8
St. Louis	36,257	51	29	2,214	16.5
Central and Mountain	42,007	44	20	15,595	2.7
Houston	6,772	43	12	601	11.2
Southwestern	29,673	39	17	13,593	2.2
San Francisco	12,375	42	19	1,990	6.2
Los Angeles	30,368	24	6	3,917	7.7
Pacific Coast	18,725	26	8	8,549	2.2
TOTAL	1,762,165	43	21	146,380	12.0

SOURCE: *American Machinist* "The Mid-Century Inventory of Metal Working Production Equipment," 1947, p. 138.

BIBLIOGRAPHY

BIBLIOGRAPHY

A. *Records in the National Archives*

Record Group 9, U.S. National Recovery Administration, Code Authority Files, 1933–1935, Machine Tool and Forging Machinery Industry.

Record Group 80, U.S. Navy Department, Office of the Secretary, General Correspondence Files, 1926–1942; Office of Procurement and Material. Machine Tool Section Files, 1940–1942.

Record Group 151, U.S. Department of Commerce, Bureau of Foreign and Domestic Commerce. General Files, Machine Tools, 1919–1950, File 221.2; General Files, Machinery—General–1930, File 221; Machinery—General 1919–1950, File 221 General; Machinery—Russia–1932, File 211 Russia; Machinery—Russia, 1924–1932, File 221 Russia; Foreign Trade—Unfair Methods—Germany, 1920–1926, File 413.0; Cooperation with Bureau—Advisory Committee—Machinery Division, File 711; Cooperation with Bureau—NMTBA, 1922–1936, File 711-N; Conventions—NMTBA—1924–1932, File 721-N.

Record Group 179, U.S. Civilian Production Administration and War Production Board. Policy Documentation File and Select Documents File (include records of the Office of Production Management and some from the Production Division of the Advisory Commission to the Council of National Defense).

Record Group 188, U.S. Office of Price Administration, Industrial Division, Director's File; Office of Industry Advisory Committee, Industry Council, Subject File, 1941–1943; Price Department, National Office, Progress Reports—Industrial Materials Price Division—Machinery; Price Department, National Office, Machinery Branch, Legal Section Misc. Commodity File.

Record Group 225, U.S. Army–Navy Munitions Board, Central File, 1922–1946, 470.1/203.2–13, Machine Tools—Commodities General.

B. Manuscripts

Brown, William H. "Innovation in the Machine Tool Industry." Unpublished. PhD. Dissertation, Yale University, New Haven, Conn., 1952, Ms. 306 pp.

Groves, Harold M. "The Machinist in Industry." Unpublished Ph.D. Dissertation, University of Wisconsin, Madison, Wisconsin, 1927. 2 Volumes. Ms. 444 pp.

Himes, Robert Stanley. "A Study of the Machine Tool Industry, With Emphasis on the Problem of Stability." Unpublished Ph.D. Dissertation, The American University, Washington, D.C., 1962, Ms. 314 pp.

U.S. National Recovery Administration. "History of the Code of Fair Competition for the Machine Tool and Forging Machinery Industry." Ms. 14 pp.

————. "History of Code of Fair Competition for Machine Tool and Equipment Distributing Trade." June 15, 1935. Ms. 36 pp.

U.S. Office of Price Administration, Industrial Division. "History of Price Control in the Machine Tool Industry." Ms. 31 pp.

U.S. War Production Board, Policy Analysis and Records Branch (PARB). "Machine Tool Policies of the War Production Board and Predecessor Agencies." May 1940 to November 1945. (Historical Reports on War Administration: Special Study No. 35), June 1947, Rough Draft, Ms.

Wickham, Lucien. "History of the Tools Division of the War Production Board and Predecessor Agencies–1940–1945." Tools Division, WPB, September 1945. Ms. 187 pp.

Wiltse, Charles M. "The Machine Tool Program, June 1950–January 1952," January 18, 1952 (U.S. Department of Commerce, National Production Authority). Ms. 42 pp.

C. Government Publications

Crowell, Benedict, Assistant Secretary of War, Director of Munitions. *America's Munitions, 1917–1918.* Washington, D.C.: Government Printing Office, 1919. 592 pp.

Coleman, Charles H. *Shipbuilding Activities of the National Defense Advisory Commission and Office of Production Management, July 1940–December 1941.* (Historical Reports on War Administration: Special Study No. 18). Washington, D. C.: Civilian Production Administration, July 25, 1945. 148 pp.

Holley, Irving Brinton, Jr. *Buying Aircraft: Material Procurement for the Army Air Forces.* (United States Army in World War

II, Special Studies). Office of the Chief of Military History, Department of the Army. Washington, D. C.: Government Printing Office, 1964. 643 pp.

Miller, Fred J. *Metal Working Machinery.* (Special Bulletin 67). Washington, D. C.: United States Bureau of the Census, 1907.

Newman, Dorothy, and Martha J. Ziegler. *Employment of Women in the Machine Tool Industry.* (United States Department of Labor, Bulletin of the Women's Bureau, No. 192–4.) Washington, D. C.: Government Printing Office, 1943. 42 pp.

Reeves, Caroline Buck. *The Disposition of Surplus Machine Tools by the War Department Following World War I.* Washington, D. C.: (United States Bureau of Labor Statistics. Historical Study No. 75.) Mimeographed. 47 pp.

Rowland, Buford, and William B. Boyd. *U.S. Navy Bureau of Ordnance in World War II.* U.S. Navy Department, Bureau of Ordnance. Washington, D. C.: Government Printing Office, no date. 539 pp.

Sitterson, J. Carlyle. *Aircraft Production Policies Under the National Defense Advisory Commission and Office of Production Management, May 1940 to December 1941.* (Historical Reports on War Administration: Special Study No. 21.) Washington, D.C.: Civilian Production Administration, May 30, 1946. 169 pp. Multilith.

———. *Development of the Reconversion Policies of the War Production Board–April 1943 to January 1945.* (Historical Reports on War Administration: Special Study No. 15.) Washington, D. C.: Civilian Producton Administration, February 26, 1945. 181 pp. Multilith.

Smith, Ralph Elberton. *The Army and Economic Mobilization.* (United States Army in World War II), Office of the Chief of Military History, Department of the Army. Washington, D. C.: Government Printing Office, 1959. 749 pp.

Thomson, Harry C., and Lida Mayo. *The Ordnance Department: Procurement and Supply.* (United States Army in World War II, The Technical Services), Office of the Chief of Military History, Department of the Army. Washington, D. C.: Government Printing Office, 1960, 504 pp.

United States Bureau of Apprenticeship. *A Half-Century of Experience in Training Machinists.* (Kearney and Trecker Corp.), 1953.

U.S. Bureau of Employment Security, *The Machine Tool Industry.* (Industry Manpower Surveys No. 25.) Washington, D. C.: U.S. Bureau of Employment Security, 1952.

U.S. Civilian Production Administration. *Industrial Mobilization for War.* (History of the War Production Board and Predecessor Agencies, 1940–1945.) Washington, D. C.: Government Printing Office, 1947. 1,010 pp.

U.S. House of Representatives, 78th Congress, 1st Session. *Hearings Before the Committee on Naval Affairs: Investigation of the Progress of the War Effort.* Vol. 2. Washington, D. C.: Government Printing Office, June 25, 1943.

U.S. Senate, 77th Congress, 2nd Session. Special Committee Investigating the National Defense Program, Senate Resolution 71 (Truman Committee). *Investigation of the National Defense Program–Additional Report.* Report No. 480, Part 5, January 15, 1942. Washington, D. C.: Government Printing Office, 1942. 288 pp.

U.S. Senate, 79th Congress, 2nd Session. Special Committee to Study Problems of American Small Business. *Economic Concentration and World War II.* Report of the Smaller War Plants Corporation. Washington, D. C.: Government Printing Office, 1946. 359 pp.

U.S. Senate, 82nd Congress, 2nd Session. Joint Committee on Defense Production, Report 1107. *Defense Production Act–Progress Report No. 13, Machine Tools.* Washington, D. C.: Government Printing Office, January 23, 1952. 105 pp.

U.S. Department of Commerce, Bureau of the Census. *Census of Manufactures:* 1919, 1923, 1929, 1931, 1933, 1935, 1937, 1939, 1947, and 1954, "Machine Tools." Washington, D. C.: Government Printing Office, various dates.

U.S. Department of Commerce, Bureau of the Census. *Historical Statistics of the United States–Colonial Times to 1957.* (A Statistical Abstract Supplement). Washington, D. C.: Government Printing Office, 1960.

U.S. Department of Commerce, Bureau of Foreign and Domestic Commerce. *Developing Machinery Markets Abroad.* (Revised Edition, 1928). Washington, D. C.: Government Printing Office, 1928. 20 pp.

U.S. Department of Labor, Bureau of Labor Statistics, *Employment and Earnings Statistics–United States* (sic 354, sic 3541) pp. 191–196.

U.S. National Resources Committee. *The Structure of the American Economy.* Part I, *Basic Characteristics,* June 1939; Part II, *Toward Full Use of Resources.* Washington, D. C.: Government Printing Office, 1939.

U.S. Office of Price Administration (OPA). *Second Report of the*

Office of Price Administration. Washington, D. C.: Government Printing Office, 1942. 151 pp.

D. Books and Monographs

Alderfer, Evan Benner and Herman Edward Michl. *Economics of American Industry.* New York: McGraw-Hill Book Co., Inc., 1942. 566 pp.

Alford, L. P. *Standardization of Machine Tools for the Benefit of the User.* NMTBA, Official Report, Tenth Annual Convention, October 10–11, 1911.

Allen, Edward Lawrence. *Economics of American Manufacturing.* New York: Henry Holt and Company, 1952. 566 pp.

Bacon, Frank R., *et al. Anatomy of an Industry–A Study of the Michigan Machine Tool Industry In Its National and International Setting.* Ann Arbor, Michigan: University of Michigan, Industrial Development Division, Institute of Science and Technology, 1963. 105 pp.

Baker, Warren and Joseph S. Kozacka. *Carbide Cutting Tools–How to Make and Use Them.* Chicago, Illinois: American Technical Society, 1949. 416 pp.

Blackall, Frederick S. Jr., President NMTBA. "A Letter to the Renegotiation Board on Behalf of the Builders of Machine Tools," Feburary 12, 1952. 51 pp.

Boston, Orlan William. *Metal Processing,* 2nd Ed. New York: John Wiley and Sons, 1951. 763 pp.

Brady, George S. *Materials Handbook.* New York: McGraw-Hill Book Company, 1947. 831 pp.

Brady, Robert A. *Business as a System of Power.* New York. Columbia University Press, 1943. 340 pp.

Broehl, Wayne G. Jr. *Precision Valley.* Englewood Cliffs, New Jersey: Prentice-Hall, 1959. 274 pp.

Calvert, Monte A. *The Mechanical Engineer in America, 1830–1910.* Baltimore, Md.: The Johns Hopkins Press, 1967. 296 pp.

Clark, John M. *Social Control of Business,* 2nd Ed. New York: McGraw-Hill Book Company, 1939. 537 pp.

Clark, Victor Selden. *History of Manufactures in the United States* (Vol. III, 1893–1928). Published for Carnegie Institution of Washington by McGraw-Hill Book Company, New York, 1929. 467 pp.

Colvin, Fred H. and Frank A. Stanley. *Drilling and Surfacing Practice,* 2nd Ed. New York: McGraw-Hill Company, 1943.

————. *Grinding Practice,* 3d Ed. New York: McGraw-Hill Company, 1950. 419 pp.

——. *Turning and Boring Practice*, 3d Ed. New York: McGraw-Hill Book Company, 1948. 531 pp.

——. *Running a Machine Shop*, 2d Ed. New York: McGraw-Hill Book Company, 1948. 521 pp.

DuBrul, Ernest Ferdinand. *The Machine Tool Industry's Code of Business Principles* (General Management Series: No. 78). New York: American Management Association, 1928.

Faulkner, Harold U. *The Decline of Laissez Faire, 1897–1917* (Vol. VII, The Economic History of the United States). New York: Rinehart and Company, Inc., 1951. 433 pp.

Flanders, Ralph Edward. *Senator from Vermont.* Boston: Little, Brown and Company, 1961, 312 pp.

Garner, S. Paul. *Evolution of Cost Accounting to 1925.* Tuscaloosa, Ala.: University of Alabama Press, 1954. 346 pp.

Geier, Frederick V. "Amortization of Machine Tools," Paper delivered to Machinery Builders Society of New York, May 1930. Pamphlet.

Hamilton, Douglas T. and Franklin D. Jones. *Automatic Screw Machines.* New York: The Industrial Press, 1916. 342 pp.

Hine, Charles R. *Machine Tools for Engineers*, 2nd Ed. New York: McGraw-Hill Book Company, Inc., 1959, 445 pp.

Johnson, Emory R. *Government Regulation of Transportation.* New York: D. Appleton-Century Company, 1938. 680 pp.

Melman, Seymour. *Our Depleted Society.* New York: Holt, Rinehart and Winston, 1965. 366 pp.

Miller, Eugene Willard. *A Geography of Manufacturing.* Englewood Cliffs, N. J.: Prentice-Hall, Inc., 1962. 490 pp.

Miller, Franklin, Basset and Company. *Uniform Cost System,* New York: National Machine Tool Builders' Association, April 1920. 71 pp.

Mitchell, Broadus. *Depression Decade, From New Era Through New Deal, 1929–1941* (Vol. IX, The Economic History of the United States). New York: Holt, Rinehart and Winston, 1962. 462 pp.

National Machine Tool Builders Association. *Machine Tools Today.* NMTBA, Cleveland, Ohio, n.d. Pamphlet. 23 pp.

NMTBA. *Official Report.* Semi-annual Convention (19th Meeting), May 18–19, 1911, Atlantic City, New Jersey.

Nevins, Allan and Frank Ernest Hill. *Ford, The Times, The Man, The Company* (Vol. 1 of 3). New York: Charles Scribner Sons, 1954. 688 pp.

——. *Ford, Expansion and Challenge, 1915–1933.* (Vol. 2 of 3). New York: Charles Scribner Sons, 1957. 714 pp .

——. *Ford, Decline and Rebirth, 1933–1962.* (Vol. 3 of 3). New York: Charles Scribner Sons, 1962. 508 pp.

Nicholson, J. Lee. *Factory Organization and Costs*. New York: Kohl Technical Publishing Company, 1909. 410 pp.

Novick, David, Melvin Anshen, and W. C. Truppner. *Wartime Production Controls*. New York: Columbia University Press, 1949. 441 pp.

Roe, Joseph Wickham. *English and American Tool Builders*. (Reprinted Ed. New York: McGraw-Hill Book Company, 1926). New Haven: Yale University Press, 1916. 315 pp.

Rolt, Thomas Caswell. *Short History of Machine Tools*. Cambridge, Mass.: M.I.T. Press, 1965. 256 pp.

Stoughton, Bradley. *History of the Tools Division, War Production Board*. New York: McGraw-Hill Book Company, Inc., 1949. 154 pp.

Strassmann, W. Paul. *Risk and Technological Innovation*. New York: Cornell University Press, 1959. 249 pp.

Terborgh, George. *Business Investment Management*. Washington, D. C.: Machinery and Allied Products Institute and Council for Technological Advancement, 1967, 357 pp.

Woodbury, Robert S. *History of the Gear-Cutting Machine: A Historical Study in Geometry and Machines*. (Technology Monographs, Historical Series No. 1.) Cambridge, Mass.: The Technology Press, 1958. 135 pp.

————. *History of the Grinding Machine*. Cambridge, Mass.: Technology Press, M.I.T., 1959. 191 pp.

————. *History of the Milling Machine*. Cambridge, Mass.: The M.I.T. Press, 1960. 107 pp.

Woytinsky, W. S., and Associates. *Employment and Wages in the United States*. New York: The Twentieth Century Fund, 1953. 777 pp.

Woytinsky, W. S., and E. S. Woytinsky. *World Population and Production–Trends and Outlook*. New York: The Twentieth Century Fund, 1953. 1,268 pp.

E. *Periodical and Journal Articles (By Author)*

Airey, John, and Carl J. Oxford. "On the Art of Milling," American Society of Mechanical Engineers (ASME), *Transactions*, 43:549–614, No. 1980. 1921.

Alexander, Magnus W. "Waste in Hiring and Discharging Men," *American Machinist*, 41:869–871, November 12, 1914.

Alford, L. P. "Developments in Machine-Shop Equipment in 1915," *American Machinist*, 43:1169–1171, December 30, 1915.

————. "Laws of Manufacturing Management," ASME, *Transactions*, 48:393–438, No. 2014, 1926.

Barth, Carl G. "Standardization of Machine Tools," ASME, *Transactions*, 38:895–922, No. 1559, 1916.

Bird, W. W. "Depreciation of Machine Tools," *American Machinist*, 33:767–769, October 27, 1910.

Boston, Orlan William. "A Research in the Elements of Metal Cutting," ASME, *Transctions*, 48:749–848, No. 2023, 1926.

Brackenbury, H. I. "Symposium on High-Speed Tools: High-Speed Tools and Machines to Fit Them," ASME, *Transactions*, 32:727–751, No. 1291a, 1910.

Brown, William H. "Innovation in the Machine Tool Industry," *The Quarterly Journal of Economics*, LXXI, No. 3, August, 1957, pp. 406–425.

Buckingham, Earle. "American Industrial Progress as Revealed by War Orders," *American Machinist*, 46:315–321, February 22, 1917.

Bunnell, Sterling H. "Expense Burden: Its Incidence and Distribution," ASME, *Transactions*, 33:535–559, 1911.

Burlingame, Luther D. "Basis for Determining the Proportions of Standard T-Slots and Bolts," ASME, *Transactions*, 48:65–79, No. 2002, 1926.

———. "The Human Factor in Industry," *American Machinist*, 46:Part 2:847–851, 931–934, May 17 and 31, 1917.

———. "Industrial Americanization," *Machinery*, 28:30–32, September 1921.

———. "War Work for Women," *Machinery*, 24:682–687, April 1918.

Cameron, Charles L. "Methods of Motor Application and Controls on Lathes," ASME, *Transactions*, 51:Part 2:178–179, 1929.

Cardullo, Forrest E. "Apprenticeship and Industrial Education," *American Machinist*, 29:244–246, February 22, 1906.

———. "Industrial Administration and Scientific Management— What Constitutes Scientific Management?" *Machinery*, Engineering Edition, 18:843–847, June 1911.

———. "Motors for Planer Service," ASME, *Transactions*, 51:Part 2:169–184, 1929.

Church, A. Hamilton. "Distribution of the Expense Burden," *American Machinist*, 34:991–992, 999, May 25, 1911.

———. "Proper Distribution of Established Charges," *The Engineering Magazine*, XXI, XXII, 1901.

Colvin, Fred H. "Putting the Machine Tool Industry Where It Belongs," *American Machinist*, 50:762–764, April 17, 1919.

———. "The War and the Machine Tool Industry," *American Machinist*, 50:Part 2:1167–1168, June 19, 1919.

Curtis, Myron S. "The Economics of Machine-Tool Replacement," *Mechanical Engineering*, 49:966–970, September 1927.

DeLeeuw, A. L. "A Foundation for Machine Tool Design nad Construction," ASME, *Transactions*, 39:185–211, No. 1589, 1917.

————. "Influence of Electric Motors on Machine Tools," *American Machinist*, 44:126, January 20, 1916.

————. "Economy of the Electric Drive in the Machine Shop," ASME, *Transactions*, 32:137–163, No. 1276a, 1910.

Dietz, Carl F. "European Conditions Affecting the American Machine Tool Trade," *American Machinist*, 53:75–77, July 8, 1920.

————. "Recent Impressions of Industrial Conditions in Europe," *Machinery*, 26:611–613, March 1920.

Doan, J. B. "Problems Facing American Machine Tool Builders," *Machinery*, 25:300, December 1918.

DuBrul, Ernest F. "Buying Machinery at the Right Time," *American Machinist*, 56:385, March 9, 1922.

————. "Compulsory Unemployment Insurance and Its Effect on the Machinery Industry," *American Machinist*, 57:205–207, August 10, 1922.

————. "Economics of the Machine Tool Industry," *Machinery*, 29:564–566, March 1923.

Einstein, S. "Machine-Tool Milestones, Past and Future," *Mechanical Engineering*, 52:959–962, November 1930.

Eldridge, R. E. "Establishment of American Banking Facilities in South America," *Machinery*, Engineering Edition, 21:255–257, November 1914.

Evans, Holden A. "What Is to Become of the Machinist?" *American Machinist*, 33:1095, December 15, 1910.

Fair, Charles. "Selecting Motors for Machine Tools," *American Machinist*, 40:1107–1109, June 25, 1914.

Ferris, J. P., and E. Weidmann. "Progress in the Use of Hydraulic Equipment on Production Machinery," *Mechanical Engineering*, 54:477–482, July 1932.

Flanders, Ralph E. "Design, Manufacture and Production Control of a Standard Machine," ASME, *Transactions*, 46:691–738, No. 1933, 1924.

————. "Scientific Management from a Social and Economic Standpoint," *Machinery*, Engineering Edition, 18:764–765, June 1912.

————. "Prospects of the Machine Tool Industry," *Machinery*, 30:765–766, June 1924.

————. "The Economics of Machine Production," *Mechanical Engineering*, 54:605–612, No. 9, September 1932.

Gantt, H. L. "The Task and Bonus System," *American Machinist,* 35:920–921, November 16, 1911.

Geier, Fred A. "Engineering and Industrial Education," *American Machinist,* 31:710–712, May 7, 1908.

Geier, Dr. Otto P. "The Human Potential in Industry," ASME, *Transactions,* 39:411–423, No. 1599, 1917.

Geschelin, Joseph. "Current Practice in Surface Broaching," ASME, *Transactions,* 56:863–870, MSP-56–1, 1934.

Graves, Benjamin P., and James A. Hall. "Effect of Variations in Design of Milling Cutters on Power Requirements and Capacity," ASME, *Transactions,* 45:165–192, No. 1896, 1923.

Harrison, R. E. W. "Motor Drives for Precision Grinding Machines," ASME, *Transactions,* 51:Part 2:175, 1929.

——. "Precision Cyclindrical Grinding," ASME, *Transactions,* 51:Part 2:133–137, 1929.

Hartness, James. "The Human Factor in Manufacturing," *American Machinist,* 36:933–994, June 20, 1912. (Article from book, *The Human Factor in Industrial Management.*)

Henn, A. W. "The Machine Tool Trade After the War," *Machinery,* 24:1096, August 1918.

——. "The Upward Trend of Business," *Machinery,* 29:775, June 1923.

Higgins, Milton P. "Progress in Industrial Education," *American Machinist,* 30:715–716, November 7, 1907.

——. "Education of Machinists, Foremen, and Mechanical Engineers," ASME, *Transactions,* 21:646–767, December 1899.

Hook, J. W. "Future for Machine Tool Exports," *Machinery,* 25:454–456, January 1919.

Kent, Fred G. "Machine-Shop Organization," ASME, *Transactions,* 39:213–227, No. 1590, 1917.

Kent, Robert Thurston. "The Utilization of Time-Study Data," *American Machinist,* 42:965–968, June 3, 1915.

Kimball, Dexter S. "Industrial Schools and Apprenticeship," *American Machinist,* 33:958–962, November 24, 1910. (Quoted from U.S. Bureau of Education Bulletin No. 6, 1908 by Carroll D. Wright on Modern Apprenticeship Systems).

Lodge, William. "Good Results from Premium Plan," *American Machinist,* 33:1017–1019, June 2, 1910.

Luchars, Alexander. "Machine Tool Prices: Few Manufacturers Favor Price Reductions Under Present Conditions," *Machinery,* 25:705–708, April 1919.

Meier, Charles. "Metal Planers and Methods of Production," ASME, *Transactions,* 39:229–243, No. 1591, 1917.

Morrow, L. C. "Shop-Equipment Policies in Representative Plants," *Mechnical Engineering*, 49:970–974, September 1927.

Nichols, W. W. "Economies Which May be Effected in Power Transmission," ASME, *Transactions*, 52:Part 2:111–114, 1930.

Norris, Edson R. "Automatic Features on Machine Tools," *American Machinist*, 39:813–814, November 13, 1913.

Norris, J. V. L. "Programs of Apprenticeship and Special Training," *American Machinist*, 54:230–232, February 10, 1921.

Norton, Charles H. "Efficient Production of Cylindrical Work," ASME, *Transactions*, 34:883–894, No. 1369, 1912.

Parsons, Fred A. "Power Required for Cutting Metal," ASME, *Transactions*, 45:193–227, No. 1897, 1923.

Riddell, John. "A User's View of Machine Tools," *American Machinst*, 33:Part 2:862–863, November 10, 1910.

Roberts, L. L. "The Use and Application of Machine Tools," ASME, *Transactions*, 51:Part 2:33–34, 1929.

Robbins, Charles. "Economical Features of Electrical Motor Applications," ASME, *Transactions*, 32:165–187, No. 1276b, 1910.

Schmidt, Ludwig W. "Machine Tool Exports During First Year of the War," *American Machinist*, 43:949–951, November 25, 1915.

————. "How Machine Tool Builders Can Cooperate in Foreign Trade," *American Machinist*, 48:839–841, May 16, 1918.

————. "Effect of Changes in Foreign Tariffs on the American Industry," *American Machinist*, 48:1047–1049, June 20, 1918.

Spence, J. C. "On Inducing Ourselves and Our Men to Earn More Money; Some Points on Securing Efficiency Through Cooperation of Employer and Employee," *Machinery*, Engineering Edition, 20:854–856, June 1914.

Sweet, John E. "What Are the New Machine Tools To Be?" ASME, *Transactions*, 25:100–106, No. 1014, 1903.

Trundle, George T. Jr. "What Information Does The Machine-Tool Buyer Need from the Machine-Tool Salesman?" ASME, *Transactions*, 52:41–45, 1930.

Tuechter, August H. "European Machinery Building Trade," *American Machinist*, 35:1203–1204, December 18, 1911.

Tupper, C. A. "Machine Tool Trade in Europe," *American Machinist*, 35:257–259, August 10, 1911.

Viall, W. A. "Conditions in the Machine Tool Industry," *American Machinist*, 43:870, 876, November 11, 1915.

Waldron, Frederick A. "Labor Dilution as a National Necessity," ASME, *Transactions*, 40:897–908, No. 1671, 1918.

Name Index

Air Corps (Air Force), Army, 263, 293
Air Corps Scheduling Unit, 263, 286
Alford, L. P., 181–182
Allied American Corporation, 211
Allison Division of G.M.C., 283
Almy, Captain E. D., USN, 250
Alter, Robert S., 211–212
Alvord, C. H., 76
American Locomotive Co., 55
American Machinist, editorial position, 103–104
American Society of Mechanical Engineers (ASME), 15, 29, 107, 168
Committee on Cutting Metals, 29
American Tool Works Company, 211, 369
Amtorg Corporation, 210–213, 219–223
Andress, J. E., 216–218
Army, 281, 283–285, 304, 350
Army-Navy Munitions Board (ANMB), 233, 244, 264–266, 280–286, 289–290, 292–293, 304, 350
cooperation with NMTBA, 233, 250
Machine Tool Committee, 233, 251–254, 280, 282, 284–286
Navy complaints against, 289
Priorities Committee, 281
Associated Patents, Inc. (API), 193–194
Australia, 383

Baldwin (Locomotive) Works, 55
Bard, Ralph, 249
Baruch, Bernard M., 101

"Battle of the Bulge," 267
Beal, Henry S., 218–219, 221–222
Belgium, 195, 201
Benedict, J. G., 148
Biggers, John D., 250
Birmingham Ordnance District, 243
Birmingham Small Arms Tools Limited (B.S.A. Tools), 194–196
Bliss, P. E., 209, 215
Boston area, (Machine tool using), 66–67, 71, 385
Brainard, George C., 257, 265, 267, 292
Bridgeport area (Machine tool using), 67, 385
British Empire, 195
British Machine Tool Board, 103, 115
Britton, Mason, 263, 281–284, 286, 288, 299
Broehl, Wayne G., Jr., 5, 310, 393
Brown, W. H., 5, 19, 389
Brown and Sharpe Mfg. Co., 13, 47, 148, 171–172, 193, 299, 346, 369, 376
Bryant Chucking Grinder Company, 145, 369, 311–312
Net profits as per cent of sales, 380
Budget, Bureau of the, 234
Buker, Henry, 148
Bullard, E. P. Jr., 76, 88, 172
Bullard Company, 48, 84, 88, 146, 172, 188, 255, 369, 376
Burger, William J., 94
Burlingame, Luther B., 171–172
Burt, Clayton R., 250, 287
Byrnes, James F., 316
California, 365–368
Canada, 195, 236, 297, 383

401

United Automobile Workers (CIO), 314
United Electrical Radio and Machine Workers of America (CIO), 271
United Kingdom, 236, 297, 383; *see also* British Empire, England, Great Britain
U.S.S.R. (Russia), 160, 195, 210–225, 232, 274, 279–280, 297, 321, 341, 354, 383
  trade with, 145, 160, 195, 210–219, 222–224
  financing of, 210–211, 215–224
  market potential, 210, 222–224
  NMTBA concern with dangers in, 224–225
U.S. recognition of, 219–220, 223–224
U.S. Lines (passenger shipping), 208
Universal Boring Machine Company, 273

Vance, Harold S., 281
Van Norman Machine Tool Co., 369, 376
Vermont, 41–42, 45–47, 69–70, 357–361, 365–368
Viall, W. A., 108
Virginia, 365–368

War Department, 233, 259, 263, 266, 281, 315
  Price Adjustment Board, 305–306, 325, 344
War Industries Board, 101–103, 114, 347
  Machine Tool Section, 101–103, 114, 347

War Manpower Commission (WMC), 315–316
War Production Board (WPB), 46, 260, 262, 264–267, 289, 313–317, 323, 326, 350–351
  Automobile Industry Advisory Committee, 314
  Automotive Division, 314
  Automotive Labor Advisory Committee, 314
  Machine Tool Industry Advisory Committee, 266–268
  Planning Committee, 235
  Production Executive Committee, 266, 292
  Tools Branch (Division), 260, 264–267, 289–292, 295, 299, 350
Warner and Swasey Co., 48, 94, 189, 209, 215, 369, 376
War Trade Board, 101
Webb-Pomerene Act, 111, 227
"Webb-Pomerene" Association, 111, 341
Webb-Pomerene Corporation, 203–205
Weinberg, Sidney, 316
Wesson, General Charles M., 244
Whipp, William E., 148
White, J. J., 303–304
Wilson, Charles E. ("Electric"), 266–267, 292, 316
Winchester Repeating Arms Co., 243
Wisconsin, 41–42, 44, 46–47, 49, 52, 69, 357–361, 365–368
Wolfe, A. J., 202
Woodbury, R. S., 5, 23, 395
Worcester, Mass., 40
Worthington Pump Co., 206
Wright Aeronautical Corp., 283
Wulfshon & Company, 211

Subject Index

Manpower, competition for, 33, 54, 86, 108–109, 113, 120–121, 161, 249, 334–335, 347
Manufacturing management, laws of, 181–183, 199
Marketing, 69, 340–341
Markets, 97–101, 109–113, 115, 340–341
domestic, 109–113, 115
foreign, 97–101, 109–113, 115
Materials, improvement in, 22
Mechanics, skilled, 28; see also Machinists
Medical care; see Insurance, health and accident; Working conditions, health and welfare
Metal-forming machinery builders, 4
"Metalworking Equipment" industry, 66, 72
"Metalworking Machinery" (SIC 354), 3, 60, 62, 65, 374–375
Metalworking practice, 14
Milling machines, 9, 24–25, 31, 357–358, 364
production in dollars for certain years, 364
production by state, 1900, 1905, 357–358
Milling operations, speeding up, 28
"Miscellaneous Machine Parts and Jobbing" industry, 66, 72
Mobilization for war, 101–107, 113–115, 141–142, 160, 231–278, 347–351
Model changes; see Design changes
"Modular construction," 9, 18, 354
"Motor Vehicles and Parts" industry, 51–53, 59, 60, 62, 64–66, 69–70, 72, 329–331, 336, 373–375, 377–378
Motors, electric, 8, 11–16, 34, 327, 335
constant speed vs. variable speed, 12–13
internal combustion; see Engines, internal combustion
"Mount Eberstadt," 264 (footnote 50)

Non-homogeneity of machine tools, 139–140, 349

Obsolescence, 131–133, 140, 151, 233, 273, 317–318, 337–338; see also Capital equipment, amortization and depreciation of; Design changes; Useful life
"Office and Store Machines" industry, 66, 374–375
Open price policy, 184–185, 189–190, 199–200, 343; see also Competition, price; Price, competition
Operation, machine, 8, 10, 327–328
Order boards, 289–290, 294–295, 322
imbalance in, 289–290
reporting revised, 294–295, 322
Order cancellation, 95–97, 110, 114–115, 258
Orders, 95, 137, 250, 263, 295–297, 319, 381–382, 384
educational, 141–142, 238–239, 243, 348
new, 137, 295, 319, 336, 384
no-cancellation clauses, 142
types of, 93
unfilled, 95, 250, 263, 295–297, 319, 381–382
Organization and concentration, 19, 36, 147, 160–161, 169–170, 173, 182, 272–273, 331–333
concentration of production, 272–273, 333
corporate form of, 36, 332–333
size of firms, 333
specialization of product, 19, 169–170, 173, 182, 333

Parts and components, interchangeable, 14, 19–20, 24, 26, 34, 57, 98, 169–170, 335, 354; see also Standardization
Patent pool, 193–194, 200
Patents, trademarks, trade names and copyrights, 184, 202–205, 209–210, 212
Patent infringement, protection against, 202–205, 209–210
Paternalism, 106
Personnel management, 105–106; see also Scientific management; Work force; Working conditions; Working hours
Planers, 15, 27, 61, 357–358, 364
production in dollars for certain years, 364

"know-how"; *see* Production methods
management, 81–83, 85, 168; *see also* Management engineering; Scientific management
methods, 8, 21–24, 26–29, 31–34, 51, 80–82, 85, 99, 102, 133, 169–172, 327–328, 333–335, 345, 349, 354; *see also* Simplification; Standardization
planning, 10, 83
Program, Machine Tool, 234, 238, 242–246, 251–258
quality of, 24–25, 27
reduction at end of World War II, 273
relation to purchasing power, 138
scheduling, 101, 172; *see also* Order boards
share produced by machine tool industry vs. other industries, 70–71
speed, 24, 27
standards, 26–27
statistics
  production by state, 361
  selected products, 377–378
  selected types of tools, 364
  by state and type, 1900, 1905, 357–358
  totals, 1941, 249–251
Productivity, 25, 28, 135, 157, 184, 201
Profits, 33, 110, 137–138, 142–143, 146, 152, 157–158, 169–170, 174–175, 182, 197, 279, 298, 304–306, 310–312, 324–325, 342–345, 355, 376, 380
as percentage of net worth, 145–146, 376
as per cent of sales, 380
ratios, 33, 123, 142–146, 158, 312
statistics for various companies, 145–146, 158, 310–312, 376
Protective devices, 15; *see also* Controls, electric and electronic; Safety; Working conditions
Punches, presses and shears, 25
Purchasing power; *see* Demand

Quality control, 26–27

"Railroad Equipment" industry, 54–

56, 62–63, 69–70, 128, 329, 374–375
locomotive production, 1900–1953, 379
stagnation of, effect on machine tool industry, 46
Railroad maintenance shops, 54–55
Raw material; *see* Requirements, materials
Reciprocal trade, 98–99; *see also* Foreign trade
Reconversion, 96–97, 109–111, 115, 119, 142–143, 314–315, 325–326, 351
"Blue plan" for automobile production, 314
planning for, 313–318, 325–326, 351
problems, 97, 109–111, 115, 351; *see also* Inventories, excess; Orders, cancellation of
service opposition to, 314–315, 325–326
Renegotiation of contracts; *see* Contracts, renegotiation of
Replacement policy, 24, 78, 125–126, 131–136, 140–142, 147, 152, 158–160, 232, 338–339
armed services, 142, 232
factors affecting, 132–134, 141–142, 232
Ford Motor Co., 126, 135–136
General Electric Co., 132–133
government-owned facilities, 142
Requirements, 25–26, 33–34, 52, 56, 92–93, 102–103, 125–126, 129–133, 140–141, 152, 159–160, 231–278, 281, 284, 294, 348–349, 351
competition between programs and contractors, 236, 252–253, 274
for "critical" types, 250, 252
for defense production, 26, 231–278, 281, 284, 294, 348–349
development of estimates of, 233–236, 252, 258, 274, 348, 351
for expansion and new products, 52, 129, 131–133
for materials, 56
for non-defense production, 281
for replacement, 125–126, 129–132, 140–141, 152, 159–160
Resale value, 20, 79, 166–167

War mobilization, 101–109, 114–115, 231–326, 347–351
World War I, 101–109, 114–115, 347–348
World War II, 231–326, 348–351
Waste; see Efficiency; Federated American Engineering Societies, Committee on Waste (Name Index)
Weapon design and tool standardization for mass production, 31–32
Work force, 21, 56, 85–86, 90, 104–105, 107–109, 112–113, 121, 130, 136–137, 151, 153–154, 161, 171, 174, 180, 249, 256, 261, 273, 315, 326, 335, 340, 345–347, 360, 365–368, 370
availability of labor, 56, 340
deterioration and waste of during depression, 273
employment of aliens, 104
employment by large firms, 370
employment by states, 360
employment of women, 104–105, 273, 346
losses from, 121, 137, 153
quality of foremen and production workers, 171
ratio of apprentices to journeymen, 90
recruitment, training, and supervision of workers, 85–86, 121, 249, 256, 261, 335, 340, 345–347
reduction of, 151, 161, 273, 326, 340, 346

relations between management, foremen and workers, 174, 180
requirements, 21, 86, 105, 108–109, 112, 130, 340, 345–346
shortages, 315, 347
surplus labor, 136, 151, 154, 161
trade union activity, 90, 107–108, 346
turnover rate, 86, 105, 112
upgrading, 104–105, 113, 345
use of unskilled helpers, 104, 113, 345–346
Work handling equipment, 11, 14, 18, 21, 34, 328
Work sharing programs, 149, 154, 156, 346
Working conditions, 104–107, 113, 150, 174, 346–347
improvements in, 104–107, 346
management opposition to mandatory social programs, 106–107, 114, 345–346
responsibility for health, accidents and safety, 106–107, 113–114, 346
theories, 345
Working hours, 85, 113, 120, 150, 153–154, 156, 161, 165–166, 238, 248–249, 254–257, 333–334, 340, 346
average weekly hours, 154, 312–313
extending or reducing hours, 238, 248–249, 254–255, 257, 340, 346
forty-hour week, 150, 156
multiple-shift operation, 248, 254–257, 340